Drawings from New York Collections   III

Drawings from
New York Collections
III

THE EIGHTEENTH CENTURY IN ITALY

Jacob Bean, Felice Stampfle

N.Y.

The Metropolitan Museum of Art
The Pierpont Morgan Library

Clothbound edition distributed by New York Graphic Society, Greenwich, Connecticut

Exhibited at The Metropolitan Museum of Art, January 30–March 21, 1971

Library of Congress catalog card number 77–134891
Cloth binding, Standard Book Number 87099–021–7
Paperbound, Standard Book Number 87099–022–5
Limited edition, Standard Book Number 87099–023–3

Foreword

WE ARE DELIGHTED to present *The Eighteenth Century in Italy*, the third in the series of exhibitions devoted to New York collections of drawings, jointly organized by The Metropolitan Museum of Art and The Pierpont Morgan Library. The first exhibition, held at the Metropolitan Museum in 1965, consisted of drawings of the Italian Renaissance; the second, held at the Morgan Library in 1967, was concerned with Italian drawings of the seventeenth century. This third exhibition, showing the splendors of eighteenth-century Italy, is the largest and richest in the series, and Venetian draughtsmanship is accounted for in a particularly magnificent fashion. This comprehensiveness is made possible by the connoisseurship of those New York collectors of the past and present who fell under the spell of eighteenth-century Italy.

The exhibition comes as a happy conclusion to The Metropolitan Museum of Art's centennial celebrations and again marks the long and felicitous collaboration between our two institutions. Once more, the exhibition and catalogue are the work of Jacob Bean and Felice Stampfle, who have been most ably assisted at every stage by Linda Boyer Gillies and Cara Dufour. We are profoundly grateful to the New York collectors, public and private, who have so generously supported this exhibition.

THOMAS P. F. HOVING
CHARLES RYSKAMP

Introduction

THE EMERGENCE and development of draughtsmanship in the principal Italian artistic centers—from the early Renaissance through the course of the seventeenth century—has been traced and illustrated in our two previous exhibitions. In the second, devoted to the seventeenth century in Italy, several forward-looking artists, Giovanni Benedetto Castiglione, Luca Giordano, and Gregorio de' Ferrari, were singled out as artistic prophets of what was to come in the following century, and the present exhibition, devoted to the eighteenth century in Italy, opens with the work of two highly influential transitional figures, the Neapolitan Francesco Solimena and the Venetian Sebastiano Ricci, whose drawings could equally well have figured in the previous show, since their working careers begin in the *Seicento* and finish in the *Settecento*.

One of the most significant features of the artistic scene in eighteenth-century Italy is the reemergence of Venice and Venetia as a major center in the peninsula and an exporter on a large scale of painters and paintings to the principal countries of northern Europe. From the relative doldrums of the seventeenth century, Venice rose again in the eighteenth to preeminence and produced in Giovanni Battista Tiepolo one of the greatest of Italian decorators, a worthy heir to his sixteenth-century predecessor, Paolo Veronese. Giambattista is supreme in his century in Venice, but the stature of his immediate forerunners, Sebastiano Ricci and Piazzetta, is considerable. They, too, are gifted, original artists, and in their figure styles, both as painters and draughtsmen, they prepare the way for Giambattista—Sebastiano with his nervous flickering line used in conjunction with transparent wash, and Piazzetta with his vigorous chiaroscuro effects.

Giambattista dominated the Venetian scene as he dominates the present exhibition with ninety-six drawings out of the total of 300. Following closely are his son Domenico with forty-six drawings, Francesco Guardi with twenty-eight, and Piranesi with twenty-three. This rich representation reflects the high merit of the work of these four masterful draughtsmen, and the incomparable resources of New York collections in the field of eighteenth-century Venetian draughtsmanship. Drawing on these local resources alone, four separate and remarkably comprehensive monographic exhibitions could have been arranged; they are offered here as four selective presentations placed within a panoramic view of the Italian artistic scene in the eighteenth century.

Both as painter and draughtsman Giambattista Tiepolo was magically inventive and enormously productive. He handled chalk, pen, and wash with consummate ease and speed. His surviving drawn *oeuvre*, which is vast, ranges from highly finished compositions produced as artistic ends in themselves to the rapid, spontaneous notations of a fleeting idea. There are long series of drawings that offer lively variations on a given theme, religious or secular, and then, of course, sheets that are clearly studies for a specific painted work. Drawings that fall in the latter category are surprisingly rare, and one can only surmise that Giambattista drew a good deal of the time for sheer pleasure, and that his drawings were kept in the studio as a working reference library of motifs; an autograph figure drawing might recall as much as adumbrate a theme in a painted composition. Indeed, a large group of chalk drawings exactly corresponding to details in Giambattista's paintings at Würzburg and formerly attributed to him are now generally considered to be records made by his pupils (see Nos. 153, 154, and 239).

The most sizable group of drawings certainly by Giambattista that can be confidently associated with a major project is to a very large extent present at this exhibition. These are the pen and wash drawings for the frescoed decoration of the Gallery of the Palazzo Clerici in Milan, a work datable 1740 (Nos. 74–95). Graphic style unifies this group; agile swelling pen contours model figures that take on an almost weightless plasticity through bold applications of transparent brown wash that contrast with the white of the page, achieving a dazzling luminosity. The wash used by Giambattista on the greater part of the Clerici drawings is of a characteristic golden brown tonality, but in other sheets equally associable with the project he uses a much darker, less transparent wash (Nos. 91–93). Some of the drawings in the Palazzo Clerici group, which represent the peak of Giambattista's seemingly effortless achievement as a draughtsman, are specifically connectible with figures in the oil sketch for the ceiling (for example, Nos. 78, 79), some with figures in the fresco itself (Nos. 88–93), while others are loosely associable with the group on stylistic and iconographic grounds (Nos. 81–87). The full gamut of Giambattista's draughtsmanship is represented, from the heavy, vigorous figure style of the 1720s to the electric, abbreviated manner of his later years, the latter particularly well exemplified by the studies for the decorations of the Palazzo Trento-Valmarana in Vicenza (Nos. 144–146).

Venetian draughtsmanship of the eighteenth century is characterized by its increasing independence of painted work—drawings were more and more often produced as ends in themselves—and the same phenomenon may be observed in contemporary France. Furthermore, draughtsmen investigated, invented, or developed new subject matter that had been only sporadically treated in previous centuries: *scherzi di fantasia* (fantastic jokes—very much to the taste of the time), scenes of contemporary life, caricatures, landscape capriccios, and, in contrast, almost photographically exact city views and landscapes.

Giambattista excelled at *scherzi di fantasia* and caricature, and even touched on the contemporary scene; all these are subjects studied with wit and elegance by his most gifted son, Domenico. As prolific a draughtsman as his father, Domenico is very strongly represented in this exhibition, which includes eight of his tolerantly ironical scenes of contemporary life and sixteen episodes from his life of Punchinello, produced at the very end of the artist's career at the turn of the century.

The landscape capriccio, in which a fanciful romantic view may by chance include a real or imaginary building or ruin, was launched in Venice by Marco Ricci, nephew of Sebastiano.

Marco's drawn and painted production served as point of departure for Canaletto and Francesco Guardi. Canaletto, of course, made a specialty as well of *vedute esatte*—exact views after nature, and both these aspects of his work are well represented here.

The strikingly individual Francesco Guardi, trained as a figure painter in his elder brother Gianantonio's studio, emerges as an independent painter of Venetian *vedute esatte* about 1750, no doubt hoping to capture some of Canaletto's market. Guardi's exact representations of the Venetian scene, often embellished with the *macchiette*—staffage figures that serve in a sense as his signature—are present here, as are some of his most brilliant architectural and landscape capriccios, all of them highly original flights of graphic fancy.

Giovanni Battista Piranesi, brilliant, original etcher of the most famous of Roman views, was Venetian by birth and training, and his origins are clearly evident in the style of a number of his drawings (Nos. 219–224). He was briefly active as a practicing architect (Nos. 227, 233), but most of his ideas for architecture and decoration had expression only on paper (Nos. 217, 233, 234).

Piranesi leads us to Rome where the artistic scene appears serious and conservative in opposition to Venice's light-hearted taste for the scherzo and the capriccio. Still an artistic center of international importance, Rome is accounted for here by Bracci's tomb designs, which testify to the vitality of the Roman sculptural tradition, and by Benedetto Luti's fine drawn *bozzetto* for an important history picture full of Marattesque solemnity. Rome itself was the subject of subjects for view painters, and Pannini, a very talented local specialist in that vein, is represented by a large drawn model for a painted view of the Palazzo di Montecitorio. Pier Leone Ghezzi is *the* Roman caricaturist of the time, while Giuseppe Cades's drawings reveal the neoclassic currents that appear in Rome relatively early in the century.

Naples remains an active center, though the rough vigor of local *Seicento* draughtsmanship is tempered in the eighteenth century by the elegance of Solimena's contours. Corrado Giaquinto, Fedele Fischetti, Paolo de Matteis, Francesco de Mura, and Domenico Mondo are all, each in his own way, conspicuously indebted to Solimena, Naples's eighteenth-century *capo scuola*.

In the north of Italy a number of regions maintain healthy independence. Bologna remains essentially conservative: Aureliano Milani reflects the persistent and invigorating influence of Ludovico Carracci; Donato Creti and the Gandolfi that of the Carracci academy and of Guido Reni; and Giuseppe Maria Crespi is more original in his paintings than in his drawings, which reveal his local academic training. Genoa produces in Magnasco an independent and idiosyncratic draughtsman, and Lorenzo de' Ferrari continues the strong local decorative tradition, following in the footsteps of his father. Florence, by now provincial, contributes the decorator Galeotti and the landscape draughtsmen Zuccarelli and Zocchi. Further north, in Lombardy, the too little known Paolo Pagani evolves a rococo style that had far-reaching influence in central Europe.

Throughout the peninsula talented and original artists appear, but in retrospect at least, Venice dominates the scene by the variety and inventiveness of her artistic contribution.

Though this is a large exhibition—the largest in our series and the largest show of drawings devoted to one school and period ever organized on this continent—it is only partially encyclopedic. A number of delightful eighteenth-century Italian draughtsmen have had to be omitted in the interest of a full presentation of the drawings of the major masters of the time. In making our selection we have been faced with a most agreeable problem, an embarrassment of riches. A long-standing and exemplary partiality among New York's institutions and private collectors for Italian—and particularly Venetian—drawings of the eighteenth century has resulted in a formidable concentration that makes possible a display of drawings by Giambattista and Domenico Tiepolo, Francesco Guardi, and Piranesi that could not easily be equaled in any other center. Giambattista is the star of this occasion, not only because he is certainly the greatest Italian figure draughtsman of the century, but because of the incomparable quality and range of the several large collections of his drawings now in New York. Of the ninety-six sheets by Giambattista on exhibition thirty-four come from the Metropolitan Museum, thirty-two from the Morgan Library, twelve from the collection of Dr. and Mrs. Rudolf Heinemann, nine from the Robert Lehman Collection. And in all of these four collections and in those of other lenders there are a great many more by Giambattista that were regretfully excluded, not for reasons of quality, but in the interest of a balanced presentation of Giambattista's production.

The provenance of several of these groups of drawings deserves attention. Professor George Knox, in the introduction to his admirable catalogue of the Tiepolo drawings at the Victoria and Albert Museum, has suggested that the nine albums of Tiepolo drawings belonging to the English *amateur* Edward Cheney (1803–1884), which were sold at Christie's in London in 1885, contained the greater part of the drawings in Tiepolo's studio at the time of his departure for Spain in 1762. Cheney had acquired some of these albums in the 1840s from a Signor Francesco Pesaro who had had them at fourth hand from the Convent of the Somaschi in Venice, to which they are said to have been given by Giambattista. The overwhelming majority of the more than one hundred drawings by Giambattista in The Pierpont Morgan Library were originally mounted in an album. Its brown mottled calf binding, which is still preserved at the Library, is labeled *TIEPOLO / DESSINS ORIGINAUX*, and the fly leaf is inscribed in Cheney's own hand *E. C. Venice 1852 May 31 / bought from the Conte Corniani-Algarotti*. Presumably this album was one of the nine sold in 1885, at which time it was probably acquired by Charles Fairfax Murray, whose collection of drawings was purchased more or less *in toto* by Pierpont Morgan in 1910.

A Cheney provenance is suggested by Knox for the better part of the pen and wash drawings by Giambattista from the collection of the Marquis de Biron that are now in the Metropolitan Museum.* The stylistic homogeneity of the better part of the Biron drawings indicates that they, like those in the Morgan Library, were once grouped together in an album. Linda Boyer Gillies points out that the Biron group may very well have formed part of a dismembered album of which the binding is preserved in the Horne Foundation in Florence. This is labeled *VARI / PENSIERI / T. I.*, and, further, on a leather label glued to the binding, *TIEPOLO ORIGINAL DRAWINGS*. On the first page of the album is inscribed the name *Beckford*, suggesting a plausible provenance, for this could be the avid collector William Beckford (1760–1844). The Florentine album, which bears no written evidence of a Cheney provenance, may have been broken up before it passed into the hands of Herbert Horne (1864–1916); in any

---

* The purchase of the Marquis de Biron's collection by the Metropolitan Museum in 1937 is discussed at length by J. Byam Shaw in an article in the centennial issue of the *Metropolitan Museum Journal*, volume 3.

case, the stubs remaining in the binding indicate that the album had 106 pages. Only forty-one are now in the Horne Foundation. Thus, there was place for the forty-four drawings now in the Metropolitan Museum. Moreover, the stylistic consistency shared by the Horne and Metropolitan drawings is further evidence that these two groups, both of which contain studies for the Palazzo Clerici, originally formed part of the same volume. Since the Morgan and the complete Horne albums both contained many studies related to the Palazzo Clerici ceiling—in fact, they contain almost all the drawings related to this project—it can be assumed that they were made up at the same time, very probably by Giambattista himself.

The two other major groups of Giambattista drawings in the exhibition are of more recent formation. Those lent by Dr. and Mrs. Rudolf Heinemann come to a large extent from the collection of drawings and prints by Giambattista and Domenico formed by the late Tomas Harris, while a good many of the Tiepolo drawings in the Robert Lehman Collection come from the Venetian material brought together by Paul Wallraf.

One important source of large-scale, highly finished drawings by Giambattista is the collection of Prince Alexis Orloff, which was dispersed at auction in Paris in 1920. A number of these splendid sheets, which because of their similarity of style, subject, and dimension, may well have been grouped together at some time in an album, have found their way to the United States, and nine are in the exhibition (Nos. 70, 72, 73, 102, 123, 124, 136, 137, 138).

Once again the catalogue entries are arranged chronologically, without regard to local schools, the date of an artist's birth determining his place in the sequence. The bibliography is selective, limited to essential references. A list of works and exhibitions cited in abbreviated form precedes the catalogue notices. Only those exhibitions recorded in a descriptive catalogue are listed. For the first time tracings of watermarks have been supplied. They are limited to marks that appear on the drawings of Giambattista and Domenico Tiepolo, Francesco Guardi, and Canaletto that are present here. Since very few of these watermarks appear in facsimile in the standard literature on the subject, this supplement should prove useful. In the entries the number following the description of a watermark refers to the corresponding number in the appendix where the marks are illustrated.

We are much indebted to the collectors and institutions that have lent so generously to this exhibition. The reader of the catalogue will constantly encounter the names of J. J. Byam Shaw and George Knox. Mr. Byam Shaw's books on the drawings of Francesco Guardi and Domenico Tiepolo are models of scholarship. Professor Knox has devoted many years to the study of the drawings of the Tiepolos, and most recently has compiled a very useful scholarly catalogue of a Tiepolo bicentenary exhibition held at the Fogg Art Museum. We have been very largely dependent on the works of these two scholars, and we gratefully acknowledge our debt to them.

Dr. George Szabo, Curator of the Robert Lehman Collection, and Elaine Evans Dee, Curator of Prints and Drawings, Cooper-Hewitt Museum, The Smithsonian Institution, have helpfully supplied much information relating to the collections in their care; Anthony M. Clark, Terisio Pignatti, Carmen Angleton, and Elizabeth Roth have also been of scholarly assistance. We are deeply indebted to Linda Boyer Gillies, Assistant Curator of Drawings, The Metropolitan Museum of Art, and to Cara Dufour and Ruth Kraemer, Curatorial Assistants at The Pierpont Morgan Library, all of whom have been of invaluable assistance in every phase of the exhibition and catalogue. Thanks are due as well to Leslie Enders Lee and Gay

Patterson Lord of The Metropolitan Museum of Art. Merritt Safford, Conservator, and Barry Byers, Restorer, of The Metropolitan Museum of Art, and Alexander J. Yow, Conservator, and Patricia A. Reyes of The Pierpont Morgan Library have provided useful counsel and service.

JACOB BEAN
Curator of Drawings
The Metropolitan Museum of Art

FELICE STAMPFLE
Curator of Drawings and Prints
The Pierpont Morgan Library

Lenders to the Exhibition

Mrs. Vincent Astor

Dr. George M. Baer

Walter C. Baker

Cooper-Hewitt Museum of Decorative Arts and Design,
    Smithsonian Institution

David Daniels

Donald P. Gurney

Dr. and Mrs. Rudolf Heinemann

Professor and Mrs. Julius Held

Christian Humann

Mr. and Mrs. E. Powis Jones

Mr. and Mrs. Jacob M. Kaplan

Robert Lehman Collection

Robert and Bertina Suida Manning

Mr. and Mrs. A. Hyatt Mayor

Joseph McCrindle

Donald Oenslager

James Parker

Janos Scholz

Harry G. Sperling

Mr. and Mrs. Donald Stralem

Mrs. Herbert N. Straus

Dr. Donald Tapley

Mr. and Mrs. Eugene Victor Thaw

Mrs. Douglas Williams

Three anonymous lenders

Table of Contents

Works Cited in an Abbreviated Form

P. d'Ancona, *Palazzo Clerici*
Paolo d'Ancona, *Tiepolo a Milano, gli affreschi di Palazzo Clerici*, [Milan], n.d.

Bean, *100 European Drawings*
Jacob Bean, *100 European Drawings in The Metropolitan Museum of Art*, New York, 1964.

Benesch, *Venetian Drawings*
Otto Benesch, *Venetian Drawings of the Eighteenth Century in America*, New York, 1947.

Bologna, *Solimena*
Ferdinando Bologna, *Francesco Solimena*, Naples, 1958.

Byam Shaw, *Domenico Tiepolo*
J. Byam Shaw, *The Drawings of Domenico Tiepolo*, London, 1962.

Byam Shaw, *Guardi*
J. Byam Shaw, *The Drawings of Francesco Guardi*, London, 1951.

Constable, *Canaletto*
W. G. Constable, *Canaletto, Giovanni Antonio Canal, 1697–1768*, 2 vols., Oxford, 1962.

Corfiato, *Piranesi Compositions*
Hector O. Corfiato, *Piranesi Compositions*, London, 1951.

De Vesme
Alexandre de Vesme, *Le Peintre-graveur italien*, Milan, 1906.

Fairfax Murray
C. Fairfax Murray, *Drawings by the Old Masters, Collection of J. Pierpont Morgan*, 4 vols., London, 1905–1912.

Fischer, *Münchner Jahrbuch*, 1968
Manfred F. Fischer, "Die Umbaupläne des Giovanni Battista Piranesi für den Chor von S. Giovanni in Laterano," *Münchner Jahrbuch der bildenden Kunst*, XIX, 1968, pp. 207–228.

Freeden and Lamb, *Würzburger Residenz*
Max H. von Freeden and Carl Lamb, *Das Meisterwerk des Giovanni Battista Tiepolo. Die Fresken der Würzburger Residenz*, Munich, 1956.

Goering, *Guardi*
Max Goering, *Francesco Guardi*, Vienna, 1944.

Hadeln, *Tiepolo Drawings*
Detlev Baron von Hadeln, *The Drawings of G. B. Tiepolo*, 2 vols., Paris, 1928.

Heawood
Edward Heawood, *Watermarks, Mainly of the 17th and 18th Centuries*, Hilversum, Holland, 1950.

Knox, *The Orloff Album*
George Knox, "The Orloff Album of Tiepolo Drawings," *Burlington Magazine*, CIII, 1961, pp. 269–275.

Knox, *Victoria and Albert*
George Knox, *Catalogue of the Tiepolo Drawings in the Victoria and Albert Museum*, London, 1960.

Lugt
Frits Lugt, *Les Marques de collections de dessins et d'estampes . . .*, Amsterdam, 1921.

Lugt S.
Frits Lugt, *Les Marques de collections de dessins et d'estampes . . . Supplément*, The Hague, 1956.

Mayor, *Piranesi*
A. Hyatt Mayor, *Giovanni Battista Piranesi*, New York, 1952.

Metropolitan Museum, *European Drawings*
Metropolitan Museum of Art, *European Drawings from the Collection of The Metropolitan Museum of Art*, I, *Italian Drawings*, New York, 1942.

Molmenti, *Tiepolo*
Pompeo Molmenti, *Tiepolo, la vie et l'oeuvre du peintre*, Paris, 1911.

Mongan and Sachs, *Drawings in the Fogg Museum*, I
Agnes Mongan and Paul J. Sachs, *Drawings in the Fogg Museum of Art*, 3 vols., Cambridge, Mass., 1940.

Morassi, 1955
Antonio Morassi, *G. B. Tiepolo, His Life and Work*, London, 1955.

Morassi, 1962
Antonio Morassi, *A Complete Catalogue of the Paintings of G. B. Tiepolo*, London, 1962.

Morgan Library, *A Review of Acquisitions, 1949–1968*
The Pierpont Morgan Library, *A Review of Acquisitions, 1949–1968*, New York, 1969.

Morgan Library, *First Fellows Report, 1950*, etc.
The Pierpont Morgan Library, Frederick B. Adams, Jr., compiler, *Annual Report to the Fellows of the Pierpont Morgan Library*, 1950 to date.

Moschini, *Guardi*
Vittore Moschini, *Guardi*, Milan, 1963.

Pallucchini, *Disegni del Guardi al Correr*
Rodolfo Pallucchini, *I Disegni del Guardi al Museo Correr di Venezia*, Venice, 1943.

Pallucchini, *Piazzetta*
Rodolfo Pallucchini, *Piazzetta*, Milan, 1956.

Pignatti, *Acqueforti dei Tiepolo*
Terisio Pignatti, *Le Acqueforti dei Tiepolo*, Florence, 1965.

Pignatti, *Disegni dei Guardi*
Terisio Pignatti, *Disegni dei Guardi*, Florence, 1967.

Pignatti, *Disegni nel Museo Correr*
Disegni veneti del Settecento nel Museo Correr di Venezia (exhibition catalogue by Terisio Pignatti), Venice, Fondazione Giorgio Cini, 1964.

Pignatti, *Disegni veneziani*
Terisio Pignatti, *I Disegni veneziani del Settecento*, [Milan], n.d.

Ripa
Cesare Ripa, *Iconologia . . .*, Siena, 1613.

Sack, *Tiepolo*
Eduard Sack, *Giambattista und Domenico Tiepolo*, Hamburg, 1910.

Stampfle, *Art Bulletin*, 1948
Felice Stampfle, "An Unknown Group of Drawings by Giovanni Battista Piranesi," *Art Bulletin*, XXX, 1948, pp. 122–141.

Thomas, *Piranesi*
Hylton Thomas, *The Drawings of Giovanni Battista Piranesi*, New York, 1954.

Tietze, *European Master Drawings*
Hans Tietze, *European Master Drawings in the United States*, New York, 1947.

Vigni, *Disegni del Tiepolo*
Giorgio Vigni, *Disegni del Tiepolo*, Venice, 1942.

Virch, *Baker Collection*
Claus Virch, *Master Drawings in the Collection of Walter C. Baker*, New York, 1962 [privately printed].

Wunder, *Extravagant Drawings*
Richard P. Wunder, *Extravagant Drawings of the Eighteenth Century from the Collection of the Cooper Union Museum*, New York, 1962.

Exhibitions Cited in an Abbreviated Form

A.F.A., 17th and 18th Century Drawings, 1966–1967
"17th and 18th Century European Drawings," circulated by the American Federation of Arts, 1966–1967.

Cailleux, Tiepolo et Guardi, 1952
Paris, Galerie Cailleux, "Tiepolo et Guardi dans les collections françaises," 1952.

Chicago, Tiepolo Exhibition, 1938
Chicago, The Art Institute, "Paintings, Drawings, and Prints by the Two Tiepolos: Giambattista and Giandomenico," 1938.

Cincinnati, Lehman Exhibition, 1959
Cincinnati, The Cincinnati Art Museum, "The Lehman Collection, New York," 1959.

Fogg, Tiepolo Exhibition, 1970
Cambridge, Mass., Fogg Art Museum, "Tiepolo, A Bicentenary Exhibition, 1770–1970," 1970.

Hamburg, Scholz Exhibition, 1963
Hamburg, Kunsthalle/Cologne, Wallraf-Richartz Museum, "Italienische Meisterzeichnungen vom 14. bis zum 18. Jahrhundert aus amerikanischem Besitz. Die Sammlung Janos Scholz, New York," 1963.

Houston, Guardi Family, 1958
Houston, Museum of Fine Arts, "The Guardi Family," 1958.

London, Arts Council, Tiepolo Exhibition, 1955
London, Arts Council, "Drawings and Etchings by Giovanni Battista Tiepolo and Giovanni Domenico Tiepolo," 1955.

London, Royal Academy, 1953
London, Royal Academy, "Drawings by the Old Masters," 1953.

London, Royal Academy, 1954–1955
London, Royal Academy, "European Masters of the Eighteenth Century," 1954–1955.

London, Savile Gallery, Tiepolo Exhibition, 1928
London, Savile Gallery, "Drawings by Giovanni Battista Tiepolo," 1928.

London, Scholz Exhibition, 1968
London, Arts Council, also Liverpool and Edinburgh, "Italian Drawings from the Collection of Janos Scholz," 1968.

Memphis-Lexington, Ricci Exhibition, 1965–1966
Memphis, Brooks Memorial Art Gallery, Lexington, University of Kentucky Art Gallery, "Sebastiano and Marco Ricci in America," 1965–1966.

New Haven, Scholz Exhibition, 1964
New Haven, Yale University Art Gallery, "Italian Drawings from the Collection of Janos Scholz," 1964.

New York, Piranesi Exhibition, 1949
New York, The Pierpont Morgan Library, "Drawings by Giovanni Battista Piranesi," 1949.

New York, The Two Sicilies, 1970
New York, Finch College Museum of Art, "The Two Sicilies. Drawings from the Cooper-Hewitt Museum," 1970.

New York, Tiepolo Exhibition, 1938
New York, The Metropolitan Museum of Art, "Tiepolo and His Contemporaries," 1938.

Oakland, Scholz Exhibition, 1957
Oakland, Mills College Art Gallery, "Drawings from Bologna, 1520–1800," 1957.

Oakland, Scholz Exhibition, 1960
Oakland, Mills College Art Gallery, "Venetian Drawings 1600–1800," 1960.

Oberlin College, Drawings of the 18th Century, 1951
Oberlin College, Allen Memorial Art Museum, "Exhibition of Master Drawings of the 18th Century in France and Italy," *Bulletin*, VIII, 1951, no. 2.

Paris, Lehman Exhibition, 1957
Paris, Musée de l'Orangerie, "Exposition de la collection Lehman de New York," 1957.

Smith College, Piranesi, 1961
Northampton, Mass., Smith College Museum of Art, "Piranesi," 1961.

Venice, Disegni di una collezione veneziana del Settecento, 1966
Venice, Fondazione Giorgio Cini, "Disegni di una collezione veneziana del Settecento," 1966.

Venice, Guardi Exhibition, 1965
Venice, Palazzo Grassi, "Mostra dei Guardi," 1965.

Venice, Scholz Exhibition, 1957
Venice, Fondazione Giorgio Cini, "Venetian Drawings from the Collection of Janos Scholz," 1957.

Venice, Wallraf Exhibition, 1959
Venice, Fondazione Giorgio Cini, "Disegni veneti del Settecento nella collezione Paul Wallraf," 1959.

Catalogue

Francesco Solimena

Canale di Serino (Avellino) 1657–Barra (Naples) 1747

1 *The Arrival of Columbus in the New World*

Pen and brown ink, gray wash, over black chalk. 10⅝ × 21⁵⁄₁₆ inches (26.3 × 54.2 cm.). Vertical crease at center.

Numbered in pen and brown ink at lower left, *37* (*36* crossed out); in pen and brown ink on verso, *270*.

Verso: Black chalk study for the same composition.

Richard Wunder recognized in the drawings on the recto and verso of this sheet Solimena's studies for one of the three large canvases painted between 1708 and 1728 to decorate the ceiling of the Sala del Minor Consiglio in the Palazzo Ducale, Genoa, which were destroyed by fire in 1777. The three compositions represented: the *Arrival of Christopher Columbus in America*, of which the only certain record is the present preparatory drawing, where Columbus is seen at left with an allegorical figure of Christian Faith dominating the composition in the sky at center; the *Martyrdom of the Giustiniani at Chios*, known through an oil sketch at the Museo di Capodimonte in Naples (Bologna, *Solimena*, pl. 150) and a preparatory drawing in the Società Napoletana di Storia Patria (identified and repr. by Vitzthum, pl. 24); and the *Arrival of the Ashes of St. John the Baptist in Genoa*, known through an oil sketch in the De' Ferrari collection in Genoa (Bologna, *Solimena*, pl. 152) and elaborate preparatory drawings in Stockholm (*Drawings from Stockholm* [exhibition catalogue], New York, The Pierpont Morgan Library, 1969, pl. 37) and at Holkham Hall.

The present drawing testifies to Solimena's extraordinary gifts as a composer of large-scale historical compositions and to his elegance as a draughtsman.

PROVENANCE: James Hazen Hyde.

BIBLIOGRAPHY: Richard P. Wunder, "Solimena Drawings at the Cooper Union Museum," *Art Quarterly*, XXIV, 1961, pp. 151–164, figs. 1 (recto), 4 (verso); *Disegni napoletani del Sei e del Settecento nel Museo di Capodimonte* (exhibition catalogue by Walter Vitzthum), Naples, Museo di Capodimonte, 1966, under no. 33.

EXHIBITIONS: Detroit, Institute of Arts, "Art in Italy, 1600–1700," 1965, no. 167, repr.; New York, The Two Sicilies, 1970, no. 25, repr.

Cooper-Hewitt Museum, Smithsonian Institution
Gift of the Trustees of the Estate of
James Hazen Hyde, 1960–1–92

2 *St. Maurus Healing an Invalid*

Brush and brown wash, over black chalk. 5¼ × 6⅝ inches (13.3 × 16.8 cm.). Several stains.

Inscribed in black chalk at lower right, *Solimeni*; in pen on old mount, *Fran:ᶜᵒ Solimeni Napolitana*.

A recently rediscovered study for the central group in a picture representing St. Maurus, disciple of St. Benedict, healing the sick during a journey to France, painted by Solimena for the Benedictine abbey of Montecassino between 1697 and 1708 and destroyed during World War II. A study for the whole horizontal composition involving other invalids being brought to St. Maurus is in the Louvre (repr. *L'Oeil*, January 1963, pp. 44–45) and oil sketches for the paintings are in Budapest and Toulon (see *Le Dessin à Naples du XVIᵉ siècle au XVIIIᵉ siècle* [exhibition catalogue by Walter Vitzthum], Paris, Musée du Louvre, 1967, under no. 76).

Transparent applications of light brown wash over an extremely free sketch in black chalk characterize many of Solimena's preliminary designs, and this procedure reveals the influence of his Neapolitan predecessor Luca Giordano.

PROVENANCE: Richard Dalton (Lugt 782).

Joseph McCrindle

3 *Deborah and Barak*

Brush and black ink, gray wash, over black chalk. 14¹⁵⁄₁₆ × 11¹⁵⁄₁₆ inches (37.9 × 30.3 cm.). Slight foxing.

Numbered in brush and gray wash at lower right, *8*; in pen and brown ink on verso, *g* [?] *18*.

Verso: Black chalk study of nude male figure wearing a helmet.

In this free, pictorial sketch Solimena represents the prophetess Deborah, seated under her palm tree, ordering Barak to take arms against Sisera (Judges 4: 5–7). The drawing is an early study for Solimena's *Deborah and Barak*, painted in Naples during the vice-regency of Alois Raimund von Harrach from 1728 to 1733, and now in the Harrach palace in Vienna (Bologna, *Solimena*, pl. 175). A finished drawing in the Uffizi (Bologna, *Solimena*, pl. 174), less pictorial and more calligraphic in character, is closer to the picture, and Vitzthum has pointed out that the two drawings represent the extreme poles of Solimena's stylistic gamut as a draughtsman. His technique is extraordinarily loose and free in his first sketches, while his finished drawings are elegant and elaborate.

PROVENANCE: Purchased by the Metropolitan Museum in London, 1963.

BIBLIOGRAPHY: *Cento Disegni Napoletani* (exhibition catalogue by Walter Vitzthum), Florence, Gabinetto Disegni e Stampe degli Uffizi, 1967, mentioned p. 64.

The Metropolitan Museum of Art
Rogers Fund, 63.98.1

Faustino Bocchi

Brescia 1659–Brescia 1742

4 *The Mock Visit of Ceremony*

Pen and brown ink, brown and gray wash, over black chalk; squared in black chalk. Sheet: $11^5/_8 \times 11^1/_2$ inches (29.5 × 29.2 cm.); drawn surface: diameter 11 3/16 inches (28.4 cm.).

Numbered in pen and brown ink at lower right margin, *1300 1511 1592. . . .*

The Brescian Faustino Bocchi made a specialty of comic genre scenes, very often of circular format, featuring absurdly costumed dwarfs and hunchbacks. Other drawings, preparatory for such pictures, are in the collection of David Rust in Washington and in the Kunsthaus, Zurich (Inv. 1943/10, as P. L. Ghezzi).

PROVENANCE: Purchased by the Metropolitan Museum in London, 1962.

The Metropolitan Museum of Art
Rogers Fund, 62.119.1

Sebastiano Ricci

Belluno 1659–Venice 1734

5 *Figure Studies*

Pen and brown ink, gray wash, over red and a little black chalk. $11^1/_8 \times 7^1/_2$ inches (28.3 × 19.1 cm.).

Inscribed in pen and brown ink on mount, *Sebastian Ricci.*

The figures on this sheet of studies are grouped with so much grace and art that one might think that Ricci was preparing a specific religious or historical composition. Actually, he seems to have been engaged in a superior form of artistic doodling. Other sheets of studies by Sebastiano in the Louvre (Inv. 14,271) and the British Museum (1960–4–9–114) have similar elegant figures jotted on the page in the same fashion, and none is related to a known picture. In drawing such sketches Ricci kept himself in practice, and when called upon to compose one of his vast pictures, his memory and his sketchbooks could supply him with a whole repertory of graceful poses and groups. Ricci is a Janus-like figure in Venetian art. At once conservative and progressive, he looks back to Paolo Veronese (and indeed this sheet recalls Veronese's own sketches) and forward to Giovanni Battista Tiepolo, on whom he had a decisive influence.

PROVENANCE: John Barnard (Lugt 1419 and 1420); Hugh N. Squire, London; purchased by the Metropolitan Museum in London, 1962.

BIBLIOGRAPHY: J. Bean, *Metropolitan Museum of Art Bulletin*, March 1963, p. 235, fig. 8; Bean, *100 European Drawings*, no. 39, repr.; Memphis-Lexington, Ricci Exhibition, 1965–1966, no. 67, repr., though not exhibited.

The Metropolitan Museum of Art
Gustavus A. Pfeiffer Fund, 62.120.6

6 *Allegory with Figures of Hope, Time, and Death*

Pen and brown ink, gray wash, over red chalk. $10^3/_4 \times 7^{11}/_{16}$ inches (27.3 × 19.5 cm.). Lined.

Inscribed in pen and brown ink at lower right, *Seb. Ricci.*

The old French inscription on the mount, *Entre le Temps et la Mort, l'Homme invoque l'Espérance*, gives a satisfactory explanation of the subject. The composition is not related to any surviving picture and may indeed be a study for a book illustration. The red chalk that appears under Ricci's elegant, meandering pen line gives an extraordinarily coloristic sparkle to this drawing, as does the subtle contrast between the brown pen lines and the transparent gray wash.

PROVENANCE: R. Willett; William Esdaile (*R. Willett's coll^n WE P 86 N164* inscribed on verso of mount, also Lugt 2617 on recto of mount); purchased by the Metropolitan Museum in Paris, 1967.

The Metropolitan Museum of Art
Rogers Fund, 67.65

7 *Venus and Cupid with Other Figures before an Altar*

Black chalk. 8 11/16 × 6 7/16 inches (22 × 16.4 cm.). Lined.

Numbered in pen and brown ink, *322* [?].

A drawing by Sebastiano Ricci that once belonged to Mariette and was certified as "Seb. Ricci" in the cartouche at the lower edge of one of the French collector's characteristic blue mats has particular interest since Mariette knew the artist personally in Venice. As Mariette reports in his *Abécédario*, "Lorsque je l'ai connu, il étoit logé dans un appartement des Procuraties et vivoit à la grande." The drawing, however, cannot be traced in the Mariette sale catalogue of 1775 unless it was possibly among the "trois compositions de fantaisie" listed as a part of lot no. 649.

The abundant use of hatching suggests that the drawing is earlier rather than later, probably dating around 1700, if not before. Among the rich sequence of 211 Ricci drawings at Windsor Castle, the Morgan drawing is best compared to the black chalk study for *Job Taunted by His Wife*, a painting, formerly at Marseilles in the Sipriot collection, that Sir Anthony Blunt places about 1695 (Anthony Blunt and Edward Croft-Murray, *Venetian Drawings of the XVII and XVIII Centuries . . . at Windsor Castle*, London, 1957, p. 55, figs. 31, 32).

PROVENANCE: Pierre-Jean Mariette (Lugt 1852); purchased by the Morgan Library in London, 1950.

BIBLIOGRAPHY: Morgan Library, *First Fellows Report, 1950*, p. 51; Morgan Library, *A Review of Acquisitions, 1949–1968*, p. 164.

EXHIBITIONS: Memphis-Lexington, Ricci Exhibition, 1965–1966, no. 21, repr.

The Pierpont Morgan Library
Gift of the Fellows, 1950.5

8 *The Education of the Virgin*

Pen and brown ink, over black chalk. 9 3/16 × 6 1/4 inches (23.3 × 15.9 cm.). Lined.

Inscribed in pen and brown ink on verso, *disegno distinto | Proviene dalla Raccolta di disegni della Galleria Corniani d'Algarotti in Venezia.*

A spirited example of Sebastiano's penmanship at its most abbreviated, where the artist's pen is working at top speed. The charming composition does not occur in a known picture by Ricci, but the subject was used in 1732 by Giambattista Tiepolo for his altarpiece in the Chiesa della Fava, Venice, further evidence of the preponderant influence of Sebastiano on Giambattista.

PROVENANCE: Corniani-Algarotti, Venice; A. de Burlet, Berlin and Basel; purchased by the Metropolitan Museum in New York, 1967.

The Metropolitan Museum of Art
Purchase, The Florence and Carl
Selden Foundation, Inc. Gift, 67.15

Paolo Pagani
Castello Valsolda, near Lugano 1661–Milan 1716

9 *Antiochus and Stratonice*

Pen and black ink, gray wash, over black chalk. 10 7/8 × 21 1/2 inches (27.6 × 54.6 cm.). Several spots.

Inscriptions in pen and black ink in the artist's hand identifying the principal figures and furniture: *Consultanti | ò medici sopra | il male di Antioco; medico | inteligente; Antioco; Seleuco; la bella Stratonica; Letto d'oro nel qual | giace Antioco; sedia di Stratonica*; long inscription in the artist's hand summarizing the story of Antiochus and Stratonice at lower margin, beginning, *Seleuco Rè in Syria che cede la moglie sua ad Antioco suo figliolo di essa inalterabilmente inamorato . . .* , and signed, *Paulo Pagani Servo Hu.^mo.*

This impressive design for a complete composition, no doubt intended for a ceiling decoration, is an important, hitherto unpublished document giving us further knowledge of the style of Paolo Pagani, an unjustly neglected artist of great significance in the formation of the rococo style. Pagani, Lombard by birth, was active in Venice, and his trips to Austria and Moravia, where he worked extensively, explain much that was to come in central European decoration. Until recently our notions of Pagani's style as a draughtsman have been somewhat unclear, though Hermann Voss (*Belvedere*, VIII, 1929) and Otto Kurz (*Dibutade*, II, 1955) published drawings that have served as useful points of reference. The Poitiers sketch published by Kurz is drawn on a letter signed by Pagani, which enables us to identify as autograph the inscriptions on the present drawing. Drawings by Pagani have been found masquerading under a variety of names. For example, a fine sheet in the British Museum (1946-7-13-585) representing the Temptation of St. Anthony, drawn with the same swelling, rounded pen line and as intensely coloristic as the present drawing, was for many years attributed to the late sixteenth-century Florentine, Passignano.

Pagani has gone to considerable pains to give an accurate representation of this historic scene with a full, rather operatic cast of characters on stage. At the center lies the lovesick Antiochus, his anguished father, Seleucus, at his side. Antiochus's beautiful stepmother is seated at the right; at left of center *il medico inteligente* prescribes the remedy: Antiochus's marriage to his stepmother.

Robert and Bertina Suida Manning

Paolo de Matteis
Cilento 1662–Naples 1728

10 *Galatea Triumphant*

Brush and brown wash, over black chalk. 10½ × 7¹³/₁₆ inches (26.7 × 19.8 cm.).

Inscribed in pen and brown ink at lower left, *P. Matteis*; unidentified paraph in pen and brown ink at lower right.

Verso: Black chalk study of the same figure.

A felicitous sample of Paolo de Matteis's draughtsmanship, strongly influenced by the example of Luca Giordano. This *Galatea* may well be a preparatory study for the *Triumph of Galatea* in the Brera, Milan (no. 610), where the sea nymph is seated in essentially the same position.

The unidentified paraph at the lower right corner of the sheet also occurs on a drawing in the Metropolitan Museum attributed to Mattia Preti, but which bears Matteis's name and initials and may be an exercise by him in the style of Preti (repr. *Drawings from New York Collections*, II, *The Seventeenth Century in Italy*, New York, 1967, no. 104).

PROVENANCE: T. Russell; purchased by the Metropolitan Museum in London, 1968.

The Metropolitan Museum of Art Rogers Fund, 68.172.1

Giuseppe Maria Crespi
Bologna 1665–Bologna 1747

11 *Marcolfa Persuades Cacasenno to Mount a Horse*

Red chalk. 7⁷/₈ × 5³/₄ inches (20 × 14.6 cm.).

A study in reverse for one of Crespi's twenty etchings (in this case, Bartsch, XIX, p. 409, no. 39) illustrating the old and rather complicated Bolognese burlesque histories of Bertoldo, Bertoldino, and Cacasenno. In this scene Marcolfa tries to persuade the recalcitrant gamin Cacasenno to mount a horse by telling him that the animal is showing its teeth as a sign of good will. The rather dry draughtsmanship is to be explained by Crespi's surprising fidelity to a long-established Bolognese academic tradition of figure drawing, for as a painter, on the contrary, his handling is very loose and intensely pictorial. Two further red chalk studies for this series of illustrations are in the Hamburg Kunsthalle (52449 and 52440, for Bartsch 41 and 35, respectively).

PROVENANCE: Purchased by the Metropolitan Museum in London, 1953.

BIBLIOGRAPHY: A. Hyatt Mayor, *Metropolitan Museum of Art Bulletin*, November 1953, p. 77, repr.; Jacob Bean, *Master Drawings*, IV, 1966, no. 4, p. 420, pl. 36 (the etching repr. fig. 3).

The Metropolitan Museum of Art The Elisha Whittelsey Collection, 53.535.23 (Print Department)

Benedetto Luti

Florence 1666–Rome 1724

12 *Pius V and the Ambassador of the King of Poland*

Black, red, and some blue chalk, brown wash, heightened with white. $15\frac{3}{8} \times 21\frac{3}{4}$ inches (39.1 × 55.2 cm.). Lined.

Inscribed in pen and brown ink on mount, *Benedetto Luti*.

The Dominican pope, St. Pius V, is here represented blessing a sample of the soil of Rome, to be taken as a relic to the king of Poland by his ambassador, who kneels before the pope. Anthony Clark points out that this elaborately finished sheet is very probably the drawn *modello* for a picture commissioned in 1712 by the General of the Dominicans as a gift to Clement XI Albani, on the occasion of the canonization of Pius V. The picture, praised by Luti's biographer, Lione Pascoli, as "per verità superbissima" and pronounced a "chef-d'oeuvre" by Dézallier d'Argenville, hung in the eighteenth century in the Palazzo Albani alle Quattro Fontane in Rome, but its present whereabouts is unknown (Vittorio Moschini, "Benedetto Luti," *L'Arte*, XXVI, 1923, p. 112).

Luti, a conscientious academic artist, has attempted an historically accurate representation of an event that took place a century and a half earlier during the reign of Pius V (1559–1565). The façade and square of St. Peter's are represented as they appeared in the 1560s; Lafreri's engraving in the *Speculum* was very possibly Luti's guide for this reconstruction. In the background, at right of upper center, may be discerned part of the dome of St. Peter's, still unfinished at Michelangelo's death in 1564.

PROVENANCE: Thomas Brand Hollis; Mr. Disney; sale, London, Christie's, July 1, 1969, no. 128, repr.; purchased by the Metropolitan Museum in London, 1969.

The Metropolitan Museum of Art
Rogers Fund, 69.169

13 *Head of a Bearded Man*

Pastel. $12\frac{11}{16} \times 10\frac{3}{8}$ inches (32.2 × 26.4 cm.). Lined.

Inscribed in pen and brown ink on verso of mount, *Roma 1715 | Il Cavalier Benedetto Luti fece -/*; unidentified collector's mark stamped in black on mount.

Benedetto Luti's Florentine training is evident in the technique of this drawing. It certainly reflects his knowledge of the pastel heads of the sixteenth-century Marchigian Federico Barocci, whose paintings and drawings were so much admired in Florence through the seventeenth and into the eighteenth century. In fact, the largest group of Barocci's drawings, many of them in pastel, was and still is conserved in the Grand Ducal collection at the Uffizi.

Luti utilized this medium on a number of occasions: the Louvre possesses a pastel self-portrait, drawn for the *dilettante romano* Nicola Pio, and there are two pastel heads of girls at Holkham Hall, one of which is inscribed in the same hand that wrote the annotations on the verso of the present drawing's mount.

Professor and Mrs. Julius Held

Alessandro Magnasco

Genoa about 1667–Genoa 1749

14 *The Peep Show*

Brush and brown watercolor, occasionally touched with white, over black chalk, on light brown paper. $9\frac{11}{16} \times 13\frac{1}{4}$ inches (24.6 × 33.7 cm.).

Verso: Slight figure sketch in black chalk.

Magnasco devoted a number of paintings to the representation of the itinerant peep show and its audience of children, cripples, and dogs, sometimes composing in horizontal format, sometimes vertically. The painting nearest to the Morgan drawing is one that, in 1949, was in the collection of Dr. Miro Martini at Cremona.

Magnasco's paintings and drawings, neglected for more than a century and a half, returned to some prominence only in the 1920s and 1930s, so at the beginning of the century it was possible for this drawing—then in the well-known Beurdeley collection—to be attributed to Fragonard, a tribute to Magnasco's swift and telling handling of the brush.

PROVENANCE: Alfred Beurdeley (Lugt 421); purchased by the Morgan Library in Amsterdam, 1961.

BIBLIOGRAPHY: Morgan Library, *Twelfth Fellows Report*,

1962, p. 82, repr.; Morgan Library, *A Review of Acquisitions, 1949–1968*, p. 155.

EXHIBITIONS: Amsterdam, Bernard Houthakker, "Dessins," 1961, no. 42, repr.

The Pierpont Morgan Library
Gift of the Fellows, 1961.37

15 *Seated Monk in a Landscape*

Brush and gray-brown wash, heightened with white, on light brown paper. 10 ³⁄₁₆ × 8 ⁵⁄₁₆ inches (25.9 × 21 cm.). Lined.

Inscribed in brush and gray-brown wash at lower margin, *B. Agustinu novelli;* in pen and brown ink, *B. Augustinus novellus Panormitanus;* in black chalk on verso, *Pietro Novelli.*

The old inscriptions on this fine sheet lead to confusion in the attribution, and the drawing is said to have passed through the London sales rooms as the work of the Sicilian artist Pietro Novelli. In fact, as Mr. Scholz has pointed out, the inscriptions identify the subject, the Augustinian hermit, the Blessed Agostino Novelli meditating over a book in a landscape. This is a characteristic example of Magnasco's draughtsmanship, revealing his partiality for the point of the brush in place of the pen.

BIBLIOGRAPHY: Janos Scholz, "Drawings by Alessandro Magnasco," *Essays in the History of Art Presented to Rudolf Wittkower*, London, 1967, p. 239, fig. 2.

EXHIBITIONS: New Haven, Scholz Exhibition, 1964, no. 80, fig. 14; Louisville, Kentucky, J. B. Speed Art Museum, Ann Arbor, University of Michigan Museum of Art, "Alessandro Magnasco," 1967, no. 12, repr.; London, Scholz Exhibiton, 1968, no. 58.

Janos Scholz

16 *Reclining Man in Meditation Visited by an Angel*

Brush and brown wash, heightened with white, on light brown paper. 10 ⁵⁄₁₆ × 8³⁄₄ inches (26.2 × 22.2 cm.).

Inscribed in pen and brown ink at lower left, *Magnaschino.*

Magnasco produced a great many such figure studies, executed with point of brush on rough beige paper. Very few of them can be connected with specific pictures, and they seem to have been done as graphic exercises on given themes. The monks and hermits that people Magnasco's paintings are also a constant subject of his drawings. In New York there are other drawings of this sort in the collections of Mrs. Richard Krautheimer and Mr. and Mrs. E. V. Thaw.

PROVENANCE: Johann Amann, Zurich; J. Hansegger, New York; purchased by the Metropolitan Museum in New York, 1953.

EXHIBITIONS: Louisville, Kentucky, J. B. Speed Art Museum, Ann Arbor, University of Michigan Museum of Art, "Alessandro Magnasco," 1967, no. 13, repr.

The Metropolitan Museum of Art
Rogers Fund, 53.169

Donato Creti
Cremona 1671–Bologna 1749

17 *Holy Family with St. John*

Pen and brown ink. 12 ¹⁄₁₆ × 9 ¹⁄₁₆ inches (30.6 × 23 cm.). Lined.

As far as could be ascertained, this typical example of Creti's graceful mature manner as a draughtsman is not related to any specific painting. It may be compared in style with a drawing like the *Holy Family with St. Catherine and Angels* at Christ Church, Oxford (*Burlington Magazine*, CXI, 1969, p. 376, fig. 59).

It was Dr. Hans Tietze who, in 1946, first properly assigned the drawing to Creti. Fairfax Murray had earlier attributed it to Guido Reni, on whose style and that of Simone Cantarini, Creti ultimately depends.

PROVENANCE: Nathaniel Hone (Lugt 2793); Charles Fairfax Murray; purchased by J. Pierpont Morgan in London, 1910.

BIBLIOGRAPHY: Fairfax Murray, I, 98 (as Guido Reni); Otto Kurz, *Bolognese Drawings in the Royal Library at Windsor Castle*, London, 1955, under no. 194; Renato Roli, *Donato Creti*, Milan, 1967, p. 109.

The Pierpont Morgan Library
No. I, 98

18 *Satyr*

Black chalk. $9\frac{7}{8} \times 8\frac{1}{8}$ inches (25.1×20.6 cm.). Inscription at upper margin of verso visible on recto.

Inscribed in pen and brown ink on verso, *Di Donato Creti detto Ragazzino Originale Bologna | No. 73*; in pen and brown ink on verso of mount, *Cav. Donato Creti, Cremonese, detto Ragazzino . . . No | 365.*

The satyr may well be Pan as he seizes the Arcadian nymph Syrinx, who is transformed into a clump of reeds. The drawing, which cannot be related to a surviving picture, is a particularly free example of Creti's chalk draughtsmanship, which, like his pen work, owes so much to Guido Reni.

PROVENANCE: Richard Philipps, Lord Milford (Lugt S. 2687); Philipps Family; Sir John Philipps.

EXHIBITIONS: Oakland, Scholz Exhibition, 1957, no. 47, repr.

Janos Scholz

Pier Leone Ghezzi
Rome 1674–Rome 1755

19 *An Ecclesiastic Playing the Cello*

Pen and brown ink, over black chalk. $9\frac{7}{8} \times 7\frac{11}{16}$ inches (25.1×19.5 cm.). Inscription on verso visible on recto; several small spots. Lined.

Inscribed in pen and brown ink on mount, *M. L'abbé*; on verso, *il virtuoso del Sigr De Bacqueville Roma 12 Marzo 1724.*

Pier Leone Ghezzi made a specialty of drawing good-humored caricatures of the celebrities and hangers-on in Roman society of the first half of the eighteenth century. An amazing number of these caricatures have survived, the bulk of them bound together in volumes conserved in the Vatican Library, the Farnesina, the print rooms of the British Museum, Berlin, and Dresden, and in the collection of the Duke of Wellington.

This cello-playing ecclesiastic is identified only as *M. L'abbé* in the inscription on the mount, but the artist has more fully described him on the verso of the sheet as "the virtuoso of Signor de Bacqueville," and has dated the drawing 1724.

Mr. Scholz possessed a complete album of Ghezzi caricatures, now in great part dispersed; nine remain in his collection, and he presented four to the Morgan Library. Also in New York, in the collection of Benjamin Sonnenberg, is an amusing Ghezzi caricature of a seated begging cleric.

PROVENANCE: Edward Goddard, London; Dr. Max A. Goldstein, St. Louis.

BIBLIOGRAPHY: "Italian Drawings from the Collection of Janos Scholz," *Metropolitan Museum of Art Bulletin*, May 1965, Part II, p. 344, repr.

Janos Scholz

20 *The Famous Castrato Il Farinelli*

Pen and brown ink, over traces of black chalk. $12 \times 8\frac{5}{16}$ inches (30.5×21.1 cm.). Stains at margins. Lined.

Inscribed in pen and brown ink in the artist's hand at lower left, *Farinello Napolitano | famoso cantore di Soprano che | cantò nel Teatro d'Aliberti nell' Anno 1724. | fatto da me Cav^{re} Ghezzi di 2 Marzo 1724*; numbered in pen and blue ink at upper right corner of mount, *30*; inscriptions in two different hands on verso giving biographical information about Farinelli.

The inscription in Ghezzi's own hand identifies the model and the occasion: we see Carlo Broschi (1705–1782), called Farinelli, the most celebrated castrato of all time, in female costume, singing at the Teatro Aliberti in Rome on March 2, 1724.

PROVENANCE: Edward Goddard, London; Dr. Max A. Goldstein, St. Louis.

BIBLIOGRAPHY: R. Kirkpatrick, *Domenico Scarlatti*, Princeton, 1953, pl. 30.

EXHIBITIONS: Hamburg, Scholz Exhibition, 1963, no. 68, fig. 58; A.F.A., 17th and 18th Century Drawings, 1966–1967, no. 26, repr.; London, Scholz Exhibition, 1968, no. 42.

Janos Scholz

Aureliano Milani
Bologna 1675–Bologna 1749

21 *Christ Healing a Possessed Man*

Pen and brown ink, brown wash, heightened with white, over traces of black chalk, on light brown paper. $11\frac{3}{4} \times 13\frac{3}{4}$ inches (29.8×34.9 cm.). Two small tears at left. Lined.

Inscribed in pen and brown ink at lower left, *[A]ureliano Milani*; numbered in red chalk at lower right, *101*.

This may well be a preparatory study for a picture mentioned by the eighteenth-century art historian Luigi Crespi in his list of works painted by Aureliano Milani before his departure for Rome in 1719: "per un altro signore, un Redentore, che libera l'indemoniato" (*Vite de' pittori bolognesi non descritte nella Felsina Pittrice*, Rome, 1769, pp. 147–148). The scene represents Jesus healing Legion, who was possessed with many devils (Luke 8: 27–33); in the background can be seen the herd of swine, possessed in its turn by the devils expelled from Legion, racing towards death by drowning in the lake. A local note is struck by the tabernacle-topped tomb at left, typically Bolognese in style and suggestive of that of Egidio Foscherari outside S. Domenico in Bologna. Luigi Crespi rightly praises Milani's competence as a draughtsman; here he shows himself a typical Bolognese, faithful to the example of Ludovico Carracci.

PROVENANCE: Major A. Merz, Ambleside, Westmoreland; purchased by the Metropolitan Museum in London, 1961.

The Metropolitan Museum of Art
Rogers Fund, 61.130.18

22 Hilly Landscape with Three Figures

Red chalk. $11\frac{1}{4} \times 17$ inches (28.6 × 43.2 cm.). Crease at upper right corner; several small spots of wash; inscription on verso visible at lower margin.

Inscribed in pen and brown ink at lower left, *Aur° Milani*; in pen and brown ink on verso, *Di Aureliano Milani Bolog°* [?] *16006*; in pen and brown ink on old mount, *Di Aureliano Milani Bolognese Pittore in Roma*.

Drawing from nature or improvising on the landscape around Bologna had been a pastime of Bolognese artists from Annibale Carracci onwards. Milani remained true to the local tradition and has here recorded, in an elegant, stylized line, a view of Appenine foothills near his native town. A similar chalk landscape drawing by Milani is in the British Museum (F.f.3.205; Gernsheim photograph 05038).

PROVENANCE: Dr. J. R. Wells; Mrs. F. A. Wells; purchased by the Metropolitan Museum in London, 1969.

The Metropolitan Museum of Art
Rogers Fund, 69.293

Giovanni Antonio Pellegrini
Venice 1675–Venice 1741

23 Head of Pompey Presented to Caesar

Pen and brown ink, brown wash, over red and black chalk. $11\frac{1}{4} \times 14\frac{5}{8}$ inches (28.6 × 37.2 cm.). Several stains, repaired tears and holes; spots of white at lower left margin.

Inscribed in pen and brown ink on verso, *N° 152 – secondi*.

Verso: Study for an elaborate doorway in pen and brown ink, brown wash, over black chalk.

Pellegrini, a peripatetic decorator who worked all across the north of Europe, has a rather mad, loose style as a draughtsman, as we see here in the present example. The distinction between the freest drawings of Diziani (see Nos. 50 and 54) and those of Pellegrini is occasionally hard to make. In this sheet the wildly indicated figures at the left and right of the composition would not be confused with Diziani's, but the figure bearing Pompey's head on a salver at right of center comes surprisingly close to Diziani in the way the bearer's head is drawn and in the scratchy, continuous hatching that suggests shadow.

PROVENANCE: John S. Newberry, New York.

BIBLIOGRAPHY: Terisio Pignatti, "Pellegrini Drawings in Venice," *Burlington Magazine*, CI, 1959, p. 451, fig. 51; *Metropolitan Museum of Art Bulletin*, October 1962, p. 65, repr.; Pignatti, *Disegni veneziani*, no. 6, repr.

The Metropolitan Museum of Art
Gift of John S. Newberry, 61.210

Sebastiano Galeotti
Florence 1676–Vico, near Mondovì 1746

24 Bacchus with Ceres and a Marine Deity

Pen and black ink, gray wash, on brownish paper. $9\frac{1}{2} \times 15\frac{1}{2}$ inches (24.1 × 39.4 cm.). Several repaired tears at margins; spots. Lined.

No doubt a study for one of the many frescoed decorations executed by Galeotti, an itinerant artist of Florentine training, in palaces across northern Italy. The brittle elegance of Galeotti's draughtsmanship reveals the preponderant influence of the

Venetian Sebastiano Ricci, who had executed important frescoes in the Palazzo Marucelli and the Palazzo Pitti in Florence in 1706.

Other characteristic drawings by Galeotti are in the collection of Robert and Bertina Suida Manning in New York.

PROVENANCE: Purchased by the Metropolitan Museum in Paris, 1965.

BIBLIOGRAPHY: Jacob Bean, review of catalogue of Italian drawings, National Gallery of Scotland, Edinburgh, *Master Drawings*, VII, 1969, no. 1, p. 56, pl. 34.

The Metropolitan Museum of Art
Rogers Fund, 65.207.1

Marco Ricci
Belluno 1676–Venice 1729

25 *Brigands Attacking Two Travelers*

Pen and brown ink, brown wash, over slight traces of black chalk. 14⅝ × 21 3/16 inches (37.2 × 53.8 cm.). Small tears and creases at right and left margins.

Inscribed in black chalk on verso of mount, *Ricci, Marco Venedig Belluno.*

Marco Ricci was heir to and a rejuvenator of a tradition of Venetian landscape draughtsmanship that goes back to the example of the Campagnolas, and ultimately, of course, to Giorgione and Titian. The romantically twisted trees seen here are very much part of this heritage. The action represented, brigands attacking two travelers, is close in spirit to the seventeenth-century Neapolitan, Salvator Rosa, whose picturesque, anecdotal landscapes were so much in fashion during the eighteenth century all over Italy.

PROVENANCE: Mestral de St. Saphorin, Switzerland.

BIBLIOGRAPHY: Janos Scholz, "Visiting Venetian Drawings at the National Gallery," *The Art Quarterly*, XXVII, 1964, p. 192, fig. 11.

EXHIBITIONS: Memphis-Lexington, Ricci Exhibition, 1965–1966, no. 41, repr.; London, Scholz Exhibition, 1968, repr.

Janos Scholz

26 *Travelers in an Italian Landscape*

Brush and brown watercolor, white tempera, on cream paper tinted brown. 15 5/16 × 21 inches (39 × 53.3 cm.). Watermark: indistinguishable, in a circle.

Executed purely with the brush and most likely made as an independent piece of decoration, this drawing reveals the facility Ricci owed, in part, to his experience as a scene painter.

PROVENANCE: Purchased by the Morgan Library in London, 1961.

BIBLIOGRAPHY: Morgan Library, *Twelfth Fellows Report, 1962*, pp. 83–84; Morgan Library, *A Review of Acquisitions, 1949–1968*, p. 164.

EXHIBITIONS: Memphis-Lexington, Ricci Exhibition, 1965–1966, no. 40, repr.

The Pierpont Morgan Library
Gift of the Fellows, 1961.35

27 *Shepherds with their Flock and Cattle at a Stream*

Pen and brown ink, brown wash, over black chalk. 14½ × 20⅞ inches (37 × 53 cm.). Lined.

Inscribed on mount in pencil at lower right, *7 Day Lot 43*; inscribed on verso of mount in pen and brown ink, *36*, in pencil, *very fine and perfect M | Dº Ph | Marco Ricci | True W.*

As the unknown collector wrote on the back of the mount, this sunlit pastoral scene is indeed a "very fine" example of Ricci's mature pen-and-wash style. The word "true" is as a rule associated with the collector Arthur Pond (Lugt 2038), who employed it to indicate the hallmark of his approval, though usually in conjunction with his signature. If the drawing did come from Pond, the words "7 Day Lot 43" on the front of the mount would not be amiss, as his sale in 1759 lasted eight days.

PROVENANCE: Charles Fairfax Murray; purchased by J. Pierpont Morgan in London, 1910.

BIBLIOGRAPHY: Fairfax Murray, I, 77; Memphis-Lexington, Ricci Exhibition, 1965–1966, no. 96, though not exhibited.

The Pierpont Morgan Library
No. I, 77

28 *Pastoral Landscape*

Gouache on kidskin. $11\frac{1}{8} \times 17\frac{1}{4}$ inches (28.3×43.8 cm.).

This and Nos. 29, 30, and 31 are characteristic examples of one of Marco Ricci's specialties, imaginary and highly picturesque landscapes executed in bright, opaque gouache on kidskin, a technique that Marco may indeed have invented. The nonporous, slightly granular surface of the kidskin serves as ideal support for Marco's thick applications of gouache in a lively gamut of colors. The subjects of these drawings, really small paintings intended to be framed and hung as such, are extremely varied, ranging from pastoral landscapes that have the air of being observed from nature, like the present example, through picturesque scenes with monkish figures inspired by Salvator Rosa (see No. 29), to architectural capricci in landscape settings, where classical buildings are grouped with imaginative caprice (see Nos. 30 and 31). Such capricci had a marked influence on Canaletto and Francesco Guardi. A further fine architectural capriccio by Marco in gouache on kidskin is in the Metropolitan Museum.

PROVENANCE: Sale, London, Christie's, March 29, 1966, no. 96, repr.; purchased by the Metropolitan Museum in London, 1967.

BIBLIOGRAPHY: *Metropolitan Museum of Art Bulletin*, March 1968, p. 302, repr.

The Metropolitan Museum of Art Rogers Fund, 67.67

29 *Monks in a Landscape*

Gouache on kidskin. $11\frac{5}{8} \times 17\frac{1}{8}$ inches (29.5×43.5 cm.), sight. Some flaking; stain at upper right margin.

See No. 28.

EXHIBITIONS: London, P. & D. Colnaghi, "Old Master Drawings," 1954, no. 22, pl. II; Memphis-Lexington, Ricci Exhibition, 1965–1966, no. 30, repr.

Harry G. Sperling

30 *Figures in Roman Ruins*

Gouache on kidskin. $11\frac{7}{8} \times 17\frac{3}{8}$ inches (30.2×44.1 cm.), sight. Some losses.

See No. 28.

PROVENANCE: Arthur Acland-Hood, Holywell Hall, Lincolnshire.

BIBLIOGRAPHY: Memphis-Lexington, Ricci Exhibition, 1965–1966, no. 86, repr., though not exhibited.

James Parker

31 *Figures under Ruined Arches*

Gouache on kidskin. $11\frac{15}{16} \times 17\frac{1}{2}$ inches (30.3×44.5 cm.), sight. Slight losses.

See No. 28.

PROVENANCE: Arthur Acland-Hood, Holywell Hall, Lincolnshire.

BIBLIOGRAPHY: Memphis-Lexington, Ricci Exhibition, 1965–1966, no. 87, repr., though not exhibited.

James Parker

32 *Roman Capriccio*

Gouache. $14\frac{11}{16} \times 24$ inches (37.2×61 cm.).

Unlike many other tempera drawings by Ricci, this capriccio is executed on paper rather than on vellum or kidskin (see Nos. 28–31). It is, however, very probably a work of the same years in the late 1720s.

PROVENANCE: Purchased by the Morgan Library in London, 1961.

BIBLIOGRAPHY: Morgan Library, *Twelfth Fellows Report, 1962*, pp. 83–84, repr.; Memphis-Lexington, Ricci Exhibition, 1965-1966, no. 88, repr., though not exhibited; Morgan Library, *A Review of Acquisitions, 1949–1968*, p. 164.

EXHIBITIONS: London, P. & D. Colnaghi, "Paintings by Old Masters," 1961, no. 9, pl. X.

The Pierpont Morgan Library Gift of the Fellows, 1961.29

Anton Maria Zanetti the Elder
Venice 1680–Venice 1767

Anton Maria Zanetti the Younger
Venice 1706–Venice 1778

33 *Album of Drawings: Delle antiche statue greche e romane*

Preparatory drawings (102) by the two Zanettis for their book *Delle antiche statue greche e romane, che nell' antisala della Libreria di San Marco, e in altri luoghi pubblici di Venezia si trovano*, Venice, I, 1740; II, 1743.

Diana

Graphite. 14 5/16 × 9 7/8 inches (36.5 × 25 cm.). Lined.

Inscribed and numbered in brown ink at lower center, *Diana / IX*.

The two-volume work by the Zanetti cousins, describing and illustrating the classical sculpture housed in their time in the Library of S. Marco and other places in Venice—and today for the most part preserved in the Archaeological Museum—was among the imposing publications of eighteenth-century Venice. The book was a project long cherished by Zanetti the Elder, the collector and amateur engraver who was an intimate of such artists as Rosalba Carriera, Canaletto, the Ricci, Piazzetta, and Tiepolo, as well as a lifelong friend of his French counterpart, P.-J. Mariette. Its production occupied him and his younger cousin, keeper of the Library of S. Marco and author of *Della pittura Veneziana*, 1771, for almost eighteen years and cost them a small fortune. The preparation involved the execution of the large quantity of preliminary red chalk drawings preserved in the Biblioteca Marciana (234) and the Morgan Library's finished drawings made for the guidance of the rather numerous engravers employed on the project. The elder Zanetti must have had the Morgan drawings mounted and bound up for himself in their present form just as soon as the second volume was published in 1743 since, as Dr. Alessandro Bettagno recently pointed out, the two volumes are listed in the inventory of his library made in 1744. The volumes, like those containing his own set of his chiaroscuro woodcuts now in the Print Room of the Boston Museum of Fine Arts, are gilt stamped with the Zanetti arms, which appropriately feature quarterings of engraver's tools. The drawings themselves, labeled in pen and set into borders of blue-gray wash, except for Piazzetta's frontispiece (see No. 44) which is framed in red, are arranged in the sequence of the printed work. In the instance of the statue of Cleopatra and that of Cupid, there are variant studies; in the case of Marcus Aurelius, a corrected proof of the engraving is included.

The statue of Diana, or Artemis, represented in the drawing to which the second volume is opened, is described by Bruna Forlati Tamaro as a good Roman copy of an Ionian Greek original of about 500 B.C. (repr. *Il Museo Archeologico del Palazzo Reale di Venezia* [Itinerari dei musei e monumenti d'Italia, no. 88], Rome, 1953, pp. 9, 46). The statue is now armless, and the head shown in the drawing has been replaced by a plaster reproduction from another more complete copy of the figure found in the ruins of Pompeii. The sculpture was part of the bequest of Cardinal Domenico Grimani in 1586.

The engraving after the drawing was executed by Giuseppe Patrini. Like all the engraved plates, it bears the inscription *Ant. M. q. Gir. e Ant. M. d'Aless. cugini Zanetti disegnarono*, but it is not possible to distinguish their hands among the drawings. The more competent draughtsmanship as exemplified in the exhibited drawing is perhaps that of the elder Zanetti rather than of the younger, who was more active as an historian than as a practicing artist.

PROVENANCE: John Quantock (bookplate); purchased by the Morgan Library in New York, 1959.

BIBLIOGRAPHY: Morgan Library, *Ninth Fellows Report*, *1958–1959*, pp. 100–102; Morgan Library, *A Review of Acquisitions, 1949–1968*, p. 178; *Caricature di Anton Maria Zanetti* (exhibition catalogue by Alessandro Bettagno), Venice, Fondazione Giorgio Cini, 1969, p. 18.

The Pierpont Morgan Library
Gift of the Fellows, 1959.3:2–104

Sebastiano Conca
Gaeta 1680–Naples 1764

34 *St. Elizabeth of Portugal Kneeling before the Crucified Christ*

Brush and gray wash, heightened with white, over black chalk, on beige paper; squared for transfer in black chalk. 15 9/16 × 7 7/8 inches (39.6 × 20 cm.).

Walter Vitzthum points out that this scene represents St. Elizabeth, dowager queen of Portugal, kneeling in a Franciscan habit before a representation of the crucified Christ. She is identified by her regal attributes, a crown and scepter, seen in the foreground. After she became a widow in 1325, St.

Elizabeth retired to a house at Coimbra near a Poor Clares convent that she had founded.

The two sources of Conca's style as painter and draughtsman are apparent here—Neapolitan emotionalism is tempered by Roman classicism. Conca, though a pupil of Solimena, was strongly influenced by Marattesque classical measure during his stay in Rome.

PROVENANCE: Chevalier de Damery (Lugt 2862); Juan Jorge Peolo (Lugt 2020); Feral (Ferrall?) sale (according to inscription on verso).

BIBLIOGRAPHY: Walter Vitzthum, review of exhibition of Neapolitan drawings from the Cooper-Hewitt Museum at Finch College, *Burlington Magazine*, CXII, 1970, p. 264.

EXHIBITIONS: New York, The Two Sicilies, 1970, no. 31, repr.

Cooper-Hewitt Museum, Smithsonian Institution
Gift of the Misses Eleanor and Sarah Hewitt,
1931–64–272

Lorenzo de' Ferrari

Genoa 1680–Genoa 1749

35 *The Triumph of Justice*

Brush and brown wash, over black chalk. $9\frac{1}{2} \times 7\frac{15}{16}$ inches (24.1 × 20.2 cm.). Lined.

Inscribed in pen and brown ink at lower margin, *abte Lorenzo Defferari*.

The old inscription correctly identifies the drawing as a characteristic example of the graphic production of Lorenzo de' Ferrari, strongly influenced by the work of his more dynamic father, Gregorio, on the one hand, and by the rather rounded, ornamental style of Domenico Piola on the other. According to Ezia Gavazza, the drawing is a preparatory study for a frescoed medallion on the ceiling of a room in the Palazzo Grimaldi, Piazza S. Luca, Genoa, described by the old guides as representing Justice Distributing Prizes to the Arts. In the drawing, however, Justice raises her attribute, a pair of scales, in her left hand and is about to be crowned by a putto who flies above.

PROVENANCE: Purchased by the Metropolitan Museum in London, 1964.

BIBLIOGRAPHY: Ezia Gavazza, *Lorenzo de' Ferrari*, Milan, 1965, pp. 94–95, pl. 47.

The Metropolitan Museum of Art
Rogers Fund, 64.49.1

36 *Hercules Triumphant*

Pen and brown ink, brown wash, over black chalk. $19\frac{7}{16} \times 14\frac{1}{4}$ inches (49.4 × 36.2 cm.). Horizontal crease at center; repaired loss at left margin.

Inscribed in pen and brown ink below pedestal on which Hercules stands, *Lorenzo Deferrari*; in pen and brown ink on verso, *Z*; in black chalk on verso, *Sol. 10*.

Lorenzo de' Ferrari was a skilled practitioner in the very Genoese art of fresco decoration, and shared the propensity for ornamental and allegorical scenes seen in very steep perspective in settings of feigned architecture. Here Hercules is seen in dizzy perspective, standing with club and oak branch in hand, his feet resting on the skull of the Erymanthian boar, the victim of his fourth labor. Above, a flying female and a putto are about to crown him, while Fame, on a winged horse, sounds two long trumpets. A further study for a Triumph of Hercules seen *di sotto in su* is in the Pinacoteca di Brera (Inv. 568). There the feigned ceiling opening is a quatrefoil rather than a circle.

PROVENANCE: Wilhelm E. Suida.

Robert and Bertina Suida Manning

Giovanni Battista Piazzetta

Venice 1682–Venice 1754

37 *Study of an Executioner*

Charcoal, heightened with white, on faded blue paper. $15\frac{7}{8} \times 10\frac{7}{16}$ inches (40.3 × 26.4 cm.). Several spots, stains, and creases. Partially lined.

Inscribed in black chalk at lower left margin, *Sebastian Piombo*; at lower left corner, *Piombo*; in pen and brown ink at lower right, *Giamb . . . a Piazzetta Venez?*

The inscription of the artist's name at the lower right corner in the calligraphy of the "Reliable Venetian Hand" more or less certifies this drawing of an executioner displaying the head of his victim as an authentic study by Piazzetta. The drawing appears to be early, and substantiating the ascription of the unknown eighteenth-century collector is the fact that the handling of the charcoal and the white chalk highlighting convincingly adumbrates Piazzetta's vigorous later style. The type of the fur-hatted executioner with his great sword and bared right arm, who appears to be a study from the model, may be compared to the swordsmen in the paintings of the *Beheading of St. John the Baptist*, S. Antonio, Padua, and the *Beheading of St. Paul* in a Venetian private collection (Pallucchini, *Piazzetta*, pls. 102–103).

PROVENANCE: "Reliable Venetian Hand" (Lugt S. 3005c–d); purchased by the Metropolitan Museum in New York, 1961.

BIBLIOGRAPHY: Pignatti, *Disegni veneziani*, no. 47, repr.

EXHIBITIONS: Venice, Disegni di una collezione veneziana del Settecento, 1966, no. 75, repr.

The Metropolitan Museum of Art
Rogers Fund, 61.204

38 *Young Man Embracing a Girl*

Black and white chalk, on blue paper faded to gray. 15 9/16 × 12 7/16 inches (39.5 × 31.6 cm.). Vertical strip added at right edge of sheet, drawing continued, this section somewhat rubbed; vertical crease near right margin; creases at left margin. Watermark: letters H P or H R.

The most familiar of Piazzetta's drawings are his large, poetically delineated heads, made as independent works of art and constituting a kind of Venetian "Iconography." Much sought after in his own time and ever since, they sometimes exist in more than one authentic version or variant as well as in contemporary copies, so that the problem of attribution is a delicate one.

The carefully modeled Baer drawing is a singularly beautiful example, notable in the preservation of the most evanescent of its white highlights. As is true of an unfortunate number of Piazzetta drawings, the once blue paper has been transformed by time to a brownish gray. This sheet enjoys the distinction of being one of the series of Piazzetta's drawings engraved by Giovanni Cattini and published under the title *Icones ad vivum expressae* in

1754, the year of the artist's death. There is an old copy of the drawing in the Minneapolis Institute of Arts (Inv. 65.62).

PROVENANCE: H. A. Vivian Smith.

EXHIBITIONS: Cambridge, Mass., Fogg Art Museum, "Drawings from the Collection of Curtis O. Baer," 1958, no. 11, repr.

Dr. George M. Baer

39 *Head of a Levantine*

Black and white chalk, on blue paper faded to brown. 15 × 11½ inches (38.1 × 29.2 cm.), sight. Vertical strip attached to sheet at left margin, drawing continued in the artist's hand; several holes and spots.

This solidly rendered masculine head strikes a strong note among the softer types of the pretty youths and girls that Piazzetta more customarily depicted in drawings made for eighteenth-century collectors like Anton Maria Zanetti the Elder, Francesco Gabburri, Pierre-Jean Mariette, and Count Tessin. Such a Middle Eastern model would not have been too hard to find among the cosmopolitan residents of a maritime city. There is another study of the same man in the Accademia, Venice, and the subject appears in reverse in a mezzotint by Johann Lorenz Haid.

As this sheet and No. 40 demonstrate, it was not unusual for Piazzetta to use a paper that had been pieced at one side or the other.

PROVENANCE: Valmarana; Corsini; Giovanni Timai, Venice.

EXHIBITIONS: Hamburg, Scholz Exhibition, 1963, no. 113, pl. 89; New Haven, Scholz Exhibition, 1964, no. 81; London, Scholz Exhibition, 1968, no. 68.

Janos Scholz

40 *Young People Feeding a Dog*

Black and white chalk, on blue paper faded to gray. 15⅛ × 20⅛ inches (38.4 × 51.1 cm.), sight. Vertical crease at center; foxing throughout sheet; repaired tears at all margins; various repaired losses throughout sheet.

The pair of drawings in the Baker collection are among the largest and most elaborate of their kind. There are two others of more or less comparable scale and impressiveness in the Royal Collection at Windsor Castle (Anthony Blunt and Edward Croft-Murray, *Venetian Drawings of the XVII and XVIII Centuries . . . of Windsor Castle*, London, 1957, nos. 32 and 33 [the latter repr. as pl. 17]) and a third in the Cleveland Museum (Benesch, *Venetian Drawings*, pl. 11). It has been suggested that together they may have been intended to constitute a series of the Five Senses. The present drawing would, of course, represent Taste and the following one, Touch.

PROVENANCE: Giuseppe Cellini, Rome.

BIBLIOGRAPHY: Virch, *Baker Collection*, no. 56, repr.

EXHIBITIONS: New York, M. Knoedler and Company, "Great Master Drawings of Seven Centuries. Benefit Exhibition for Columbia University," 1959, no. 37, pl. XL.

Walter C. Baker

41 *Young Girl Selling a Fowl*

Black and white chalk, on blue paper faded to gray. $15\frac{1}{8} \times 20\frac{1}{8}$ inches (38.4 × 51.1 cm.), sight. Vertical crease at center; foxing and small abrasions throughout sheet; repaired tear at left margin; repaired losses at upper left and right corners; stain at lower right corner.

See No. 40.

PROVENANCE: Giuseppe Cellini, Rome.

BIBLIOGRAPHY: Virch, *Baker Collection*, no. 57.

Walter C. Baker

42 *Young Woman Holding a Pear*

Black chalk, heightened with white, on faded blue paper. $16\frac{3}{4} \times 13\frac{1}{2}$ inches (42.6 × 34.2 cm.). Foxed.

Inscribed on verso at lower right in black lead, *10*; below, *45*.

As was suggested by the late Dr. Otto Benesch, this drawing and two others in the Morgan Library, one of which is exhibited as No. 43, could conceivably have been designed as part of a series of the Five Senses. If so, the pear held by the young woman would mark this sheet as the Sense of Taste; the jingle ring would identify No. 43 as the Sense

of Hearing; and the gesture of the woman in the third Morgan sheet (repr., Fairfax Murray, IV, 91) might be regarded as consistent with a representation of the Sense of Touch, although her glance heavenward and the difference in feminine type may suggest another meaning. In the Gallerie dell' Accademia, Venice, there is a drawing of a young woman holding a rose, which could be interpreted as the Sense of Smell in such a sequence of the Senses (Rodolfo Pallucchini, *Piazzetta*, 1956, pl. 156).

All three Morgan sheets display the same kind of white lead chalk, and, contrary to Benesch's statement, there is no evidence of reworking, although there have been some surface losses. When examined under ultraviolet light, the white chalk areas fluoresce consistently. It is possible that the heavy, "loaded" effects in some areas were produced by the draughtsman's moistening of the chalk before he used it.

PROVENANCE: Charles Fairfax Murray; purchased by J. Pierpont Morgan in London, 1910.

BIBLIOGRAPHY: Fairfax Murray, IV, 89; Charles de Tolnay, *History and Techniques of Old Master Drawings*, New York, 1943, no. 140, repr.

EXHIBITIONS: New London, Connecticut, Lyman Allyn Museum, "Fourth Anniversary Exhibition: Drawings," 1936, no. 104.

The Pierpont Morgan Library
No. IV, 89

43 *Young Woman Holding a Jingle Ring*

Black chalk, heightened with white, on faded blue paper. $16\frac{3}{4} \times 13\frac{1}{2}$ inches (42.9 × 34.3 cm.). Foxed.

Inscribed on verso at lower left in graphite, *43*.

See No. 42

PROVENANCE: Charles Fairfax Murray; purchased by J. Pierpont Morgan in London, 1910.

BIBLIOGRAPHY: Fairfax Murray, IV, 90.

EXHIBITIONS: New York, Tiepolo Exhibition, 1938, no. 34; New York, Pierpont Morgan Library, "Illustrated Catalogue of an Exhibition Held on the Occasion of the New York World's Fair," 1939, no. 74.

The Pierpont Morgan Library
No. IV, 90

44 *Minerva's Homage to Venice*

Red chalk, over graphite. $15\frac{1}{2} \times 10\frac{15}{16}$ inches (39.3 $\times$ 27.7 cm.). Lined.

Preparatory drawing for the frontispiece of *Delle antiche statue greche e romane, che nell' antisala della Libreria di San Marco, e in altri luoghi pubblici di Venezia si trovano*, Venice, I, 1740, by Anton Maria Zanetti the Elder and Anton Maria Zanetti the Younger (see No. 33).

Anton Maria Zanetti had long been familiar with Piazzetta's work when he and his younger cousin of the same name commissioned the artist to design the frontispiece of their large two-volume *Delle antiche statue greche e romane . . .*, Venice, 1740–1743. As early as the summer of 1726, he had arranged for two drawings of heads by Piazzetta to be sent to his fellow collector Gabburri (Giovanni Bottari, *Raccolta di lettere sulla pittura scultura ed architettura*, II, Rome, 1757, pp. 140–142). Piazzetta's first book illustration, a design for a frontispiece of Antonio da Venezia's *La Chiesa di Gesù Cristo*, had appeared a little earlier in 1724, but his real activity as an illustrator started in the last half of the 1730s with the appearance of the first volumes of a ten-volume edition of Bossuet's *Oeuvres* (1736–1757), published by Giovanni Battista Albrizzi.

Piazzetta's drawing for the frontispiece of the first volume of the Zanetti work depicts the ermine-robed personification of Venice, the city's winged lion at her side, seated on a dais before which Minerva stands pointing to two classical torsos and some coins or medals lying at her feet; another female figure, perhaps History, sits recording the treasures in a large tome. Overhead there hovers a palm-bearing Victory who points below to a corner of the Doge's Palace and the Libreria, with a glimpse of a ship's prow and a gondola. The design was engraved in the same direction by Felicità Sartori, the woman painter and engraver who was a pupil of Rosalba Carriera, and between Piazzetta's drawing and the printed illustration, there were several changes in detail. A bust and a relief were substituted for the two torsos in the foreground of the drawing, and the Ionic capital resting in the right corner of the drawing was eliminated entirely. It is not illogical to assume that the two men behind the figure of Venice represent the two Zanetti—Anton Maria the Elder perhaps to be identified by the medallion he wears on a chain, a reference to his role as a collector of gems and coins, and the younger cousin, the historian, by the book he carries.

Piazzetta's design may have been the ultimate inspiration of the drawing *Venice as Protector of the Sciences and Arts* by Pietro Antonio Novelli in the Hermitage (repr. *Disegni veneti del Museo di Leningrado* [exhibition catalogue by Larissa Salmina], Venice, Fondazione Giorgio Cini, 1964, no. 117).

PROVENANCE: Purchased by the Morgan Library in New York, 1959.

BIBLIOGRAPHY: Morgan Library, *Ninth Fellows Report, 1958–1959*, pp. 100–102, repr.; Morgan Library, *A Review of Acquisitions, 1949–1968*, p. 178; *Caricature di Anton Maria Zanetti* (exhibition catalogue by Alessandro Bettagno), Venice, Fondazione Giorgio Cini, 1969, p. 18.

The Pierpont Morgan Library
Gift of the Fellows, 1959.3:1

45 *Apollo and the Muses*

Black chalk. $17\frac{1}{16} \times 11\frac{7}{8}$ inches (43.3 $\times$ 30.3 cm.). Lined.

This sheet and Nos. 46 and 47 come from a red morocco album of 201 drawings mounted on 94 leaves ($20\frac{5}{8} \times 15\frac{1}{16}$ inches, 52.4 $\times$ 38.3 cm.) decorated with borders brushed in red and gold; ornamented title page by another hand, pen and black ink with gray wash, lettered, *Raccolta / delle opere / piu segnalate in disegno / a lapis rosso e nero / inventate e delineate dal celebre / Giambatista Piazzetta / Veneto pittore.* Shortly after the drawings entered the Library, they were removed from the binding but not from the album leaves on which they are mounted; the binding is preserved separately.

One of the most elaborate sheets of the album presented to the Morgan Library by the Samuel H. Kress Foundation in 1961 is this slightly variant design, in the reverse, of Piazzetta's frontispiece of Tasso's *La Gerusalemme Liberata*. The book was produced in 1745 by the Venetian publisher Giovanni Battista Albrizzi, Piazzetta's devoted friend whose many commissions for book illustration provided a needed supplement for the artist's income as a painter. The chief difference between the drawing and the engraved illustration by Martin Schedel is the substitution of the portrait of Tasso for the winged figure of Virtue and motto *sola sibi satis* of the black chalk design, but there are several other changes as well. In the print, the two putti scattering flowers in the sky do not appear, and the relationship of the lutist's arms and instrument has been altered so that she is shown holding the face of the lute toward the spectator but still playing with her right hand. Otherwise, the reversal of the figure would have resulted in a left-handed performance. Certain weaknesses, like the poor articulation of the reclining figure holding up a crown, also carry over into the printed illustration.

The Kress series also contains eleven other drawings of *Gerusalemme* subjects, namely designs for tailpieces, but each of them invariably duplicates a superior version in the long sequence of Piazzetta's drawings for book illustration in the Biblioteca Reale at Turin (Mss. Var. 204 and 205). The subject of the present drawing, however, does not occur in the Turin albums and is, as far as could be ascertained, the only known drawing relating to the frontispiece.

PROVENANCE: Sir William Eden; Count Alessandro Contini-Bonacossi; Samuel H. Kress; Samuel H. Kress Foundation.

BIBLIOGRAPHY: Giuseppe Morazzoni, *Il libro illustrato veneziano del Settecento*, Milan, 1943, p. 125; Pallucchini, *Piazzetta*, pp. 54–62, pl. 193; Morgan Library, *Twelfth Fellows Report, 1962*, pp. 85–87; Pignatti, *Disegni nel Museo Correr*, under no. 40; Morgan Library, *A Review of Acquisitions, 1949–1968*, p. 159.

EXHIBITIONS: New York, Tiepolo Exhibition, 1938, no. 33.

The Pierpont Morgan Library
Gift of the Samuel H. Kress Foundation, 1961.12:74

See No. 45. The finely worked red chalk design is preparatory for an *antiporta* in the Venetian edition of a manual on surgery written by Johann Zacharias Platner (1694–1747). The distinguished German physician's *Institutiones chirurgicae rationalis tum medicae tum manualis in usus discentium variis nonnullorum ferramentorum aliorumque quae ad chirurgi officinam pertinent*, first published in Leipzig in 1745, appeared in Venice in 1747 under the auspices of Giovanni Battista Albrizzi. The engraved illustration, which is in the same direction as the drawing and is very nearly the same size ($8\frac{11}{16} \times 6\frac{5}{16}$ inches, 22.1×16.1 cm.), is inscribed *Gio. Batta. Piazzetta inv. Giulian Gianpiccoli sculp.* The surgeon shown pulling up his frilled cuff seems about to make an incision in the patient's outstretched arm, in the unusual setting of a landscape.

The book for which the black chalk border with martial symbols was designed has yet to be discovered.

When the sheet is examined on a light table, it is possible to see yet a third drawing, in black chalk, mounted beneath the red chalk drawing; it shows the portrait of a queen (Maria Theresa?) in an oval.

PROVENANCE: Sir William Eden; Count Alessandro Contini-Bonacossi; Samuel H. Kress; Samuel H. Kress Foundation.

BIBLIOGRAPHY: Giuseppe Morazzoni, *Il libro illustrato veneziano del Settecento*, Milan, 1943, p. 125; Pallucchini, *Piazzetta*, pp. 61–62; Morgan Library, *Twelfth Fellows Report, 1962*, pp. 85–87; Pignatti, *Disegni nel Museo Correr*, under no. 40; Morgan Library, *A Review of Acquisitions, 1949–1968*, p. 159.

EXHIBITIONS: New York, Tiepolo Exhibition, 1938, no. 33, repr.

The Pierpont Morgan Library
Gift of the Samuel H. Kress Foundation, 1961.12:8

46 *Surgeon and His Patient, Attended by Her Maid*

Red chalk, over black chalk. Design area, $8\frac{15}{16} \times 6\frac{5}{16}$ inches (22.7×16 cm.). Lined.

Border Design for the Page of a Book

Black chalk. $16\frac{1}{4} \times 12\frac{3}{16}$ inches (41.2×3.1 cm.). Width at sides, $1\frac{3}{8}$ inches (3.3 cm.); at top and bottom, $1\frac{13}{16}$ inches (4.6 cm.). Watermark: probably a crossbow. Lined.

47 *Male Nude Lying on a Standard*

Black chalk. $10\frac{3}{16} \times 15\frac{1}{8}$ inches (25.9×38.5 cm.). Lined.

See No. 45. In 1760, six years after Piazzetta's death, the Venetian publisher Albrizzi issued the *Studi di pittura*, a drawing book consisting of twenty-four plates of studies of heads and the human body, engraved by Marco Alvise Pitteri with duplicate plates in outline by Francesco Bartolozzi, after the designs of Piazzetta. In the preface Albrizzi states that, some years before his death, Piazzetta had been induced to execute these designs for instruction in the fundamentals of figure drawing, whether for professional use or for pleasure. In 1764, Albrizzi also published the plates with a French text, and for some time they continued to be a standard manual for draughtsmen.

The Kress album includes the drawings for the full sequence of plates as well as the frontispiece. The present sheet is one of eight devoted to the male figure, but there are studies as well of the female (a single torso) and infant nude, plus details of eyes and ears, and hands and feet in a variety of attitudes. All are executed in the same direction as the printed plates, which faithfully transcribe them with only an occasional slight deviation. The beautiful copy of the *Studi di pittura*, preserved in the Museo Correr (its Copy I), shows the plates in what must be the first state since none of the nudes display the addition of the fig leaves found in the plates of many other copies. Significantly, none of the drawings show the fig leaves.

The nude figure of the sheet exhibited here occurs as the dead Abel in an oil sketch owned by Aldo Ravà and reproduced as plate 60 of his Piazzetta monograph published in 1921. This may well be an instance of the use of the drawing book by a follower. Pallucchini makes no mention of the painting.

PROVENANCE: Sir William Eden; Count Alessandro Contini-Bonacossi; Samuel H. Kress; Samuel H. Kress Foundation.

BIBLIOGRAPHY: Giuseppe Morazzoni, *Il libro illustrato veneziano del Settecento*, Milan, 1943, p. 125; Pallucchini, *Piazzetta*, p. 62; Morgan Library, *Twelfth Fellows Report*, *1962*, pp. 85–87; Pignatti, *Disegni nel Museo Correr*, 1964, under no. 40; Morgan Library, *A Review of Acquisitions*, *1949–1968*, p. 159.

EXHIBITIONS: New York, Tiepolo Exhibition, 1938, no. 33, repr.

The Pierpont Morgan Library
Gift of the Samuel H. Kress Foundation, 1961.12:55

Alessio de Marchis
Naples 1684–Perugia 1752

48 *Landscape with a Bridge and Two Horsemen*

Brush and brown wash, over black and red chalk. 10 7/16 × 14 1/8 inches (26.5 × 35.9 cm.).

Inscribed in pen and brown ink on verso, *Originale di Alessio de' Marchis Napolitano.*

Neapolitan by birth and earliest training, De Marchis, who worked in Rome, Umbria, and the Marches, was a specialist in decorative landscape painting. As a draughtsman he has been little known until recently when Marco Chiarini called attention to the charm and relative originality of his landscape drawings (*Master Drawings*, V, 1967, no. 3, pp. 289–291). The present example is typical; the artist's touch is somewhat hesitant, but the composition is given an atmospheric unity by the way the red and black chalk under the drawing shines through the transparent wash. His example, of course, was the work of the Dutch Italianizing landscape draughtsmen.

Janos Scholz possesses a De Marchis landscape that is similar in style to the present drawing (repr. New York, Scholz Exhibition, 1968, no. 49).

EXHIBITIONS: New York, The Two Sicilies, 1970, no. 35, repr.

Cooper-Hewitt Museum, Smithsonian Institution
Gift of Mrs. Grafton H. Pyne, 1948–118–130

Baldassare de Caro
1686–1752

49 *Design for a Monument*

Pen and black ink, gray wash, over black chalk; squared for transfer in black chalk. 16 3/8 × 10 13/16 inches (41.7 × 27.5 cm.).

Numbered in blue crayon at upper right, *23*; in pen and black ink on verso, *Baldassare de Caro.*

Richard Wunder has suggested that this is a design for a painted monument in honor of the Emperor Charles VI. Allegorical female figures of Prudence, Fortitude, Abundance, and Justice stand or recline below the emperor, about to be crowned by Fame, while Minerva leads his horse. The old inscription attributing the drawing to De Caro is presumably acceptable, though surprising, for he is largely known as a painter of animal and flower pieces. In any case, the very Solimenesque handling of the chalk and wash fit well with the time and place.

PROVENANCE: Giovanni Piancastelli (no mark, see Lugt S. 2078a); Mr. and Mrs. Edward Brandegee (no mark, see Lugt S. 1860c).

BIBLIOGRAPHY: Wunder, *Extravagant Drawings*, no. 16, repr.

EXHIBITIONS: New York, The Two Sicilies, 1970, no. 36, repr.

Cooper-Hewitt Museum, Smithsonian Institution
1938–88–2996

Gaspare Diziani
Bologna 1689–Venice 1767

50 *Hercules and Omphale*

Pen and brown ink, brown wash, over red chalk; squared for transfer in black chalk. $11\frac{3}{4} \times 7\frac{3}{4}$ inches (29.8×19.7 cm.). Large stain of blue watercolor at upper right.

Inscribed in pen and brown ink on verso, *Gasparo Diziani V⁰* and a long receipt in Italian.

Gaspare Diziani was a bravura draughtsman whose enormous production owes a great deal to the example of Sebastiano Ricci. Note, for instance, the coloristic effect achieved by the use of a red chalk underdrawing. As a painter Diziani is a rather plodding, provincial figure. A painted version of this subject, composed horizontally rather than vertically, exists in the Musée des Beaux-Arts at Geneva (repr. *Arte Veneta*, II, 1948, fig. 160).

PROVENANCE: James Jackson Jarves.

BIBLIOGRAPHY: Pignatti, *Disegni veneziani*, no. 32, repr.

EXHIBITIONS: Minneapolis, University of Minnesota Gallery, "The Eighteenth Century, One Hundred Drawings by One Hundred Artists," 1961, no. 19, pl. XII.

The Metropolitan Museum of Art
Gift of Cornelius Vanderbilt, 80.3.384

51 *The Virgin of Sorrows*

Pen and brown ink, brown wash, heightened with white tempera, over black chalk. $22\frac{5}{16} \times 13\frac{15}{16}$ inches (56.7×35.4 cm.). Ruled border with arched top in pen and brown ink.

Inscribed in pen and brown ink at lower center on verso, *S*.

In its imposing dimensions and narrow vertical format as well as in the brilliance of its browns and whites, this religious composition of the Venetian painter and theater decorator could be said to anticipate the devotional drawings of Giovanni Domenico Tiepolo. Whether or not the drawing was intended, like the younger Tiepolo's series, to be an independent work is not known, but the drawing is certainly an example of Diziani's mature style.

The subject is the widely favored baroque motif of the stricken Virgin seated at the foot of the cross with the body of the dead Christ supported against her knees, her heart pierced with the swords symbolic of her Seven Sorrows, and grieving angels at her side and in the clouds. In her right hand she holds a scapular, symbolic of her dead Son's cross and yoke, and perhaps associating her with Our Lady of the Carmelite legends of St. Simon Stock.

PROVENANCE: Purchased by the Morgan Library in London, 1962.

BIBLIOGRAPHY: Morgan Library, *Thirteenth Fellows Report, 1963–1964*, p. 102; Morgan Library, *A Review of Acquisitions, 1949–1968*, p. 141.

EXHIBITIONS: London, P. & D. Colnaghi, "Old Master Drawings," 1962, no. 17.

The Pierpont Morgan Library
Gift of the Fellows, 1962.14

52 *Apollo and Daphne*

Pen and brown ink, watercolor, over traces of black chalk. $10\frac{3}{4} \times 7\frac{1}{4}$ inches (27.3×18.4 cm.). Foxing; small tear at right margin.

This dashing sketch and its companion, No. 53, are unusual, if not unique, in Diziani's enormous graphic production in being extensively heightened in watercolor.

EXHIBITIONS: London, Scholz Exhibition, 1968, no. 30; Venice, Palazzo Ducale, "Dal Ricci al Tiepolo. I Pittori di figura del Settecento a Venezia," 1969, no. 105, repr.

Janos Scholz

53 Adam and Eve Driven from Paradise

Pen and brown ink, watercolor, over traces of black chalk. 11 × 7⅜ inches (27.9 × 18.7 cm.). Foxing.

See No. 52.

EXHIBITIONS: London, Scholz Exhibition, 1968, no. 29; Venice, Palazzo Ducale, "Dal Ricci al Tiepolo. I Pittori di figura del Settecento a Venezia," 1969, no. 106, repr.

Janos Scholz

54 Venice Receiving Homage

Pen and black ink, gray-green wash, over traces of black chalk. 11⅞ × 8⅟₁₆ inches (30.2 × 20.5 cm.). Horizontal creases at center. Watermark: bird.

Inscribed in pen and black ink at lower right, *Gasparo Diziani Bellunese.*

This is no doubt a project for a ceiling decoration in which the allegorical figure of Venice, identified by a doge's cap, receives the homage of a kneeling female. The shield held by the seated male figure at upper right is blank, and thus it is impossible to identify the family for which this project was intended. The rapid pen work, the indication of shadow by broad areas of uninterrupted angular hatching, and the abbreviated facial types are all characteristic of Diziani.

There are a good many typical drawings by this productive master in New York collections: the Metropolitan Museum, the Morgan Library, and the collections of Janos Scholz, E. V. Thaw, David Daniels, and of Robert and Bertina Suida Manning.

PROVENANCE: "Reliable Venetian Hand" (Lugt S. 3005c–d); J. MacGowan (Lugt 1496); purchased by the Metropolitan Museum in Paris, 1962.

EXHIBITIONS: Venice, Disegni di una collezione veneziana del Settecento, 1966, no. 91, repr.

The Metropolitan Museum of Art
Rogers Fund, 62.121.2

Giovanni Paolo Pannini
Piacenza 1691/1692–Rome 1765

55 Drawing of the Lottery in Piazza di Montecitorio

Pen and gray ink, watercolor, over black chalk. 13 ⁷⁄₁₆ × 21⅜ inches (34.1 × 54.3 cm.). Repaired tear at lower right corner.

Inscribed in pen and gray ink at lower right, *1743*; in pen and brown ink on eighteenth-century mount, *Bozzetto Originale del' Cavalᵉ Giõ Paulo Panini del Quadro dell'Estrazione del Lotto di Roma, da esso eseguito per L. Emo Cardinale Domenico Orsini*; unidentified collector's mark on eighteenth-century mount.

An elaborate preparatory *modello* for one of Pannini's finest Roman views, a painting dated 1747 in the collection of Lt. Col. Norman Colville, London, representing the drawing of the papal lottery on the balcony of the Palazzo di Montecitorio in the presence of a vast crowd of excited spectators. The Palazzo di Montecitorio, a familiar monument in present-day Rome and now the seat of the Italian Chamber of Deputies, was in Pannini's time the Curia Innocenziana, the papal court of justice, and from February 1743 its central balcony was the official site of the lottery drawing. The façade of the palace remains just as we see it in Pannini's drawing, which was no doubt made on the spot. However, the view through to the Column of Marcus Aurelius was blocked in the 1830s by the construction of the Palazzo Wedekind. The base of the Column of Antoninus Pius that we see to the right in Pannini's drawing was excavated near the Palazzo di Montecitorio in 1703, and in 1705 was set up by Carlo Fontana in the square, where it remained until 1764. It is now in the Cortile della Pigna of the Vatican. The obelisk that we see today in the center of the square was only erected there between 1788 and 1792.

In general composition the drawing corresponds closely to the Colville picture, but in the latter the figures are larger in scale and differently grouped. Edward Croft-Murray identified a number of chalk figure studies for the Colville picture in a Pannini sketchbook at the British Museum (*Old Master Drawings*, XI, March 1937, pp. 61–65, pls.

57–63), and James Draper has found further figure studies in the West Berlin Print Room, the Witt Collection at the Courtauld Institute, London, and in a private collection in Paris.

The old inscription, affixed to the mount of the drawing, states, very plausibly, that the picture was painted for Domenico Orsini (1719–1789), created cardinal in 1743. The inscription itself, though in an eighteenth-century hand, must postdate both the drawing and the picture, since Pannini is described as *Cavaliere*; the painter received the title of "Cavaliere dello Sperone d'Oro" in October 1749.

PROVENANCE: Purchased by the Metropolitan Museum in London, 1968.

BIBLIOGRAPHY: James David Draper, "The Lottery in Piazza di Montecitorio," *Master Drawings*, VII, 1969, no. 1, pp. 27–34, pls. 16, 17 (the Colville picture repr. figs. 1–3).

The Metropolitan Museum of Art
Rogers Fund, 68.53

56 *Young Gentleman Holding His Hat*

Brush and brown wash, over black chalk. 8½ × 4 ³⁄₁₆ inches (21.6 × 10.6 cm.). Foxed. Lined.

This stylish young man must have been studied for a participant in one of Pannini's vast Roman views, which are often peopled with crowds of elegant or popular spectators. The technique, warm transparent brown wash over slight indications in black chalk, is often used by Pannini, one of the most charming figure draughtsmen of the eighteenth century.

PROVENANCE: Duke of Aosta, Turin.

Harry G. Sperling

Giuseppe Galli Bibiena, attributed to
Parma 1696–Berlin 1756

57 *Design for a Stage Set: The Temple of Jupiter*

Pen and brown ink, with gray-brown and blue wash. 13⅞ × 20 inches (35.3 × 50.8 cm.). Vertical crease at center. Watermark: fleur-de-lis (?) in circle.

Numbered on verso in pen and brown ink in an old hand *N° 5*.

This drawing has traditionally gone under the generic name of the Bibiena family with a more specific, if tentative, ascription to Giuseppe. Recently, however, Dr. Per Bjurström has questioned its inclusion even within the wide circle of the Bibiena family, stating that he has "not found any related works in the authenticated material . . . . The baroque language of the Bibienas has here been mingled with classicizing elements that look unfamiliar even for works of the later representatives of the family." At this point in our knowledge of theater drawings, however, such a drawing is possibly best still retained under the Bibiena label with which its baroque vocabulary is at least in sympathy.

Hopefully, in time it may be possible to identify the opera that featured a king and his queen appearing with their offerings within the lofty confines of the remarkable temple of Jupiter depicted here. (The design in its general outlines may be interestingly compared with a drawing by Bernardino Galliari [repr. Janos Scholz, *Baroque and Romantic Stage Design*, New York, 1950, no. 49].) A companion drawing, showing a garden scene, in the Metropolitan Museum also carries an old inscription *N° 5* on the verso (repr. Philadelphia exhibition catalogue, no. 26), suggesting that both may be designs for the same production. The Metropolitan drawing has been ascribed to Ferdinando as well as to Giuseppe Bibiena.

PROVENANCE: Purchased by the Morgan Library in London, 1950.

BIBLIOGRAPHY: Morgan Library, *First Fellows Report*, 1950, pp. 52–53; Per Bjurström, review of exhibition, "Drawings by the Bibiena Family," Philadelphia Museum of Art, 1968, *Burlington Magazine*, CX, 1968, p. 484; Morgan Library, *A Review of Acquisitions, 1949–1968*, p. 131.

EXHIBITIONS: Philadelphia, Museum of Art, "Drawings by the Bibiena Family," 1968, no. 31, repr.

The Pierpont Morgan Library
Gift of Walter C. Baker, 1950.2

Francesco de Mura
Naples 1696–Naples 1784

58 *Design for the Frame of a Portrait*

Pen and black ink, gray wash, over black chalk. 14 15/16 × 11 1/16 inches (37.9 × 28 cm.).

Inscribed in pen and black ink on verso, *Franᶜ di Mura.*

The traditional attribution of this design for the frame of a portrait, possibly intended as an over-door, may be accepted. The style of the drawing and the elegance of the decorative motifs reveal the strong influence of Francesco Solimena, De Mura's master. The chalk portrait sketch of the warrior at center is particularly Solimenesque, and indeed the drawings of master and pupil are often confused.

PROVENANCE: Giovanni Piancastelli (no mark, see Lugt S. 2078a); Mr. and Mrs. Edward Brandegee (no mark, see Lugt S. 1860c).

BIBLIOGRAPHY: Wunder, *Extravagant Drawings*, no. 68, repr.

EXHIBITIONS: New York, The Two Sicilies, 1970, no. 37, repr. cover.

Cooper-Hewitt Museum, Smithsonian Institution
1938-88-7068

Giovanni Battista Tiepolo
Venice 1696–Madrid 1770

59 *Figures around a Pyramid*

Pen and brown ink, brown wash, heightened with white, over black chalk. 16 9/16 × 10 13/16 inches (42.1 × 27.5 cm.). Spot of red paint at lower right; slight foxing.

The mood and even the paraphernalia of Giambattista's later *scherzi di fantasia* (see No. 96) are already present here: the funerary pyramid, the enigmatic group of brooding figures—two soldiers, a "philosopher," and a nude youth—as well as the skulls, the mask, the scabbard, and the snake at lower left. Morassi, however, very convincingly suggested in his catalogue of the Wallraf exhibition that the drawing is quite early, datable about 1725. The vigorous, monumental Piazzettesque figures

and the dramatic, mysterious lighting are characteristic of Giambattista's work at this time.

PROVENANCE: Paul Wallraf, London.

EXHIBITIONS: Venice, Wallraf Exhibition, 1959, no. 52, repr.

Robert Lehman Collection

60 *Group of Fighting Figures*

Pen and brown ink, brown wash, over black chalk. 14 1/16 × 20 7/8 inches (35.7 × 53 cm.). Spot of red paint at lower right corner; slight foxing. Watermark: trefoil above the letters E S C (see watermark no. 34).

Inscribed in black chalk at lower right, *Tiepolo f.*

In their vigor and energy these mysterious struggling figures come close to the heroic participants in the series of ten scenes from Roman history, painted, probably, in the mid-1720s for the Ca' Dolfin in Venice, and now divided between the Metropolitan Museum (Morassi, 1955, fig. 15; 1962, figs. 294, 306), the Hermitage in Leningrad (Morassi, 1962, figs. 295–299), and the Kunsthistorisches Museum in Vienna (Morassi, 1955, fig. 12). In this important early drawing Giambattista's contour line has an almost brutal incisiveness.

PROVENANCE: Giuseppe Vallardi, Milan (according to Morassi in the Wallraf catalogue); Paul Wallraf, London.

EXHIBITIONS: Venice, Wallraf Exhibition, 1959, no. 53, repr.

Robert Lehman Collection

61 *Beheading of St. Nazarius and St. Celsus in Milan*

Pen and brown ink, brown wash, heightened with white, over black chalk; traces of red chalk at upper and lower right. 19 11/16 × 14 7/16 inches (50 × 36.8 cm.). Lined.

Blind stamp, a mounter's mark, at lower right corner, *F. R.* (Lugt 1042).

Nos. 61 and 62, both drawings of exceptional size, elaborate finish, and impressive monumentality, must have been made as ends in themselves, as independent works of art rather than preparatory studies. In any case, they do not relate directly to any of Giambattista's paintings. Stylistically, however, they are strikingly similar to the frescoes in the Colleoni Chapel at Bergamo, where Giambattista worked in 1732 and 1733. The vigorous physical types, the steep perspective, and the dramatic Piazzettesque chiaroscuro that characterize the drawings are all apparent in the Bergamo fresco representing the Beheading of St. John the Baptist (Morassi, 1962, fig. 44). Benesch suggested a much earlier date for the drawings, placing them anterior to Tiepolo's work in Udine in the mid-1720s, but Harry Wehle's suggestion that they are the work of the Bergamask period, a dating also proposed by Morassi, seems entirely convincing.

The identification of the subjects is modern, not traditional. At the time of their acquisition in 1937 by the Metropolitan Museum they were described in the Biron inventory as the *Martyrdom of the Baptist* and the *Martyrdom of Two Saints*, respectively. The present title of No. 61, the *Beheading of St. Nazarius and St. Celsus*, seems to have been suggested by Wehle; it is a very plausible identification, for these two saints were venerated in Milan, the scene of their martyrdom, and Tiepolo worked in Lombardy in the early 1730s. The Martyrdom of St. Cyprian and Justina at Nicomedia has been proposed as the subject of No. 62, but there does not appear to be any particular iconographical or geographical justification for this identification.

Another scene of martyrdom of similar dimensions and finish, stylistically very close to the two present drawings, is in a private collection in Milan. It figured in the Orloff collection and is reproduced in the sale catalogue thereof (no. 162). An old copy of No. 61 is in the Hermitage in Leningrad (Inv. 20113; repr. Larissa Salmina, *Hermitage Bulletin*, VIII, 1964, no. 3, p. 246); a copy of No. 62 is in the Musée Départemental des Vosges at Épinal (Cailleux, Tiepolo et Guardi, 1952, pl. 1).

PROVENANCE: Marquis de Biron, Paris and Geneva; purchased by the Metropolitan Museum in Geneva, 1937.

BIBLIOGRAPHY: Benesch, *Venetian Drawings*, no. 12, repr.; Antonio Morassi, "Some Drawings by the Young Tiepolo," *Burlington Magazine*, XCI, 1949, p. 85; *Disegni veneti dell'Albertina di Vienna* (exhibition catalogue by Otto Benesch), Venice, Fondazione Giorgio Cini, 1961, p. 72; Bean, *100 European Drawings*, no. 40, repr.

The Metropolitan Museum of Art
Rogers Fund, 37.165.14

62 *Beheading of a Male and a Female Saint*

Pen and brown ink, brown wash, heightened with white, over black chalk. 19⅝ × 14⅜ inches (49.8 × 36.3 cm.). Lined.

Blind stamp, a mounter's mark, at lower right corner, F. R. (Lugt 1042).

See No. 61.

PROVENANCE: Marquis de Biron, Paris and Geneva; purchased by the Metropolitan Museum in Geneva, 1937.

BIBLIOGRAPHY: Metropolitan Museum, *European Drawings*, no. 36, repr.; Benesch, *Venetian Drawings*, pp. 29–30; Antonio Morassi, "Some Drawings by the Young Tiepolo," *Burlington Magazine*, XCI, 1949, p. 85; *Disegni veneti dell'Albertina di Vienna* (exhibition catalogue by Otto Benesch), Venice, Fondazione Giorgio Cini, 1961, p. 72; Knox, *Victoria and Albert*, under no. 311; Bean, *100 European Drawings*, under no. 40.

EXHIBITIONS: New York, Tiepolo Exhibition, 1938, no. 37, repr.

The Metropolitan Museum of Art
Rogers Fund, 37.165.15

63 *Enthroned Madonna Attended by St. Sebastian, St. Francis, and Angels*

Pen and brown ink, brown wash, heightened with white, over a little black chalk. 12 1/16 × 9¾ inches (30.7 × 24.8 cm.).

A fine, highly finished presentation drawing. Such sheets, unrelated to documented paintings, are extremely difficult to situate chronologically, and a dating in the early 1730s is proposed here with considerable caution. Knox points out that a copy of this drawing, signed by one of Giambattista's assistants Francesco Lorenzi is in the Martin von Wagner Museum at Würzburg (Fogg, Tiepolo Exhibition, 1970, fig. 4).

PROVENANCE: Marquis de Biron, Paris and Geneva; purchased by the Metropolitan Museum in Geneva, 1937.

BIBLIOGRAPHY: Metropolitan Museum, *European Drawings*, no. 37, repr.

EXHIBITIONS: New York, Tiepolo Exhibition, 1938, no. 38, repr.

The Metropolitan Museum of Art
Rogers Fund, 37.165.6

64 *Design for a Ceiling:*
Truth Appearing before a Group of Elders

Pen and brown ink, gray-brown wash, over black chalk. 12 $\frac{7}{16}$ × 12 $\frac{1}{4}$ inches (31.6 × 31.1 cm.). Watermark: six-pointed star, letters B F (see watermark no. 33).

Comparison with the earlier, sketchier drawing of the same subject at Trieste (Vigni, *Disegni del Tiepolo*, no. 24) shows that in the present sheet the perspective has been corrected by a careful plotting of the construction lines, the putto with the wreath has been moved from the right to a more central point, the position of the woman's legs has been reversed, and the whole has been developed with extreme finesse. The cowering figures at the bottom of the steps, scarcely suggested in the Trieste sketch, are possibly identified as personifications of Falsehood and Hypocrisy banished from the presence of the nude figure of Truth who reveals herself to the gathering of dignitaries. No painted ceiling of the composition is known.

The Morgan drawing is regarded by Byam Shaw as an indisputable work by Giovanni Battista in the decade of the 1730s. George Knox, on the other hand, assigns it just as firmly to Giovanni Domenico with the further suggestion that the subject is the Story of Phryne. The drawing is not too far removed in style from the other ceiling design in the exhibition (No. 69), which the late Hylton A. Thomas placed in the 1730s. In its completeness and careful finish, the sheet is somewhat unusual in the context of the other drawings of the Morgan album. Its watermark also appears in the paper of the Metropolitan Museum's drawing of Time and Truth exhibited as No. 121.

PROVENANCE: Count Francesco Algarotti (and thence presumably to his brother and heir, Count Bonomo Algarotti; his daughter Maria Algarotti-Corniani; her son Count Bernardino Corniani); Edward Cheney; Colonel Alfred Capel Cure (Cheney's brother-in-law); sale, London, Sotheby's, April 29, 1885, presumably part of lot 1024; Charles Fairfax Murray; purchased by J. Pierpont Morgan in London, 1910.

BIBLIOGRAPHY: Fairfax Murray, IV, 95.

The Pierpont Morgan Library
No. IV, 95

65 *St. Dominic Borne Upward by Three Angels*

Pen and brown ink, brown wash, over black chalk. 9 $\frac{3}{4}$ × 8 $\frac{7}{8}$ inches (24.8 × 22.5 cm.). Upper corners diagonally cropped.

Identified by his long billowing scapular and hooded cloak, the saint in this and the two following drawings is clearly St. Dominic, and it is presumed that the three drawings were made in the course of the artist's preliminary preparations for the frescoed ceiling in the Jesuit church of S. Maria del Rosario, Venice (1737–1739), apparently Tiepolo's only executed project involving the representation of this saint. None of the three drawings corresponds with the ceiling although the present drawing offers some analogies to the figure of the saint in the compartment showing his apotheosis (Morassi, 1962, fig. 93): the position of the feet is almost identical, there is the same steep foreshortening of the head so that only the chin and the nose are visible, and the elbow of the supporting angel at the far right projects in similar fashion. In the fresco, the saint appears more nearly frontal with his arms outstretched much as in No. 66.

PROVENANCE: See No. 64.

BIBLIOGRAPHY: Fairfax Murray, IV, 100.

The Pierpont Morgan Library
No. IV, 100

66 *St. Dominic with Arms Outstretched*

Pen and brown ink, brown wash, over black chalk. 8 $\frac{1}{16}$ × 7 $\frac{5}{16}$ inches (20.5 × 18.5 cm.). Upper corners diagonally cropped.

This drawing and the preceding sheet appear to be executed on paper that is slightly heavier than that of the following drawing.

PROVENANCE: See No. 64.

The Pierpont Morgan Library
No. IV, 116d

67 *St. Dominic, His Hands in Prayer,*
Borne Upward

Pen and brown ink, brown wash, over black chalk. 13 $\frac{1}{8}$ × 10 $\frac{11}{16}$ inches (33.4 × 27.2 cm.). Watermark: letters F C (see watermark no. 28).

The late Dr. Benesch first associated this drawing with the ceiling of the Gesuati but made no mention of the two preceding drawings. George Knox has commented that on a stylistic basis "one would prefer to put the drawing substantially later" than the years 1737–1739. The drawing is singularly successful in its effect of airy upward movement.

PROVENANCE: See No. 64.

BIBLIOGRAPHY: Fairfax Murray, IV, 99; Benesch, *Venetian Drawings*, no. 18, repr.; Larissa Salmina, "Some Drawings by Giuseppe Petrini," *Burlington Magazine*, CII, 1960, pp. 118, 121, fig. 24 (wrongly as Petrini).

The Pierpont Morgan Library
No. IV, 99

68 *The Adoration of the Magi*

Pen and brown ink, brown wash, over black chalk. 16 7⁄₁₆ × 11 7⁄₁₆ inches (41.7 × 29 cm.). Slight foxing.

Numbered in black chalk on verso, *N6*.

A brilliant, highly pictorial exercise that may date from the late 1730s. The same Magi, similarly costumed but quite differently placed in relation to the seated Virgin and Child, appear in Adorations of the Magi in the West Berlin Print Room (Hadeln, *Tiepolo Drawings*, II, pl. 107) and in the Cleveland Museum of Art (repr. H. S. Francis, *Bulletin of the Cleveland Museum of Art*, January 1946, p. 1).

PROVENANCE: Marquis de Biron, Paris and Geneva; purchased by the Metropolitan Museum in Geneva, 1937.

The Metropolitan Museum of Art
Rogers Fund, 37.165.16

69 *Design for a Ceiling: The Triumph of Hercules*

Pen and brown ink, brown wash, over black chalk; some corrections in brush and white tempera. 18 1⁄₆ × 24 inches (45.8 × 61 cm.). Vertical crease at center. Watermark: circle (see watermark no. 4).

Inscribed on verso in pen and brown ink at upper right, *660–661*.

This finished design for a ceiling, complete with the representation of the illusionistic, painted architectural setting, is of the utmost rarity in Tiepolo's

oeuvre. It was perhaps made as a guide for the specialist in architectural painting, who was to do that part of the ceiling, or it might have been a *modello* to be submitted to the patron. No such ceiling now survives, if ever it was done. A drawing in the Horne Foundation at Florence (repr. *Disegni della Fondazione Horne, Firenze* [exhibition catalogue by Licia Ragghianti Collobi], Florence, 1963, no. 105) shows a slightly different version of the central group of Hercules and Fame along with the surrounding figural motifs, which appear to juxtapose themes of Peace and War. The Horne drawing has been associated with the *Triumph of Hercules*, the ceiling formerly in the Palazzo Canossa at Verona, but the drawing style is certainly at least fifteen or twenty years earlier than the date of the fresco, 1761–1762.

PROVENANCE: Adrien Fauchier-Magnan (sale, London, Sotheby's, December 4, 1935, no. 55 [withdrawn]); sale, Paris, Palais Galliéra, June 16, 1966, no. 7, repr.; purchased by the Morgan Library, 1968.

The Pierpont Morgan Library
Gift of the Fellows, 1968.8

70 *Virgin and Child Attended by St. Sebastian and Two Monastic Saints*

Pen and brown ink, brown wash, over black chalk. 17 15⁄₁₆ × 11 13⁄₁₆ inches (45.6 × 30 cm.). Four corners of sheet replaced. Watermark: small trefoil, letters V d (see watermark no. 30).

Agnes Mongan and Paul J. Sachs were first to call attention to the close similarity of subject and composition between this drawing and a fine sheet in the Fogg Museum (repr. Fogg, Tiepolo Exhibition, 1970, no. 15). The Virgin's raised throne in its niche is the same in both drawings, and in both St. Sebastian stands leaning against the base of the throne looking upwards at the Virgin. Knox dates the Fogg drawing about 1735, but it might well be somewhat later and immediately before the drawings associated with the Palazzo Clerici of 1740.

PROVENANCE: Prince Alexis Orloff, Paris; Orloff sale, Paris, Galerie Georges Petit, April 29–30, 1920, no. 130, repr.; Paul Wallraf, London.

BIBLIOGRAPHY: Hadeln, *Tiepolo Drawings*, no. 43, repr.; Mongan and Sachs, *Drawings in the Fogg Museum*, I, pp. 172–173; Knox, *The Orloff Album*, pp. 273–274, no. 10; Fogg, Tiepolo Exhibition, 1970, under no. 15.

EXHIBITIONS: Venice, Wallraf Exhibition, 1959, no. 56, repr.

Robert Lehman Collection

71 *Virgin and Child Attended by Three Ecclesiastics*

Pen and brown ink, brown wash, over black chalk. 14 × 10⅛ inches (35.6 × 25.7 cm.). Lined.

Inscribed in black chalk at lower right, *Gio Batta Tiepolo Vares*[e].

This fine sheet corresponds very closely in style to the previous drawing, No. 70. The similarity of facial notation is striking, especially the abbreviated indication of the eyes. A similar composition is adumbrated in a rapid sketch in the Museo Civico at Trieste (Vigni, *Disegni del Tiepolo*, fig. 69), where the monk holding the staff appears kneeling at the right.

The inscription, *Gio Batta Tiepolo Vares*[e], is puzzling, as the Venetian Tiepolo had to our knowledge no family connection with this Lombard town. It may merely suggest that the drawing has some relation with a project intended for Varese.

BIBLIOGRAPHY: "Italian Drawings from the Collection of Janos Scholz," *Metropolitan Museum of Art Bulletin*, May 1965, Part II, repr. opp. p. 337.

EXHIBITIONS: Oakland, Scholz Exhibition, 1960, no. 77, repr. as frontispiece; Hamburg, Scholz Exhibition, 1963, no. 153; London, Scholz Exhibition, 1968, no. 94.

Janos Scholz

72 *Virgin and Child Appearing to a Group of Worshipers*

Pen and brown ink, brown wash, over black chalk. 16⅜ × 11¼ inches (41.6 × 28.6 cm.).

Erased and almost illegible number inscribed in black chalk at upper right, *28* [?].

Another fine, large-scale drawing from the Orloff group, presumably done as an end in itself and not directly connectable with a painting. Morassi has suggested a date between 1730 and 1735, but this now seems too early a dating.

PROVENANCE: Prince Alexis Orloff, Paris; Orloff sale, Paris, Galerie Georges Petit, April 29–30, 1920, no. 133, repr.; Paul Wallraf, London.

BIBLIOGRAPHY: Knox, *The Orloff Album*, pp. 273–275, no. 14.

EXHIBITIONS: Venice, Wallraf Exhibition, 1959, no. 55, repr.

Robert Lehman Collection

73 *Virgin and Child Appearing to Two Monks*

Pen and brown ink, brown wash, over black chalk. 16¹¹⁄₁₆ × 11¼ inches (42.4 × 28.6 cm.). Several spots.

This very luminous drawing from the Orloff collection is closely related stylistically to the previous drawing, No. 72. The Virgin and Child appear as they do there, seated on a cloud and facing to the left. The two standing monks are also present, though the other worshipers and spectators have disappeared.

PROVENANCE: Prince Alexis Orloff, Paris; Orloff sale, Paris, Galerie Georges Petit, April 29–30, 1920, no. 132; Charles Crocker, San Francisco.

BIBLIOGRAPHY: Hadeln, *Tiepolo Drawings*, no. 106, repr.; Knox, *The Orloff Album*, pp. 273–274, no. 13.

EXHIBITIONS: Oakland, Mills College Art Gallery, Portland Museum of Art, "Old Master Drawings," 1937–1938, no. 80; Chicago, Tiepolo Exhibition, 1938, no. 56, repr.

Private Collection

74 *Apollo Supported by a Genius with Butterfly Wings*

Pen and brown ink, brown wash, over a little black chalk. 10⁹⁄₁₆ × 8⁹⁄₁₆ inches (26.8 × 21.7 cm.).

Numbered in black chalk on verso, *30*.

An early Clerici-style drawing. Apollo appears thus, supported by a winged genius, in the center of the oil sketch representing Olympus in the Hausammann collection, Zurich (Morassi, 1962, fig. 319). The oil sketch may well be a preliminary *modello* for the frescoed ceiling of the Gallery of the Palazzo

Clerici in Milan, painted by Giambattista in 1740. Apollo's pose as studied in this sheet was utilized for an anonymous flying figure that appears at the south end of the Gallery. A copy of the present drawing is in the National Gallery of Art, Washington, D.C. (B–21–680), Gift of Howard Sturges.

PROVENANCE: Marquis de Biron, Paris and Geneva; purchased by the Metropolitan Museum in Geneva, 1937.

BIBLIOGRAPHY: Benesch, *Venetian Drawings*, no. 25, repr.; Fogg, Tiepolo Exhibition, 1970, under no. 19.

The Metropolitan Museum of Art
Rogers Fund, 37.165.21

75 *Apollo, with Lyre and Quiver, His Arm Upraised*

Pen and brown ink, brown wash, over black chalk. 8⅝ × 7¼ inches (21.8 × 18.4 cm.).

This Clerici study seems to have preceded the above Metropolitan sheet since the god is shown alone, his quiver occupying part of the space that was to be used for the winged genius. The presence of the second figure also necessitated a change in the pose of the legs.

PROVENANCE: See No. 64.

The Pierpont Morgan Library
No. IV, 112a

76 *Apollo Seated on Clouds, Two Figures at Left*

Pen and brown ink, brown wash, over traces of black chalk. 8⅛ × 8 ¹³⁄₁₆ inches (21.6 × 22.4 cm.). Watermark: small trefoil, letters V d (see watermark no. 30).

Numbered in black chalk on verso, 47.

Another Clerici drawing for Apollo, presumably an intermediary stage between No. 74, where the god is supported by a winged genius, and the Clerici palace ceiling, where the standing Apollo drives his quadriga across the sky.

PROVENANCE: Marquis de Biron, Paris and Geneva; purchased by the Metropolitan Museum in Geneva, 1937.

The Metropolitan Museum of Art
Rogers Fund, 37.165.52

77 *Apollo Standing in His Chariot*

Pen and brown ink, brown wash, over a little black chalk. 9½ × 9 ⁹⁄₁₆ inches (24.1 × 24.2 cm.).

A further Clerici Apollo, closer to the final solution where the Sun God, facing the spectator, races his quadriga across the width of the Gallery of the Palazzo Clerici (P. d'Ancona, *Clerici*, pl. 12).

PROVENANCE: Marquis de Biron, Paris and Geneva; purchased by the Metropolitan Museum in Geneva, 1937.

EXHIBITIONS: New York, Tiepolo Exhibition, 1938, no. 41, repr.

The Metropolitan Museum of Art
Rogers Fund, 37.165.35

78 *Reclining River God, Nymph, and Putto*

Pen and brown ink, dark brown and lighter brown wash, over black chalk. 9¼ × 12 ⁵⁄₁₆ inches (23.5 × 31.3 cm.). Watermark: large trefoil, small letters V d (see watermark no. 32).

Numbered in black chalk on verso, 8.

This group appears in the Hausammann oil sketch that is presumably preparatory for the Palazzo Clerici ceiling (Morassi, 1962, fig. 319). In the ceiling itself the river god and the nymph, without the oar and accompanying putto, reappear seated on the south cornice (P. d'Ancona, *Clerici*, pl. 35). Giambattista used a very similarly seated river god and nymph a little more than ten years later in the frescoed ceiling of the Kaisersaal of the Würzburg Residenz (Morassi, 1955, pl. 65).

PROVENANCE: Marquis de Biron, Paris and Geneva; purchased by the Metropolitan Museum in Geneva, 1937.

BIBLIOGRAPHY: Metropolitan Museum, *European Drawings*, no. 41, repr.; Freeden and Lamb, *Würzburger Residenz*, pl. 44; Bean, *100 European Drawings*, no. 42, repr.; Fogg, Tiepolo Exhibition, 1970, under no. 19.

EXHIBITIONS: Chicago, Tiepolo Exhibition, 1938, no. 70, repr.; New York, Tiepolo Exhibition, 1938, no. 45, repr.

The Metropolitan Museum of Art
Rogers Fund, 37.165.32

79 *Two Zephyrs with a Horse of Apollo*

Pen and brown ink, brown wash, over black chalk. $9\frac{5}{8} \times 15\frac{5}{16}$ inches (24.4 × 38.9 cm.). Upper corners diagonally cropped. Watermark: small trefoil, letters V d (see watermark no. 30).

This spirited group appears in the lower center section of the Hausammann oil sketch below the figure of Apollo. In the oil sketch the horse is given more prominence by elevating the neck to a vertical position and turning the head in stricter profile.

PROVENANCE: See No. 64.

BIBLIOGRAPHY: Fairfax Murray, IV, 120.

EXHIBITIONS: Fogg, Tiepolo Exhibition, 1970, p. XVIII, no. 19, repr.

The Pierpont Morgan Library
No. IV, 120

80 *Ariadne with a Winged Putto and Two Other Figures*

Pen and brown ink, brown wash, over black chalk. $8\frac{3}{8} \times 10\frac{7}{8}$ inches (21.2 × 27.6 cm.).

The nude female of this group was used for the figure of Ariadne in the left corner of the Hausammann oil sketch where Bacchus stands on her right, replacing the putto and the seated figure. In the oil sketch her left arm is obscured by the presence of a putto, and the shield at her right becomes a vase; above her in the sky are the two Zephyrs with the horse of Apollo represented in No. 79.

PROVENANCE: See No. 64.

BIBLIOGRAPHY: Fairfax Murray, IV, 127; Fogg, Tiepolo Exhibition, 1970, under no. 19.

The Pierpont Morgan Library
No. IV, 127

81 *Hercules with an Attendant Male and a Female Figure*

Pen and brown ink, brown wash, over black chalk. $10\frac{5}{8} \times 13\frac{5}{8}$ inches (27 × 34.7 cm.). Watermark: small trefoil, letters V d (see watermark no. 30).

Although clearly drawn in the Clerici manner, Hercules, holding his club over his shoulder and wrapped in his lion skin, a paw dangling below his right foot, makes no appearance in either the Hausammann oil sketch or the Clerici ceiling itself. The aquiline profile lightly sketched at the right of the sheet brings to mind such types in the fresco as the man smoking a pipe in the Allegory of Painting (P. d'Ancona, *Clerici*, pl. 18). The watermark is one found on a number of drawings of the Clerici group.

PROVENANCE: See No. 64.

The Pierpont Morgan Library
No. IV, 113a

82 *Truth with Two River Gods and Putti*

Pen and brown ink, brown wash, over black chalk. $10\frac{1}{2} \times 13\frac{15}{16}$ inches (26.5 × 35.5 cm.). Upper corners diagonally cropped. Watermark: small trefoil, letters V d (see watermark no. 30).

This may have been a preliminary idea, admittedly several times removed, for the group of a river god, naiad, and fisher boy at the far end of the south portion of the Clerici ceiling (P. d'Ancona, *Clerici*, pl. 33). A stage nearer the final solution may, as Knox has suggested, be represented by the Metropolitan Museum's drawing 37.165.50 (not exhibited). It, like the present sheet, shows a feminine personification of Truth with a river god, although in the ceiling the female figure is without any allegorical significance. In the ceiling and the Metropolitan drawing, the river god faces left rather than right as he does here. Indicative of the permutations of Tiepolo's ideas is the fact that although the river god in the Metropolitan drawing is positioned as in the ceiling, his attribute is not the urn of the ceiling and the Morgan drawing, but an oar.

PROVENANCE: See No. 64.

BIBLIOGRAPHY: Fairfax Murray, IV, 113; Rudolf Wittkower, *Art and Architecture in Italy 1600–1750*, second rev. ed., Baltimore, 1965, pp. XX, 320, pl. 186B.

The Pierpont Morgan Library
No. IV, 113

83 *Apollo Flanked by Two Figures and a Putto Holding a Quiver*

Pen and brown ink, brown wash, over black chalk. 10 × 14 inches (25.4 × 35.5 cm.).

A multifigured composition in the Clerici style, like No. 82, this sheet would seem to embody yet another scheme for the Apollo group.

PROVENANCE: See No. 64.

BIBLIOGRAPHY: Fairfax Murray, IV, 110.

The Pierpont Morgan Library
No. IV, 110

84 *Standing Figure of Prudence and a Seated River God*

Pen and brown ink, brown wash, over black chalk. 12 × 11⅝ inches (30.4 × 29.6 cm.).

Several measurements written in pencil on verso.

A puzzling drawing in the large Clerici-style group. A very similar figure of Prudence, seen in steep perspective, holding a large mirror and fitted out with her usual attribute, an extra masklike face on the back of her head, appears in one of the lateral canvases in the ceiling of the Scuola dei Carmini in Venice, on which Tiepolo worked intermittently from 1740 to 1744 (Morassi, 1962, fig. 205). In the Carmini canvas, however, Prudence is attended not by a river god but by allegorical female figures said to represent Grace and Innocence. The stance of Prudence in the present drawing, and even her skirt, looped over the thighs and caught by a clip in the form of a mask, reappear in the Hausammann oil sketch (Morassi, 1962, fig. 319) and in the Clerici ceiling itself, where the figure is reversed (P. d'Ancona, *Clerici*, pl. 22). However, in both these instances Prudence has become Ceres. Mirror and mask have disappeared, and the standing female holds a luxuriant symbolic plant. The drawing seems thus preparatory for neither one nor the other contemporaneous project—the Scuola dei Carmini or the Palazzo Clerici—but for *both*. This beautiful sheet may serve as an example of the

difficulty in securely associating Giambattista's preparatory drawings with his painted work.

PROVENANCE: Marquis de Biron, Paris and Geneva; purchased by the Metropolitan Museum in Geneva, 1937.

BIBLIOGRAPHY: Benesch, *Venetian Drawings*, no. 21, repr.; G. Mazzariol and T. Pignatti, *Itinerario Tiepolesco*, Venice, 1951, p. 126, fig. 71; Knox, *Victoria and Albert*, pp. 14, 39, note 28; Fogg, *Tiepolo Exhibition*, 1970, under no. 19.

The Metropolitan Museum of Art
Rogers Fund, 37.165.44

85 *Seated Woman with Mirror and Vase, Putto with Serpent, and a River God*

Pen and brown ink, brown wash, over black chalk. 11⅜ × 10 1/16 inches (28.9 × 25.6 cm.).

A fine drawing in the Clerici style of 1739–1740, but not associable with any group in the Milanese ceiling or the preparatory oil sketch in Zurich. The convex-faced mirror held by the seated female figure and the serpent held by the putto suggest that she may be intended to represent Prudence (see No. 84).

PROVENANCE: Eugène Rodrigues (Lugt and Lugt S. 897); Marquis de Biron, Paris and Geneva; purchased by the Metropolitan Museum in Geneva, 1937.

The Metropolitan Museum of Art
Rogers Fund, 37.165.45

86 *Two Seated Women and a Boy*

Pen and brown ink, brown wash, over black chalk. 8¼ × 9 9/16 inches (21 × 24.2 cm.).

Numbered in black chalk on verso, *28*.

A brilliant exercise in the Clerici style. The seated female spectator reappears in a drawing of the same period at Princeton (*Italian Drawings in the Art Museum, Princeton University*, Princeton, 1966, pl. 78).

PROVENANCE: Marquis de Biron, Paris and Geneva; purchased by the Metropolitan Museum in Geneva, 1937.

The Metropolitan Museum of Art
Rogers Fund, 37.165.36

87 *Two Women and a Putto*

Pen and brown ink, brown wash, over black chalk. 7 $7/16$ × 8$5/8$ inches (18.9 × 21.9 cm.). Watermark: large trefoil, small letters V d (see watermark no. 32).

Numbered in black chalk on verso, *53*.

A drawing in the Palazzo Clerici style that may be connectible with Giambattista's contemporaneous work in the Scuola dei Carmini in Venice. In one lateral canvas in the Carmini (Morassi, 1962, fig. 204), there is a differently grouped representation of Hope and Charity, the former identified as usual by an anchor, the latter by the presence of a child.

PROVENANCE: Marquis de Biron, Paris and Geneva; purchased by the Metropolitan Museum in Geneva, 1937.

The Metropolitan Museum of Art
Rogers Fund, 37.165.34

88 *Seated Satyr Holding a Cornucopia*

Pen and brown ink, gray-brown wash, over black chalk. 8 $1/16$ × 9 $1/16$ inches (20.5 × 23 cm.).

Numbered in black chalk on verso, *52*.

This drawing and Nos. 89 and 90 are studies for the satyrs that appear in steep perspective seated on the *quadratura* cornice of the Gallery of the Palazzo Clerici. Satyrs in Nos. 89 and 90 appear at the north end of the Gallery, their positions somewhat altered; the satyr in No. 89 loses his companions, while No. 90 is transformed into a satyress. No. 88 appears at the south end, holding a garland instead of a cornucopia (Morassi, 1955, pl. 26). The second satyr at the south end is studied in a further drawing in the Metropolitan Museum (37.165.38; repr. Fogg, Tiepolo Exhibition, 1970, no. 20). A sheet with studies of a satyr and satyress, probably also related to the Clerici decoration, is in the Horne Foundation, Florence (*Disegni della Fondazione Horne, Firenze* [exhibition catalogue by Licia Ragghianti Collobi], Florence, 1963, pl. 88).

PROVENANCE: Marquis de Biron, Paris and Geneva; purchased by the Metropolitan Museum in Geneva, 1937.

The Metropolitan Museum of Art
Rogers Fund, 37.165.47

89 *Two Seated Satyrs and a Satyr Child*

Pen and brown ink, brown wash, over red chalk. 8$1/4$ × 9$15/16$ inches (21 × 25.2 cm.).

Inscribed in black chalk on verso, *Tiepolo 30 /*.

See No. 88.

PROVENANCE: Marquis de Biron, Paris and Geneva; purchased by the Metropolitan Museum in Geneva, 1937.

EXHIBITIONS: Chicago, Tiepolo Exhibition, 1938, no. 67; New York, Tiepolo Exhibition, 1938, no. 43, repr.

The Metropolitan Museum of Art
Rogers Fund, 37.165.33

90 *Seated Satyr Looking Downward*

Pen and brown ink, gray-brown wash, over black chalk. 7 $13/16$ × 7$7/8$ inches (19.9 × 20 cm.).

Numbered in black chalk on verso, *54*.

See No. 88.

PROVENANCE: Marquis de Biron, Paris and Geneva; purchased by the Metropolitan Museum in Geneva, 1937.

The Metropolitan Museum of Art
Rogers Fund, 37.165.49

91 *Time and Cupid*

Pen and brown ink, brown wash, over black chalk. 10$9/16$ × 12 $7/16$ inches (26.8 × 31.5 cm.). Watermark: letters V d (see watermark no. 30).

This brilliant study was used with very little alteration for the figures of Time and Cupid in the group with Venus in the south portion of the great ceiling of the Palazzo Clerici, Milan. In the fresco, Time's scythe gains a more complicated handle and his right wing covers most of his right arm; further, one no longer sees his left arm athwart Cupid's body, and the hourglass is omitted.

PROVENANCE: See No. 64.

BIBLIOGRAPHY: Fairfax Murray, IV, 125; Benesch, *Venetian Drawings*, no. 30, repr.

EXHIBITIONS: Cambridge, Mass., Fogg Museum of Art, "Venice in the Eighteenth Century," 1948, no. 36; Hartford, Wadsworth Atheneum, "The Pierpont Morgan Treasures," 1960, no. 81.

The Pierpont Morgan Library
No. IV, 125

92 *Time with a Chariot Wheel, a Dragon's Wing and Tail to Left*

Pen and brown ink, brown wash, over traces of black chalk. 9¾ × 16⅛ inches (24.8 × 41 cm.).

Nos. 92 and 93, studies for a seated figure of Time, are clearly related iconographically, stylistically, and technically to the Morgan Library study for Time as he appears in the Clerici ceiling (see No. 91). The present drawings are no doubt both alternative studies for the same figure. All three are executed in a dark brown ink and wash that are markedly different from the golden brown ink and wash that characterize the bulk of the drawings that can with certainty or plausibility be associated with the Palazzo Clerici. Nonetheless, Nos. 91, 92, and 93 are part of the Clerici group.

PROVENANCE: Eugène Rodrigues (according to Biron inventory); Marquis de Biron, Paris and Geneva; purchased by the Metropolitan Museum in Geneva, 1937.

BIBLIOGRAPHY: Benesch, *Venetian Drawings*, no. 28, repr.

EXHIBITIONS: Chicago, Tiepolo Exhibition, 1938, no. 68.

The Metropolitan Museum of Art
Rogers Fund, 37.165.9

93 *Time Seated, Clutching a Putto*

Pen and brown ink, brown wash, over traces of black chalk. 10 1/16 × 12 13/16 inches (25.6 × 27.5 cm.). Watermark: small trefoil, letters V d (see watermark no. 30).

Numbered in black chalk on verso, *4*.

See No. 92.

PROVENANCE: Marquis de Biron, Paris and Geneva; purchased by the Metropolitan Museum in Geneva, 1937.

BIBLIOGRAPHY: Metropolitan Museum, *European Drawings*, no. 42, repr.; Benesch, *Venetian Drawings*, no. 30, repr.

EXHIBITIONS: Chicago, Tiepolo Exhibition, 1938, no. 69; New York, Tiepolo Exhibition, 1938, no. 42, repr.

The Metropolitan Museum of Art
Rogers Fund, 37.165.7

94 *Three Zephyrs*

Pen and brown ink, brown wash, over black chalk. 12⅝ × 10 13/16 inches (32.1 × 27.5 cm.). Lower left corner repaired.

Though typical of the many figures with butterfly wings fluttering in the skies of the Clerici ceiling, this soaring triad does not correspond with any specific group, nor can it be related to the Hausammann oil sketch.

PROVENANCE: See No. 64.

BIBLIOGRAPHY: Fairfax Murray, IV, 129.

EXHIBITIONS: Chicago, Tiepolo Exhibition, 1938, no. 60; Allentown Art Museum, "Gothic to Baroque," 1960, no. 95.

The Pierpont Morgan Library
No. IV, 129

95 *Bacchant and Bacchante*

Pen and brown ink, brown wash, over black chalk. 10 15/16 × 9 15/16 inches (27.8 × 25.2 cm.).

According to whether the sketchily indicated wand held by the male figure is interpreted as a caduceus or thyrsus, he may be identified as Mercury or as a youthful bacchant, both of whom are actors on the Clerici scene although not in this pose.

PROVENANCE: See No. 64.

The Pierpont Morgan Library
No. IV, 109a

96 *Scherzo di Fantasia: Standing Warrior and King Attended by Five Figures*

Pen and brown ink, brown wash, over a little black chalk. 13 13/16 × 10 15/16 inches (35 × 27.8 cm.). Watermark: small trefoil, letters V d (see watermark no. 30).

Numbers 96, 97, and 98 are all related in format, figure style, mysterious subject matter, even in their exotic costumes and accessories, to Giambattista's series of twenty-three etchings called the *Scherzi di Fantasia*—Fantastic Jokes (Pignatti, *Acqueforti dei Tiepolo*, pls. XIII–XXXV). No one of the drawings, however, is a study for any specific Scherzo. Indeed, no complete study for any of the Scherzi seems to have survived, though George Knox has loosely associated a number of sketches with the series (see G. Knox, *Burlington Magazine*, CVIII, 1966, pp. 585–586; Fogg, Tiepolo Exhibition, 1970, under no. 17). Knox argues that the Scherzi as well as the Capricci, Giambattista's other series of etchings, were executed in the years 1743–1749. The present drawings relate technically and stylistically to certain drawings associated with the preparations for the Palazzo Clerici fresco (see Nos. 91, 92, and 93), and thus may date from the late 1730s or early 1740s.

PROVENANCE: Eugène Rodrigues (according to Biron inventory); Marquis de Biron, Paris and Geneva; purchased by the Metropolitan Museum in Geneva, 1937.

BIBLIOGRAPHY: Benesch, *Venetian Drawings*, no. 20, repr.

The Metropolitan Museum of Art
Rogers Fund, 37.165.17

97 *Scherzo di Fantasia: Two Standing Orientals and a Standing Youth*

Pen and brown ink, brown wash, over traces of black chalk. 13⅝ × 9¹⁵⁄₁₆ inches (34.6 × 25.2 cm.).

See No. 96.

PROVENANCE: Marquis de Biron, Paris and Geneva; purchased by the Metropolitan Museum in Geneva, 1937.

BIBLIOGRAPHY: Metropolitan Museum, *European Drawings*, no. 43, repr.

EXHIBITIONS: Chicago, Tiepolo Exhibition, 1938, no. 80, repr.; New York, Tiepolo Exhibition, 1938, no. 53, repr.

The Metropolitan Museum of Art
Rogers Fund, 37.165.13

98 *Scherzo di Fantasia: Seated Warrior and Standing Youth*

Pen and brown ink, brown wash, over black chalk. 13¾ × 10¹³⁄₁₆ inches (34.9 × 27.4 cm.).

Stamped in black ink at upper margin of verso, *5*.

See No. 96.

PROVENANCE: Marquis de Biron, Paris and Geneva; purchased by the Metropolitan Museum in Geneva, 1937.

BIBLIOGRAPHY: Metropolitan Museum, *European Drawings*, no. 44, repr.

EXHIBITIONS: New York, Tiepolo Exhibition, 1938, no. 52, repr.

The Metropolitan Museum of Art
Rogers Fund, 37.165.18

99 *Three Standing Men and an Angel*

Pen and brown ink, brown wash, over black chalk. 14 × 10⅜ inches (35.6 × 26.2 cm.). Diagonal crease at lower right. Lined.

Inscribed in black chalk at lower left, *tiepolo*.

The three standing, draped men wearing fanciful Oriental headdresses are very similar to the exotic figures that people Giambattista's *Scherzi di Fantasia*. Indeed, the drawing might be thought to be a free study for this secular series if it were not for the presence of the angel behind.

Private Collection

100 *Psyche Transported to Olympus*

Pen and brown ink, brown wash, over black chalk. 9¾ × 9 inches (24.8 × 22.9 cm.), sight. Several spots of brown wash at lower margin.

The identification of the subject is due to M. Mauricheau Beaupré, and at the time this drawing was exhibited at the Galerie Cailleux in Paris in 1952, it was suggested that this forms part of a series illustrating the story of Psyche. A drawing now in the collection of Mrs. Vincent Astor representing Psyche seated by a blindfolded Cupid was also associated with this theme. No painted version by Giambattista of this subject has survived.

In No. 101 below the subject is the same, Psyche looking upward as she is transported heavenward by putti, but the group has been reversed and the number of putti increased to three. Stylistically the drawings seem to date from about 1740 and are close in handling to the drawings related to Giambattista's work in the Palazzo Clerici, Milan.

PROVENANCE: Victor de Cock; A. Doucet; José Maria Sert (according to labels on back of frame).

EXHIBITIONS: Cailleux, Tiepolo et Guardi, 1952, no. 16, pl. 12.

Dr. and Mrs. Rudolf Heinemann

101 *Psyche Transported to Olympus*

Pen and brown ink, brown wash, over black chalk. $8^3/_4 \times 8^{11}/_{16}$ inches (22.3 × 22 cm.).

Inscribed in pen and brown ink on verso, *Tiepolo*; numbered in black chalk on verso, *No 19 32/14 33/9 smie*.

See No. 100.

PROVENANCE: Marquis de Biron, Paris and Geneva; purchased by the Metropolitan Museum in Geneva, 1937.

The Metropolitan Museum of Art
Rogers Fund, 37.165.20

102 *Virgin and Child Seated on a Globe*

Pen and brown ink, brown and yellow wash, over black chalk. $17^3/_4 \times 12^1/_8$ inches (45.1 × 30.8 cm.). Several spots.

Byam Shaw has suggested that this is probably a design for a processional mace, and Knox proposes that it may have been planned as part of Giambattista's work for the Scuola dei Carmini, executed between 1740 and 1743. The presence in the drawing of an angel holding the Carmelite scapular gives weight to this association. A similar scapular-bearing angel appears at the center of Giambattista's large ceiling canvas in the principal room of the Scuola dei Carmini.

PROVENANCE: Prince Alexis Orloff; Orloff sale, Paris, Galerie Georges Petit, April 29–30, 1920, no. 138, repr.; Tomas Harris, London.

BIBLIOGRAPHY: Knox, *The Orloff Album*, pp. 273, 275, no. 44, fig. 102.

EXHIBITIONS: Venice, "Mostra del Tiepolo," 1951, no. 34; London, Royal Academy, 1953, no. 166; London, Arts Council, Tiepolo Exhibition, 1955, no. 1, repr., pl. IV.

Dr. and Mrs. Rudolf Heinemann

103 *Nobility and Virtue*

Pen and brown-black (iron gallnut) ink, gray wash, over black chalk. $10^7/_8 \times 9^{13}/_{16}$ inches (27.6 × 25 cm.).

This drawing is one of a group of four closely related studies in the Morgan Library (see also Nos. 104, 105, and 106). These, together with another Morgan drawing (No. 107) and a further sheet in the Metropolitan Museum (No. 108) form a sequence that illustrates Tiepolo's remarkable fertility of invention in the manipulation of a motif.

Such paired Virtues constitute the theme of a number of ceilings dated between 1740 and 1750: Palazzo Barbarigo, Venice (now Museo di Ca' Rezzonico); Palazzo Caiselli, Udine (now Museo Civico); Villa Cordellina, Montecchio Maggiore; Palazzo Gallarati-Scotti, Milan; and Palazzo Manin, Venice (now Florence, Contini-Bonacossi collection). But with none of these is there any true correspondence of finished work and surviving drawings. The Virtues have often been identified as Strength (or Fortitude) and Wisdom, but an interpretation as Virtue and Nobility would seem to be more strictly in accordance with Ripa. According to that authority, "Nobiltà" is personified as a woman carrying a lance in her right hand and the "simolacro di Minerva" in her left (Pt. II, pp. 89–90); "Virtù," as a winged woman who holds a lance in her right hand, a crown of laurel in the left, and wears a sun on her breast (Pt. II, pp. 356–357). With the exception of the laurel wreath and an obvious disregard for left and right, these elements are present here. The Metropolitan Museum's drawing incorporates all of the attributes with the exception of the lances, an omission that must have seemed desirable from the point of view of composition.

The four Morgan drawings, as Knox and others have remarked, are perhaps best linked with the Villa Cordellina ceiling, which was painted late in 1743 (Morassi, 1962, fig. 347); for instance, the putto of the present sheet has a near counterpart in the Dulwich *modello* (Morassi, 1962, fig. 346) for the Cordellina ceiling, and the chalk indications of a second putto and the foot of another figure may be regarded as fragmentary first notations for the group of Vice, who falls headlong away from the central Virtues.

For yet another drawing that has been associated with this group in the Villa Cordellina ceiling, see Vigni, *Disegni del Tiepolo*, no. 81.

PROVENANCE: See No. 64.

BIBLIOGRAPHY: Fairfax Murray, IV, 107.

EXHIBITIONS: Montreal, Museum of Fine Arts, "Five Centuries of Drawings," 1953, no. 63, repr.

The Pierpont Morgan Library
No. IV, 107

104 *Virtue and Nobility*

Pen and brown-black (iron gallnut) ink, gray wash, over black chalk. 10¼ × 9 9/16 inches (26.1 × 24.4 cm.). Watermark: letters A S (see watermark no. 29).

It will be noted that the statuette of Minerva, which is Nobility's attribute, is indicated only in the preliminary chalk sketch, where her left arm is shown in a raised position. An alternate placement was also apparently considered in relation to the lowered arm; just above it one sees a few hasty chalk strokes that appear to outline the small standing form of the goddess. The winged figure here appears on the left as it does in all the painted versions of the subject except that now in the Contini-Bonacossi collection, Florence (Morassi, 1962, fig. 351). That the figure may be identified as Virtue would seem to be indicated by the chalk circle on her breast, an abbreviated reference to the sun disk.

Morgan drawing Inv. IV, 111c, showing a small putto and part of a second figure, which can be identified as Vice (Virtue's opposite who appears in the various paintings below the central pair of figures), was at one time attached at the lower left corner of the sheet. The extreme acidity of the ink in which this drawing and its companions (Nos. 103, 105, and 106) are executed tends to "burn" through the paper in those areas where the deposit is heaviest. The watermark of this sheet also appears in Nos. 105 and 106.

PROVENANCE: See No. 64.

BIBLIOGRAPHY: Fairfax Murray, IV, 106.

EXHIBITIONS: New York, Staten Island Museum, "Italian Drawings and Sculpture from the Renaissance to the Present," 1958–1959, no. 26.

The Pierpont Morgan Library
No. IV, 106

105 *Nobility and Virtue*

Pen and brown-black (iron gallnut) ink, gray wash, over black chalk. 9 13/16 × 9 13/16 inches (25 × 25 cm.). Watermark: letters A S (see watermark no. 29).

Although these figures display no attributes, with the possible exception of the summarily outlined sun disk on the breast of the standing figure, they clearly belong to the same sequence of drawings as those discussed above and below.

PROVENANCE: See No. 64.

BIBLIOGRAPHY: Fairfax Murray, IV, 108.

The Pierpont Morgan Library
No. IV, 108

106 *Nobility, Liberality, and a Third Virtue*

Pen and brown-black (iron gallnut) ink, gray wash, over black chalk. 10⅛ × 12 5/16 inches (25.8 × 31.3 cm.). Watermark: letters A S (see watermark no. 29).

The third allegorical figure who joins Nobility and her companion here is very possibly to be interpreted as Abundance or Liberality in view of the overflowing cornucopia supported by the putto. Ripa (Pt. II, pp. 6–7) writes that the "horns of plenty mean that Abundance brings forth Liberality when it is accompanied by Nobility of the Generous Spirit. . . ."

Knox cites the ceiling painting formerly in the collection of the Baron Gustave de Rothschild, Paris (Sack, *Tiepolo*, fig. 213), as containing a number of the elements of this drawing, but there is little significant relationship.

PROVENANCE: See No. 64.

BIBLIOGRAPHY: Fairfax Murray, IV, 112.

The Pierpont Morgan Library
No. IV, 112

107 *Virtue and Nobility*

Pen and brown ink, brown wash, over black chalk. 12 × 10⅛ inches (30.4 × 25.7 cm.).

Though dealing with the same theme as Nos. 103–106 and 108, this drawing is so different in execution that it probably originated within the context of another project, possibly somewhat later than the Villa Cordellina. Among the various paintings and drawings of the subject, this appears to be the only instance in which Tiepolo employed the attractive device of placing the small statue of Minerva in the hand of the attendant putto. It has often been suggested that the drawing is to be associated with the Palazzo Barbarigo ceiling, now the Ca' Rezzonico; such a relationship cannot be ruled out but it is more easily postulated for the following drawing (No. 108).

PROVENANCE: See No. 64.

108 *Virtue and Nobility*

Pen and brown ink, brown wash, over black chalk. $10\frac{1}{2}$ × $9\frac{13}{16}$ inches (26.6 × 24.9 cm.). Watermark: letters F C (see watermark no. 28).

Numbered in black chalk on verso, *29*.

Tiepolo here explicitly illustrates Ripa's characterization of "Virtù" and "Nobiltà" (see No. 103). The presence of the putto holding a wreath could be regarded as an argument for associating this study with the Ca' Rezzonico painting, where the wreath is a prominent feature, although as with all the drawings on this theme there is no truly precise correspondence with any of the paintings. The date of the Ca' Rezzonico painting, 1744–1745, would be acceptable for the style of the drawing.

PROVENANCE: Marquis de Biron, Paris and Geneva; purchased by the Metropolitan Museum in Geneva, 1937.

The Metropolitan Museum of Art
Rogers Fund, 37.165.29

109 *Time Holding a Nude Female Figure, a Putto at Right*

Pen and brown ink, gray-brown wash, over black chalk. $8\frac{3}{4}$ × $7\frac{13}{16}$ inches (22.2 × 20.1 cm.).

Verso: Black chalk tracings over principal contours of recto.

Time and his nude female companion, possibly to be identified as Beauty, appear, reversed and somewhat altered, above the frescoed representation of the Banquet of Anthony and Cleopatra in the Palazzo Labia, Venice (Morassi, 1955, pl. 46). The Ca' Labia frescoes are assigned to the summer of 1744 by Knox.

PROVENANCE: Marquis de Biron, Paris and Geneva; purchased by the Metropolitan Museum in Geneva, 1937.

BIBLIOGRAPHY: Freeden and Lamb, *Würzburger Residenz*, p. 71 (where it is mistakenly suggested that the drawing relates to figures in the Kaisersaal), pl. 44.; Knox, *Victoria and Albert*, p. 19, note 34.

EXHIBITIONS: New York, Tiepolo Exhibition, 1938, no. 49, repr.

The Metropolitan Museum of Art
Rogers Fund, 37.165.31

110 *The Meeting of Anthony and Cleopatra*

Pen and brown ink, brown wash, over a little black chalk. $16\frac{1}{16}$ × $11\frac{1}{2}$ inches (40.8 × 29.2 cm.). Watermark: large trefoil, large letters V d (see watermark no. 31).

Inscribed in black chalk on verso, *Ce Dessin a été doublé.*

The meeting of Anthony and Cleopatra, in a splendid setting of illusionistic architecture by Mengozzi-Colonna, is the subject of one of Giambattista's frescoes in the Salone of the Palazzo Labia in Venice, painted in the mid-1740s (Morassi, 1955, pl. 47). The poses of the two principal figures in the drawing differ considerably from the Palazzo Labia fresco, but the drawing, on stylistic grounds, may well date from the same time. The two figures grouped as they are in the drawing occur in an oil sketch in the collection of Mr. and Mrs. Charles Wrightsman, New York (Morassi, 1955, fig. 30). This sketch is a study for a large canvas by Giambattista, dated 1747, at Arkhangelskoye, the former country house of the Jusopov family near Moscow, where the figures of Anthony and Cleopatra are arranged in yet another fashion (Morassi, 1962, fig. 313). The complex relationships among the Palazzo Labia fresco, the Wrightsman oil sketch, the painting at Arkhangelskoye, and the present drawing pose a typically difficult problem in Tiepolo chronology.

PROVENANCE: Marquis de Biron, Paris and Geneva; purchased by the Metropolitan Museum in Geneva, 1937.

BIBLIOGRAPHY: Metropolitan Museum, *European Drawings*, no. 38, repr.; Bean, *100 European Drawings*, no. 43, repr.

The Metropolitan Museum of Art
Rogers Fund, 37.165.10

111 Bacchus and Ariadne

Pen and brown ink, brown wash, over black chalk. 10 × 7⅝ inches (25.4 × 19.4 cm.).

Numbered in black chalk on verso, 35.

This brilliant drawing is closely related in style and composition to two other studies of Bacchus seated, raising a cup of wine in his right hand and holding a flask in his left, with Ariadne seated at his right. One is in the collection of Mrs. Joan K. Davidson, New York (repr. Fogg, Tiepolo Exhibition, 1970, no. 36), the other in the collection of Madame Z. Birtschansky in Paris (Cailleux, Tiepolo et Guardi, 1952, no. 23, pl. 6).

In discussing Mrs. Davidson's drawing Knox pointed out convincingly that the three sketches are studies for a ceiling fresco in the Palazzo Labia representing Bacchus and Ariadne (Morassi, 1962, fig. 265). In the fresco certain changes were made and the composition given a horizontal axis: Ariadne is farther from Bacchus, but turns towards him in profile, while hovering putti are moved to the right. Knox assigns Giambattista's decorations in the Palazzo Labia to 1744.

PROVENANCE: Marquis de Biron, Paris and Geneva; purchased by the Metropolitan Museum in Geneva, 1937.

BIBLIOGRAPHY: Fogg, Tiepolo Exhibition, 1970, under no. 36.

The Metropolitan Museum of Art
Rogers Fund, 37.165.27

112 Bacchus and Ariadne

Pen and brown ink, brown wash, over black chalk. 12¼ × 9½ inches (31.1 × 24.1 cm.). Slight foxing. Lined.

Knox tentatively associates this justly celebrated drawing with Giambattista's *Bacchus and Ariadne* ceiling fresco in the Palazzo Labia, which he dates 1744 (Fogg, Tiepolo Exhibition, under no. 36). Except for the presence of a seated figure of Bacchus, the drawing has little in common with the composition of the Labia ceiling, and the style of the drawing, the way in which wash is used to suggest light and shade, even the color of the wash, would seem to indicate a somewhat earlier date,

closer to the drawings associated with Giambattista's work in the Palazzo Clerici, Milan, in 1740. (See No. 111 for a drawing Knox has most convincingly identified as a study for the *Bacchus and Ariadne*.)

PROVENANCE: William Bateson (Lugt S. 2604a); Bateson sale, London, Sotheby's, April 23–24, 1929, no. 99; Philip Hofer, Cambridge, Mass.

BIBLIOGRAPHY: Sack, *Tiepolo*, p. 237, fig. 230; W. Gaunt, "Tiepolo," *Drawings and Design*, III, 1927, p. 64, repr.; Hadeln, *Tiepolo Drawings*, no. 73, repr.

EXHIBITIONS: London, Burlington Fine Arts Club, "Eighteenth Century Venetian Exhibition," 1911, no. 66; London, Burlington Fine Arts Club, "Drawings by Deceased Masters," 1917, no. 71; London, Warren Gallery, "Magnasco Society Exhibition," 1927; Buffalo, Albright Art Gallery, "Master Drawings Selected from the Museums and Private Collections of America," 1935, no. 64, repr.; New London, Conn., Lyman Allyn Museum, "Fourth Anniversary Exhibition: Drawings," 1936, no. 106, repr.; Chicago, Tiepolo Exhibition, 1938, no. 71, repr.; Paris, Lehman Exhibition, 1957, no. 128; Cincinnati, Lehman Exhibition, 1959, no. 226, repr.

Robert Lehman Collection

113 Three Studies of Bacchus

Pen and brown ink, brown wash, over black chalk. 13 × 10¹³⁄₁₆ inches (33 × 27.5 cm.). Watermark: letters V d (see watermark no. 30).

The problem of placing this splendid drawing in its proper context may be judged by the fact that Knox links it with the drawings related to the Hausammann oil sketch and at the same time suggests that it may be a study for the ceiling of *Bacchus and Ariadne* in the Palazzo Labia (Fogg, Tiepolo Exhibition, 1970, under nos. 19 and 36). In favor of a connection with the Hausammann *modello* is the point that Bacchus is there depicted as a standing figure, seen in steep perspective, his thyrsus at his side, although presented frontally rather than in the three-quarter aspect of the rotund god of this sheet. The color of the ink and wash, as well as the style, is nearer that of the Lehman *Bacchus and Ariadne* (No. 112) and the Morgan *Harvesters* (No. 114) than the golden brown tone so consistently characteristic of the drawings of the Hausammann group. Compare, for example, the clearly preparatory Morgan study for Bacchus's companion (No. 80) in the oil sketch.

Beyond the fact that they are seated, the other two figures of the sheet have little in common with the Bacchus of the Labia ceiling and do not agree with the drawing style of that project, which is firmly established by the group of drawings to which the Metropolitan drawing No. 111 belongs. If the Morgan and Lehman sheets are to be associated with the Palazzo Labia, it would seem necessary to postulate that there were two campaigns of drawing productive of two series of designs as in the Hausammann-Clerici project.

PROVENANCE: See No. 64.

BIBLIOGRAPHY: Fogg, Tiepolo Exhibition, 1970, under nos. 19, 36.

The Pierpont Morgan Library
No. IV, 117a

114 *Harvesters with Rakes and a Sieve*

Pen and brown ink, brown wash, over black chalk. 8³/₄ × 10¹⁵/₁₆ inches (22.2 × 27.7 cm.). Upper corners diagonally cropped.

It has not been possible to trace this delightful rustic motif in any of Giambattista's painted works. While at first glance such a theme would not seem to carry any iconographical significance, George Knox has pointed out that according to Ripa (Pt. I, pp. 194–196), the rake and the sieve, because they separate good from bad, are the attributes of the personification "Distintione del bene et del male." Stylistically, the drawing appears to be a work of the mid-forties. Morgan drawing Inv. IV, 129a, was formerly a part of this sheet.

PROVENANCE: See No. 64.

BIBLIOGRAPHY: Benesch, *Venetian Drawings*, no. 29, repr.; Arthur Millier, *The Drawings of Tiepolo*, Los Angeles, 1956, p. 45.

The Pierpont Morgan Library
No. IV, 117b

115 *Zephyr and Flora*

Pen and brown ink, brown wash, over black chalk. 9 × 9 inches (22.8 × 22.8 cm.). Upper corners replaced.

Inscribed in black chalk on verso, *40*.

Knox has convincingly identified this free sketch as a study for the elliptical ceiling fresco in the Palazzo Labia, Venice, representing Zephyr gazing lovingly at Flora (Morassi, 1962, fig. 257). In the fresco the group is reversed, and Zephyr appears at the right; this solution is announced in a drawing now in the Barber Institute of Fine Arts, Birmingham (Sack, *Tiepolo*, fig. 113). A drawing in Trieste may be related to the fresco; Flora appears at center, Zephyr at right, and an unidentified additional figure at right (Vigni, *Disegni del Tiepolo*, fig. 105).

PROVENANCE: Marquis de Biron, Paris and Geneva; purchased by the Metropolitan Museum in Geneva, 1937.

BIBLIOGRAPHY: Fogg, Tiepolo Exhibition, 1970, under no. 36.

The Metropolitan Museum of Art
Rogers Fund, 37. 165. 51

116 *Zephyr and Flora*

Pen and brown ink, brown wash, over black chalk. 11¹¹/₁₆ × 10³/₄ inches (29.8 × 27.3 cm.). Watermark: large trefoil, small letters V d (see watermark no. 32).

Although allied in subject to the ceiling of *Zephyr and Flora* in the Palazzo Labia, this drawing appears to be earlier in style and bears little relation to the drawings discussed in the preceding entry (No. 115).

PROVENANCE: See No. 64.

BIBLIOGRAPHY: Fairfax Murray, IV, 109.

The Pierpont Morgan Library
No. IV, 109

117 *Three Angels in Flight*

Pen and brown ink, brown wash. 10 × 8 inches (25.5 × 20.4 cm.). Watermark: fir tree (see watermark no. 46).

This is one of a unit of twenty-one drawings from the Morgan-Cheney album, all executed, without any preliminary chalk indications, in the same rough penwork and "flooded" with large areas of a very wet, dark brown wash. The papers for the most part are watermarked with a fir tree or the letters I F Q, the latter possibly a countermark of the tree device. Almost all the drawings represent flying figures depicted in attitudes of upward support (in this, the present drawing is not entirely typical). On the basis of George P. Mras's identification of a drawing at Princeton as a study for the Virgin in the *Miracle of the Holy House of Loreto* (1745)—the now demolished ceiling fresco of the Chiesa degli Scalzi, Venice, George Knox associated this group and others from different sources with the Scalzi commission. He also included another Morgan group of five small drawings of spectators executed in a more careful manner, but the group is more likely linked with the Villa Contarini at Mira. None of the figures in the Morgan drawings has its precise counterpart in the ceiling, but attention may be drawn to the figure with outspread legs in the group of angelic musicians in the upper third of the ceiling, whose pose seems to be forecast in the central figure of Morgan Inv. IV, 123a.

The other drawings of this group are Inv. IV, 95 b–f; 98b–e; 102a; 103a, b, d; 116a; 119a; 123a; 128a; 132b; 134a; 137; 138.

PROVENANCE: See No. 64.

BIBLIOGRAPHY: George Knox, "G. B. Tiepolo and the ceiling of the Scalzi," *Burlington Magazine*, CX, 1968, p. 397; Fogg, Tiepolo Exhibition, 1970, under no. 39.

The Pierpont Morgan Library
No. IV, 95a

118 *Angelica and Medoro*

Pen and brown ink, brown wash, over black chalk. 15⅛ × 11⅜ inches (38.4 × 28.9 cm.). Crease at lower right corner. Watermark: large trefoil, small letters V d (see watermark no. 32). Lined.

This affective representation of the famous lovers of Ariosto's *Orlando Furioso* (Canto XIX: 1–41) differs from tradition in that it is Angelica who carves their names on the tree trunk rather than Medoro, the wounded young Moorish soldier whom the princess of Cathay succored and married to the despair and madness of Orlando. This variation was, however, one which Tiepolo favored; it occurs in a drawing in the National Gallery of Art, Rosenwald Collection, as well as in the famed frescoes of the Villa Valmarana, and Domenico followed suit in drawings now at Oxford and Milan.

The Thaw drawing until recently had as a companion the *Rinaldo and Armida* now in the Smith College Museum of Art at Northampton, a drawing of similar size and execution; both drawings are reported in the Wellesley exhibition catalogue to have been in the Calando collection but only the Smith College sheet is listed in the sale of March 17, 1927 (no. 237). The two drawings are discussed at length by Professor Rensselaer Lee. He appropriately dates them around 1745.

PROVENANCE: Duke of Saxe-Altenburg.

BIBLIOGRAPHY: Rensselaer W. Lee, "Giambattista Tiepolo's Drawing of Rinaldo and Armida," *Smith College Museum of Art Bulletin*, 1961, no. 41, pp. 18–21, fig. 10.

EXHIBITIONS: Wellesley College, Jewett Arts Center, "Eighteenth Century Italian Drawings," 1960, no. 59; Allentown Art Museum, "Gothic to Baroque," 1960, no. 96, repr.

Mr. and Mrs. Eugene Victor Thaw

119 *Time and Truth*

Pen and brown ink, brown wash, over black chalk. 10 × 8 11/16 inches (25.4 × 22.1 cm.).

Time, embracing a nude figure of Truth, identified by the sun symbol she holds in her hand or that appears above her, are a standard allegorical couple in Giambattista's iconographic repertory (see for example Morassi, 1962, figs. 322, 323, 325, 327). Neither this nor the following two fine variations on a theme can be clearly associated with a painted work. The present drawing is perhaps earlier and differs stylistically from Nos. 120 and 121, which have in common a looser, more transparent handling of pen and wash, as does a related representation of Time and Truth in the Morgan Library (Inv. IV, 101).

A copy of the present sheet was sold at Sotheby's in London, October 21, 1963, no. 169.

PROVENANCE: Marquis de Biron, Paris and Geneva; purchased by the Metropolitan Museum in Geneva, 1937.

BIBLIOGRAPHY: Benesch, *Venetian Drawings*, no. 22, repr.

The Metropolitan Museum of Art
Rogers Fund, 37.165.23

120 Time and Truth

Pen and brown ink, brown wash, over black chalk. 10 × 9 3/16 inches (25.3 × 23.3 cm.).

Inscribed in black chalk on verso, *Tiepolo*.

See No. 119.

PROVENANCE: Marquis de Biron, Paris and Geneva; purchased by the Metropolitan Museum in Geneva, 1937.

The Metropolitan Museum of Art
Rogers Fund, 37.165.19

121 Time and Truth

Pen and brown ink, brown wash, over black chalk. 10 1/4 × 10 1/4 inches (26 × 26 cm.). Watermark: six-pointed star with letters B F (see watermark no. 33).

Inscribed in black chalk on verso, *Tiepolo*.

See No. 119.

PROVENANCE: Marquis de Biron, Paris and Geneva; purchased by the Metropolitan Museum in Geneva, 1937.

BIBLIOGRAPHY: Metropolitan Museum, *European Drawings*, no. 39, repr.

EXHIBITIONS: New York, Tiepolo Exhibition, 1938, no. 40, repr.

The Metropolitan Museum of Art
Rogers Fund, 37.165.42

122 Two Old Men, a Marine Deity, and a Putto Looking over a Balustrade

Pen and brown ink, brown wash, over black chalk. 6 5/8 × 10 1/2 inches (16.8 × 26.7 cm.). Lower right corner replaced. Watermark: large trefoil, small letters V d (see watermark no. 32).

These four figures gathered at a balustrade must have been studied with a ceiling fresco in mind, but they cannot be directly associated with any existing decoration by Giambattista. The style suggests the 1740s. The Morgan Library possesses a study of a similar group of figures looking over a balustrade very close in style to the present example (Inv. IV 128a; repr. Benesch, *Venetian Drawings*, no. 26), and four smaller studies of such groups are to be found in this collection (Inv. IV 122a, 123d, 123e, 132c). The Morgan Library drawings have been associated with the ceiling decoration for the Villa

Contarini at Mira, now in the Musée Jacquemart-André in Paris, where a crowd of spectators looks down over a high-placed balustrade.

PROVENANCE: William Bateson (Lugt S. 2604a); Bateson sale, London, Sotheby's, April 23–24, 1929, no. 97; Paul Wallraf, London.

BIBLIOGRAPHY: Sack, *Tiepolo*, p. 252, no. 104; *The Vasari Society for the Reproduction of Drawings by Old Masters*, Part IX, London, 1928, no. 6, repr.

EXHIBITIONS: London, Burlington Fine Arts Club, "Drawings by Deceased Masters," 1917, no. 84; Venice, Wallraf Exhibition, 1959, no. 57, repr.

Robert Lehman Collection

123 The Flight into Egypt

Pen and brown ink, brown wash, over traces of black chalk. 16 1/2 × 11 3/4 inches (41.9 × 29.8 cm.). Some black chalk or charcoal spots.

A particularly luminous example of a large-scale drawing from the Orloff collection that was clearly drawn as an independent work of art. Domenico Tiepolo borrowed this design by his father for one of his etchings in the *Flight into Egypt* series, where Giambattista's composition is reversed (Pignatti, *Acqueforti dei Tiepolo*, pl. LXI).

PROVENANCE: Prince Alexis Orloff, Paris; Orloff sale, Paris, Galerie Georges Petit, April 29–30, 1920, no. 90, repr.

BIBLIOGRAPHY: Knox, *The Orloff Album*, pp. 273, 275, no. 29, fig. 101.

Mrs. Vincent Astor

124 Christ Healing a Paralytic Man

Pen and brown ink, brown wash, over black chalk. 12 1/8 × 16 13/16 inches (30.8 × 42.7 cm.). Slightly foxed; small repaired loss at lower right margin; touches of red chalk at lower right corner.

The setting of this biblical scene, the Pool of Bethesda, is represented as a sumptuous classical loggia, and the horizontal disposition of the composition harks back, as Knox has pointed out, to the example of Paolo Veronese, whose style had such a profound and exhilarating influence on Tiepolo. Knox dates this drawing between 1740 and 1750. The horizontal format of this sheet is unusual among the drawings from Prince Orloff's collection, though it shares this feature with another biblical scene from the same source, now in the collection of the late Frits Lugt, Institut Néerlandais, Paris (Orloff sale, no. 144). This latter sheet represents figures seated around a table in a splendid architectural setting reminiscent of Paolo Veronese.

PROVENANCE: Prince Alexis Orloff, Paris; Orloff sale, Paris, Galerie Georges Petit, April 29–30, 1920, no. 96, repr.; Charles Crocker, San Francisco.

BIBLIOGRAPHY: Knox, *The Orloff Album*, pp. 273, 275, no. 46.

EXHIBITIONS: Oakland, Mills College Art Gallery, Portland, Museum of Art, "Old Master Drawings," 1937–1938, no. 77.

Private Collection

125 *Venus Entrusting an Infant in Swaddling Clothes to Time*

Pen and brown ink, brown wash, over black chalk. 11 $\frac{15}{16}$ ×9 $\frac{15}{16}$ inches (30.3×25.2 cm.). Watermark: graduated triple crescents (see watermark no. 15).

This group, somewhat altered and in reverse, appears in a ceiling painting formerly in the Bischoffsheim collection and now in the National Gallery, London (Morassi, 1962, pp. 18, 71; repr. F. J. B. Watson, *Apollo*, LXXXI, 1965, p. 187). The painting may be dated in the later 1740s, and this is a very plausible dating for the drawing as well.

PROVENANCE: Marquis de Biron, Paris and Geneva; purchased by the Metropolitan Museum in Geneva, 1937.

BIBLIOGRAPHY: Benesch, *Venetian Drawings*, no. 34, repr.

The Metropolitan Museum of Art Rogers Fund, 37.165.11

126 *Elderly Man Attended by Mercury and Prudence*

Pen and brown ink, brown wash, over black chalk. 11 $\frac{5}{8}$ ×9 $\frac{3}{4}$ inches (29.6×24.8 cm.).

Inscribed in black chalk on verso, *10*.

The figures stand on a cornice and are seen in very steep perspective. This same compositional device was used by Giambattista, as Knox points out, in the *Marriage Allegory of the Cornaro Family*, a ceiling painting now in the Contini-Bonacossi collection, Florence, that Morassi dates about 1745–1750 (Morassi, 1955, fig. 26). In the painted ceiling, however, figures of a bride and bridegroom appear on the cornice.

PROVENANCE: Marquis de Biron, Paris and Geneva; purchased by the Metropolitan Museum in Geneva, 1937.

The Metropolitan Museum of Art Rogers Fund, 37.165.43

127 *Magus and His Attendants*

Pen and brown ink, brown wash, over black chalk; framing lines in pen and blue ink. 15 $\frac{3}{16}$ × 10 $\frac{1}{16}$ inches (38.6× 25.6 cm.).

This group must be studied for an Adoration of the Magi, but cannot be directly associated with a painting. The most celebrated version of this subject painted by Giambattista is the *Adoration* dated 1753, executed in Germany for the church of the Benedictines at Schwarzach and now in the Alte Pinakothek, Munich (Morassi, 1955, pl. 50). The drawing is said by Morassi to have a German provenance, but it differs so considerably from the painting in Munich that it is difficult to establish a connection with that *Adoration*, just as it is difficult to date the drawing.

PROVENANCE: Convent of Nonnberg near Salzburg; Professor Neufang, Munich (according to Morassi in the Wallraf catalogue); Paul Wallraf, London.

EXHIBITIONS: Venice, Wallraf Exhibition, 1959, no. 61. repr.

Robert Lehman Collection

128 *Young Man Seated on a Cloud*

Pen and brown ink, brown wash. 6 $\frac{1}{4}$ × 5 $\frac{3}{4}$ inches (15.9× 14.6 cm.), sight. Repaired loss at upper left corner.

This free sketch and its pendant, No. 129, come from an album of studies by Giambattista devoted exclusively to figures seen in steep perspective, seated on clouds. This series must have been used as a kind of pictorial repertory in the Tiepolo studio, for cloud-borne figures were a constant feature in Giambattista's decorative schemes. This album, which was broken up in the 1920s, was labeled *Sole Figure per Soffitti*, and once probably belonged to the great nineteenth-century collector Edward Cheney. There was another now dismembered volume from the same source labeled *Sole Figure Vestite T: I:*. This contained drawings of standing figures, often in Oriental costume. A good many drawings from these two albums are now in New York collections, and the present two examples testify to the versatility of Giambattista's imagination as a figure draughtsman.

PROVENANCE: The Library of the Somasco Convent (S. Maria della Salute), Venice; Cicognara; Canova; Monsignor Canova; Francesco Pesaro; Edward Cheney, London; sale, London, Sotheby's, April 29, 1885, no. 1042.

Dr. and Mrs. Rudolf Heinemann

129 Young Woman Seated on a Cloud

Pen and brown ink, brown wash. 8 1/16 × 5 13/16 inches (20.5 × 14.8 cm.), sight. Several spots of wash.

See No. 128.

PROVENANCE: Same as No. 128.

Dr. and Mrs. Rudolf Heinemann

130 Design for an Overmantel

Pen and brown ink, brown wash, over black chalk. 13 1/2 × 10 inches (34.3 × 25.4 cm.).

A most unusual drawing showing Giambattista's skill and fantasy as a decorator. Here he proposes an overmantel decoration comprising a figured medallion with a mask above and a shell motif below, flanked by two asymmetrically placed putti, one standing and one seated.

PROVENANCE: J. Böhler, Lucerne; Tomas Harris, London.

EXHIBITIONS: London, Royal Academy, 1953, no. 202; London, Arts Council, Tiepolo Exhibition, 1955, no. 16, repr.

Dr. and Mrs. Rudolf Heinemann

131 Studies of Vases

Pen and brown ink, brown wash, over black chalk. 12 1/2 × 9 1/8 inches (31.8 × 23.2 cm.). Slight creases below center and at upper right corner. Watermark: six-pointed star above letters B [F] (see watermark no. 33).

This beautiful sheet is closely related in style and subject to a group of designs by Giambattista for ornamental vases, conserved in the Museo Civico in Trieste (Vigni, *Disegni del Tiepolo*, figs. 36–59).

The three nude winged female figures with corkscrew tails at the upper left are studies for vase handles, and the bearded mask studied at upper left is used on the vase at right.

Private Collection

132 Holy Family with an Attendant Boy at Left

Pen and brown ink, brown wash. 11 3/8 × 7 7/8 inches (28.9 × 20 cm.). Watermark: letters B T (see watermark no. 27).

Inscribed in black chalk on verso, *Giov B Tiepolo*.

Giambattista designed a long series of entrancing variations on the theme of the Holy Family, involving the subtlest changes in the grouping of the three central figures and their attendants. Many of these studies, which are certainly done as ends in themselves, were preserved in an album that passed to the Somasco Convent in Venice at the departure of the Tiepolo family for Madrid in 1762, was brought to England in the nineteenth century, and was finally dismembered at some point after the Cheney sale at Sotheby's in 1885. Other fine versions of this theme are in the Metropolitan Museum and in the collection of Dr. and Mrs. Rudolf Heinemann (see Nos. 135 and 136), and a series of eleven were formerly in the collection of the Duc de Talleyrand (repr. A. Morassi, *Dessins vénitiens du dix-huitième siècle de la collection du Duc de Talleyrand*, Milan, 1958, nos. 6–16). Both Morassi and Knox date these drawings in the late 1750s.

PROVENANCE: The Library of the Somasco Convent (S. Maria della Salute), Venice; Cicognara; Canova; Monsignor Canova; Francesco Pesaro; Edward Cheney, London; sale, London, Sotheby's, April 29, 1885, no. 1042; Paul Wallraf, London.

EXHIBITIONS: London, Savile Gallery, Tiepolo Exhibition, 1928, catalogue number uncertain; London, Royal Academy, 1954–1955, no. 559; Venice, Wallraf Exhibition, 1959, no. 70, repr.

Robert Lehman Collection

133 *Holy Family with St. Joseph Standing*

Pen and brown ink, brown wash. 11 $\frac{7}{16}$ × 7 $\frac{15}{16}$ inches (29.1 × 20.2 cm.). Watermark: bird (see watermark no. 1).

See No. 132.

PROVENANCE: Same as No. 132, and as well, Henry S. Reitlinger, London; Reitlinger sale, London, Sotheby's, December 9, 1953, no. 109, repr.; Paul Wallraf, London.

BIBLIOGRAPHY: *The Connoisseur*, CXXXIII, 1954, p. 265, repr.

EXHIBITIONS: London, Savile Gallery, Tiepolo Exhibition, 1928, catalogue number uncertain; London, Royal Academy, 1954–1955, no. 563; Venice, Wallraf Exhibition, 1959, no. 69, repr.

Robert Lehman Collection

134 *Holy Family under a Tree with St. Joseph Standing at a Pedestal*

Pen and brown ink, brown wash, over black chalk. 8$\frac{3}{8}$ × 11$\frac{1}{2}$ inches (21.3 × 29.2 cm.).

See No. 132.

PROVENANCE: Same as No. 132, through Cheney sale, and as well, Mark Oliver; Tomas Harris, London.

EXHIBITIONS: London, Savile Gallery, Tiepolo Exhibition, 1928, no. 11, repr.; Venice, "Mostra del Tiepolo," 1951, no. 35; London, Arts Council, Tiepolo Exhibition, 1955, no. 3, pl. v.

Dr. and Mrs. Rudolf Heinemann

135 *Holy Family with St. Joseph Kneeling*

Pen and brown ink, brown wash. 13$\frac{7}{8}$ × 9$\frac{1}{4}$ inches (35.2 × 23.5 cm.).

Signed in pen and brown ink at lower left, *Giovanni Battista Tiepolo*.

See No. 132.

PROVENANCE: Same as No. 132, through Cheney sale, and as well, Mark Oliver; Tomas Harris, London.

EXHIBITIONS: London, Savile Gallery, Tiepolo Exhibition, 1928, no. 10, repr.; London, Royal Academy, 1953, no. 171; London, Arts Council, Tiepolo Exhibition, 1955, no. 2.

Dr. and Mrs. Rudolf Heinemann

136 *Holy Family with Child Asleep*

Pen and brown ink, brown wash. 11$\frac{1}{2}$ × 8 inches (29.2 × 20.3 cm.). Upper and lower right corners replaced.

In style and subject this *Holy Family* is to be associated with the large group of studies of the Holy Family that once formed part of an album left by Giambattista Tiepolo with the Somasco Convent in Venice on his departure for Madrid (see No. 132). In this case the provenance is different: the drawing comes from the Orloff collection. Like the four Holy Families discussed above, this drawing may be dated in the late 1750s.

PROVENANCE: Prince Alexis Orloff, Paris; Orloff sale, Paris, Galerie Georges Petit, April 29–30, 1920, no. 78, repr.; Tomas Harris, London.

BIBLIOGRAPHY: Knox, *The Orloff Album*, p. 275, no. 77.

EXHIBITIONS: London, Royal Academy, 1953, no. 179; London, Arts Council, Tiepolo Exhibition, 1955, no. 4.

Dr. and Mrs. Rudolf Heinemann

137 *Bishop Seated*

Pen and brown ink, brown wash, over black chalk. 11$\frac{1}{4}$ × 8 inches (28.6 × 20.3 cm.). Lower right corner replaced.

A fine, free drawing that cannot be associated with a painted work and possibly dates from the 1750s.

PROVENANCE: Prince Alexis Orloff, Paris; Orloff sale, Paris, Galerie Georges Petit, April 29–30, 1920, no. 121, repr.; Tomas Harris, London.

BIBLIOGRAPHY: Knox, *The Orloff Album*, p. 275, no. 73.

EXHIBITIONS: London, Royal Academy, 1954–1955, no. 564; London, Arts Council, Tiepolo Exhibition, 1955, no. 9.

Dr. and Mrs. Rudolf Heinemann

138 *Group of Figures*

Pen and brown ink, brown wash, over red chalk. 11$\frac{1}{4}$ × 8 inches (28.6 × 20.3 cm.). Repaired loss at lower right corner; repaired tear at upper left margin.

The subject of this composition study is uncertain. In the Orloff sale catalogue the central figure was described as female, but J. J. Byam Shaw has proposed an alternative solution, that this is a Passion subject, and that here Christ is represented as he was shown to the people. The drawing must be late.

PROVENANCE: Prince Alexis Orloff, Paris; Orloff sale, Paris, Galerie Georges Petit, April 29–30, 1920, no. 145, repr.; Tomas Harris, London.

BIBLIOGRAPHY: Knox, *The Orloff Album*, pp. 274, 275, no. 75.

EXHIBITIONS: London, Royal Academy, 1954–1955, no. 560; London, Arts Council, Tiepolo Exhibition, 1955, no. 8.

Dr. and Mrs. Rudolf Heinemann

139 *Apotheosis of a Warrior*

Pen and brown ink, brown wash, over a little black chalk. 9¾ × 12½ inches (24.9 × 31.7 cm.).

While this drawing and the following pair all deal with the apotheosis theme, differences in style and technique suggest that they may relate to separate projects. Of the various painted versions of the subject showing the laurel-crowned hero with a lion at his side, the Metropolitan sheet is perhaps most logically associable with the *Apotheosis of Francesco Barbaro*, the painting on canvas formerly in the Palazzo Barbaro, Venice, and now likewise in the Metropolitan Museum (Morassi, 1955, fig. 27). The painting is usually assigned to the period 1745–1750, but Sack dated it somewhat later, after Tiepolo's return from Würzburg. Knox groups the present drawing with Nos. 140 and 141 as a part of the preparation for the decoration of the Palazzo Rezzonico.

PROVENANCE: Marquis de Biron, Paris and Geneva; purchased by the Metropolitan Museum in Geneva, 1937.

The Metropolitan Museum of Art
Rogers Fund, 37.165.26

140 *Apotheosis of Merit*

Pen and brown ink, gray-brown wash, over black chalk. 11½ × 14 inches (29.2 × 35.5 cm.). Four corners diagonally cropped.

This drawing is perhaps closest to the ceiling fresco *Merit between Nobility and Virtue* of the Palazzo Rezzonico, Venice (Morassi, 1955, fig. 54), one of two painted in celebration of the marriage of Ludovico Rezzonico and Faustina Savorgnan in 1758. The distinctive motif of the putti carrying the book provides a significant clue for the connection al-

though its placement in the fresco is different. The slight chalk outlines of a column, barely perceptible at the right of the group, may be the genesis of the idea for the circular Temple of Virtue that is similarly located in the fresco. In the intricacies of eighteenth-century allegory, the laurel-crowned bearded man with a book, who personifies Merit, may at the same time have been intended to represent a member of the Rezzonico family. It may be remarked that, as in the fresco, he is shown without the sword hilt or baton of the preceding and following drawings. See also Nos. 139 and 141.

PROVENANCE: See No. 64.

BIBLIOGRAPHY: Fairfax Murray, IV, 105; Knox, *Victoria and Albert*, p. 33, note 62; Fogg, Tiepolo Exhibition, 1970, under no. 77.

The Pierpont Morgan Library
No. IV, 105

141 *Apotheosis of Merit*

Pen and brown ink, gray-brown wash, over black chalk. 8 15/16 × 10¾ inches (22.7 × 27.2 cm.). Four corners diagonally cropped. Watermark: letters A S (see watermark no. 29).

Here the central figure of the hero who faces left in the above drawing is turned to the right as in the Rezzonico fresco. In the closely connected study at Yale University (repr. Fogg, Tiepolo Exhibition, 1970, no. 77), the winged figure of Fame is moved forward, her trumpet shown silhouetted against the sky at the right instead of against her wing at the left as in the Morgan drawing.

PROVENANCE: See No. 64.

BIBLIOGRAPHY: Fairfax Murray, IV, 104; Fogg, Tiepolo Exhibition, 1970, under no. 77.

The Pierpont Morgan Library
No. IV, 104

142 *Constancy and Fame*

Pen and brown ink, gray-brown wash, over black chalk. 7¾ × 10 1/16 inches (19.8 × 25.6 cm.). Upper corners diagonally cropped. Watermark: letters A S (see watermark no. 29).

Iconographically, as Knox has pointed out, this sheet and its companion, No. 143—both of which show the pomegranate, emblem of fruitfulness—appear to fit with the marriage theme of the Rezzonico ceilings (see No. 140). It may also be remarked that this sheet bears the same watermark as No. 141, which could help to confirm a connection. There are no corresponding groups in either of the Rezzonico ceilings.

PROVENANCE: See No. 64.

BIBLIOGRAPHY: Fairfax Murray, IV, 114.

The Pierpont Morgan Library
No. IV, 114

143 *Constancy and Fame*

Pen and brown ink, gray-brown wash, over black chalk. $8\frac{1}{8} \times 10\frac{3}{8}$ inches (20.7 × 26.3 cm.). Upper corners diagonally cropped. Watermark: letter B (see watermark no. 25).

See No. 142.

PROVENANCE: See No. 64.

BIBLIOGRAPHY: Fairfax Murray, IV, 115.

The Pierpont Morgan Library
No. IV, 115

144 *Error and Falsehood*

Pen and brown ink, brown wash, over black chalk. $7\frac{5}{8} \times 10\frac{1}{8}$ inches (19.5 × 25.7 cm.). Four corners diagonally cropped.

Tiepolo's decorations at the Villa Valmarana, S. Bastiano at Monte Berico near Vicenza, bear the date 1757, and it is assumed that his work at the Palazzo Trento-Valmarana in Vicenza itself dates from about the same time. Knox, Morassi, Vigni, and others have identified more than twenty drawings that are preparatory for the Palazzo Trento-Valmarana, which was unfortunately destroyed by bombardment in 1945. No other Tiepolo commission is so extensively documented among his surviving drawings. Six of the extant preparatory studies, including the present sheet and Nos. 145 and 146, are in the Morgan Library; the others are divided among the print rooms of Princeton, Trieste, and the Victoria and Albert Museum, London. (For a detailed list, see the Fogg exhibition catalogue of 1970 under nos. 72 and 76.)

The personifications of Error, the blindfolded man with a staff, and Falsehood, the recumbent woman, figure in the *Triumph of Truth*, the oval ceiling of the principal salon of the palace (Morassi, 1955, fig. 51), although in a somewhat different spatial context.

Not included in the exhibition are three Morgan sketches: Inv. IV, 97 and 98, which are variant ideas for the sole surviving remnant of the Trento frescoes, the tondo in a private collection in Milan with the figure of a man writing, his hand guided by the genius at his side (Morassi, 1962, fig. 407), and Inv. IV, 98g, a sketch for the group of putti presenting the Mirror of Intellect to Truth, for which No. 146 below is also preparatory.

PROVENANCE: See No. 64.

BIBLIOGRAPHY: Fairfax Murray, IV, 136; Knox, *Victoria and Albert*, under no. 262.

EXHIBITIONS: Fogg, Tiepolo Exhibition, 1970, p. xx, no. 74, repr.

The Pierpont Morgan Library
No. IV, 136

145 *Female Figure with Mirror and Serpent and Two Companions*

Pen and brown ink, brown wash, over black chalk. $7\frac{1}{4} \times 6\frac{3}{4}$ inches (18.5 × 17.2 cm.). Three corners repaired. Lined.

As Morassi and Knox independently observed, the figure at upper left was used without change at the right end of the main ceiling of the Palazzo Trento-Valmarana. There she is grouped with another female figure with a column, the symbol of Fortitude and also of Constancy; the present figure's attributes of mirror and serpent, commonly those of Prudence, may here be associated with Intelligence, as Knox noted. The same authority suggests the winged figure is a sketch for the figure of History in one of the four roundels grouped about the main oval.

PROVENANCE: See No. 64.

BIBLIOGRAPHY: Fairfax Murray, IV, 131.

EXHIBITIONS: Fogg, Tiepolo Exhibition, 1970, p. xx, no. 76, repr.

The Pierpont Morgan Library
No. IV, 131

146 *Three Putti Bearing a Mirror*

Pen and brown ink, brown wash, over red chalk. $7\frac{3}{4} \times 5\frac{7}{16}$ inches (19.8 × 13.8 cm.). Repaired losses upper and lower right. Lined.

Both the single putto and the group of three appear in the main ceiling of the Palazzo Trento-Valmarana, the former high in the sky above and to the left of the central figure of Truth and the latter to the right of Truth to whom they hold up a mirror.

PROVENANCE: See No. 64.

BIBLIOGRAPHY: Knox, *Victoria and Albert*, pp. 32–33, 85, no. 262 (verso).

EXHIBITIONS: Fogg, Tiepolo Exhibition, 1970, p. XX, no. 75, repr.

The Pierpont Morgan Library
No. IV, 131a

147 *Bacchus and Fauns*

Pen and brown ink, brown wash, over red chalk, on brown paper. $7\frac{3}{4} \times 12\frac{3}{8}$ inches (19.7 × 31.4 cm.).

This powerful representation of the drunken Bacchus and his drowsing companions is most likely a late drawing, perhaps to be dated in the latter years of the 1750s. It has not as yet been associated with any project.

PROVENANCE: See No. 64.

BIBLIOGRAPHY: Fairfax Murray, IV, 139; Arthur Millier, *The Drawings of Tiepolo*, Los Angeles, 1956, p. 46.

EXHIBITIONS: Stockholm, Nationalmuseum, "Pierpont Morgan Library gästra Nationalmuseum," 1970, no. 43, repr.

The Pierpont Morgan Library
No. IV, 139

148 *The Angel at the Tomb*

Pen and black ink, gray wash, over black chalk. 10 × 16 inches (25.3 × 40.6 cm.). Upper corners diagonally cropped. Watermark: coat of arms (see watermark no. 5).

This monumental late design presented in steep foreshortening may well have been executed with a ceiling composition in mind, but no related painted work is known. Fairfax Murray not implausibly identified the subject as the Annunciation, most likely by reason of the lily carried by the angel. The attitude of the almost recumbent female figure lifting her veil, however, suggests a possible alternate identification as one of the Marys at the Tomb, the opened lid of the sepulcher being just visible behind her while the angel gestures in the direction of the risen Christ. For the facial type of the woman, compare the Virgin in the late drawing owned by Mr. and Mrs. Jacob M. Kaplan (repr. Fogg, Tiepolo Exhibition, 1970, no. 89 [dated about 1760]).

PROVENANCE: See No. 64.

BIBLIOGRAPHY: Fairfax Murray, IV, 134.

The Pierpont Morgan Library
No. IV, 134

149 *Family Group*

Pen and brown ink, gray and brown wash. $10\frac{7}{8} \times 16\frac{1}{2}$ inches (27.6 × 41.9 cm.).

Giambattista did three drawings of this family, and they are presumably studies for a never-executed group portrait rather in the manner of Paolo Veronese. Rizzi has speculated that the family in question may be the Pisani, whose villa at Strà Giambattista decorated in 1761–1762, just before his departure for Spain. The other two studies for this portrait group are in the Horne Foundation in Florence (repr. *Disegni del Tiepolo* [exhibition catalogue by Aldo Rizzi], Udine, 1965, no. 116), and with Wildenstein & Co. in New York (repr. Fogg, Tiepolo Exhibition, 1970, no. 95).

PROVENANCE: Tomas Harris, London.

EXHIBITIONS: London, Royal Academy, 1953, no. 174; London, Arts Council, Tiepolo Exhibition, 1955, no. 10, repr.

Dr. and Mrs. Rudolf Heinemann

150 *Design for a Dedication Page to Charles III*

Pen and brown ink, brown wash, over black chalk. $14\frac{1}{16} \times 9\frac{3}{4}$ inches (35.6 × 25 cm.).

Inscribed in pen and brown ink at lower left, *Do Juán Bautista Tiepolo*; at lower right, *lo grecho* (?) . . . *Volpato*.

As one of the few known examples of Tiepolo's drawing style during his last years, which were spent in Spain (1762–1770), this drawing is of particular significance. As was noted by the late Dr. Rudolf Berliner some years ago, it is a study for the dedicatory frontispiece of a book on the ruins of Paestum by Paolantonio Paoli (*Paesti quod Posidoniam etiam dixere rudera. Rovine della città di Pesto detta ancora Posidonia*, Rome, 1784). Most of the material for the book was collected over a period of years, even decades, by Count Felice Gazola, an artillery general and amateur archaeologist, who became interested in Paestum when he was resident in Naples. However, like Tiepolo he spent the later years of his life in the service of Charles III in Spain and died there in 1780, four years before the appearance of the book on Paestum. From correspondence of the year 1761 preserved in Madrid, it is known that Gazola was intermediary in the arrangements for Tiepolo's Spanish sojourn, and it seems likely that he personally ordered the design for the frontispiece of his projected book from the artist. The Spanish form of Tiepolo's name in the inscription on the drawing suggests that the drawing was done some time after Tiepolo arrived in Spain, but by 1769 it was in the hands of the engraver Giovanni Volpato, who was working in Venice at that moment (see G. B. Verci, *Notizie intorno alla vita e alle opere de' pittori, scultori e intagliatori della città di Bassano*, Venice, 1775, pp. 305, 307). Preserved with the drawing is an early state of the engraved frontispiece that differs in several details from the version in the book itself. The dedicatory inscription to Charles III is in Italian, and Count Gazola is specifically named as the dedicator, whereas only Paoli's initials appear in the Latin dedication of the frontispiece in the book. The face of the portrait bust of Charles III has also been changed in the engraving in the book so that the gaze is more nearly frontally oriented, but otherwise the plate appears unaltered.

Dr. Berliner's notes, which Dr. Wunder states that he followed when he published the drawing, refer to an edition of the book published at Bassano in 1770, but it has not been possible to trace such an early edition. Dr. Pignatti reports that it is not in the library at Bassano where one might expect to find it.

Tiepolo's design was in the main followed in the engraving, which is in the same direction as the drawing, but there are a certain number of changes, chiefly in the ornamentation of the pedestal and the disposition of the symbols of the arts and of war.

PROVENANCE: Erskine Hewitt.

BIBLIOGRAPHY: Wunder, *Extravagant Drawings*, no. 69, repr.

EXHIBITIONS: New York, Cooper Union Museum, "Five Centuries of Drawing," circulated by the American Federation of Arts, 1959-1961, no. 29; Fogg, Tiepolo Exhibition, 1970, no. 96, repr.

Cooper-Hewitt Museum, Smithsonian Institution Bequest of Erskine Hewitt, 1938-57-219

151 *Portrait of Palma Giovane*

Red chalk, heightened with white, on blue paper. $9\frac{1}{4} \times 6$ inches (23.5 × 15.2 cm.). Stains at margins.

Sir Karl Parker was the first to identify the subject of this drawing. It is a copy by Giambattista Tiepolo of the portrait bust of the late sixteenth-century Venetian painter Jacopo Palma, Il Giovane, by his contemporary, the sculptor Alessandro Vittoria. Vittoria's original, which is now in the Kunsthistorisches Museum in Vienna (illustrated in K. E. Maison's article), or a plaster cast thereof must have been on hand in the Tiepolo studio, for Giambattista and his sons Domenico and Lorenzo made a number of drawings after the bust, studying it from many angles. Maison recently published fourteen of these studies, and on the basis of the quality of these sheets, attributed five of them, including the present drawing, Mr. Scholz's drawing (No. 152), a drawing in the Rasini collection, Milan, another at Princeton, and a sheet in the collection of Dr. Schrafl in Zurich to Giambattista himself, one to Domenico, and all the rest to the much less talented younger son Lorenzo.

PROVENANCE: Hans Wendland, Lugano; sale, Berlin, Hermann Ball, Paul Graupe, April 24, 1931, no. 102; Tomas Harris, London.

BIBLIOGRAPHY: Hadeln, *Tiepolo Drawings*, no. 164, repr.; Ugo Ojetti, editor, *Il Settecento italiano*, I, Milan, 1932, no. 277, pl. CLXXXV; K. T. Parker, *Old Master Drawings*, IX, 1935, p. 62, fig. 13; Morassi, 1955, p. 146; K. E. Maison, "The Tiepolo Drawings after the Portrait Bust of Palma Giovane by Alessandro Vittoria," *Master Drawings*, VI, 1968, no. 4, pp. 392-394, pl. 34.

EXHIBITIONS: London, Savile Gallery, "Drawings by Giovanni Battista Tiepolo," 1930; London, Royal Academy, 1953, no. 168; London, Arts Council, Tiepolo Exhibition, 1955, no. 17, repr.

Dr. and Mrs. Rudolf Heinemann

152 *Portrait of Palma Giovane*

Red chalk, heightened with white, on blue paper. $9\frac{11}{16} \times 7\frac{1}{8}$ inches (24.6 × 18.1 cm.).

Inscribed in pen and brown ink at upper right corner, *Tiepol.*

See No. 151.

BIBLIOGRAPHY: K. T. Parker, *Old Master Drawings*, IX, 1935, p. 61; K. E. Maison, "The Tiepolo Drawings after the Portrait Bust of Palma Giovane by Alessandro Vittoria," *Master Drawings*, VI, 1968, no. 4, pp. 392–394, pl. 36.

EXHIBITIONS: Oakland, Scholz Exhibition, 1960, no. 83; Hamburg, Scholz Exhibition, 1963, no. 154, repr.; New Haven, Scholz Exhibition, 1964, no. 84; A.F.A., 17th and 18th Century Drawings, 1966–1967, no. 32, repr.; London, Scholz Exhibition, 1968, no. 95.

Janos Scholz

Giovanni Battista or Domenico Tiepolo

153 *Three Studies of Dogs, after Paolo Veronese*

Black chalk, heightened with white chalk, on blue paper. $13\frac{1}{8} \times 9\frac{7}{8}$ inches (33.3 × 25.1 cm.). Margins irregular; all four corners trimmed. Watermark: letters RO SA (see watermark no. 36).

Inscribed in pen and brown ink on verso, *80 X*ʳˢ*. 12. No. 3103.*

These three dogs' heads are, as Knox pointed out, copied from details in Paolo Veronese's *Family of Darius before Alexander*, now in the National Gallery, London, which could have been seen by the Tiepolos in Venice, probably in the Palazzo Pisani a S. Polo. The two spaniels appear at the extreme left of Veronese's composition; the dog seen in profile at the lower right of the sheet appears at the extreme right in the painting. That the Tiepolos should copy Veronese is hardly surprising. The work of the great sixteenth-century Venetian master had a predominant influence on the style of Giambattista.

Like No. 154, this sheet formed part of a group of more than eight hundred drawings, largely chalk studies on blue paper, that appeared at the Bossi-Beyerlen sale in Stuttgart in 1882. Drawings from this source are identifiable by characteristic, cryptic code numbers inscribed in pen on the verso of the sheets (see Knox in Fogg catalogue, 1970, p. XIV). These drawings were once attributed *en bloc* to Giambattista, but in recent years Tiepolo scholars have come to agree that the majority of the drawings, many of them literal copies after details in the painted work of Giambattista, are the work of members of the Tiepolo studio, and above all Domenico. George Knox and others attribute Nos. 153 and 154 to Giambattista himself, on the grounds of the high quality of execution. They may indeed be his work, but the distinction between the chalk styles of father and son is far from clear for the present. No doubt Knox's forthcoming volume on the chalk drawings of the Tiepolos will very considerably clarify this complex question.

It should be added that the two spaniels studied in the present sheet appear, grouped exactly as they are in Veronese's painting, in an etching by Domenico inscribed *Io. Bapta Tiepolo inv. et pinx.* (Pignatti, *Acqueforti dei Tiepolo*, pl. LXV).

Hadeln, followed by Freeden and Lamb, suggested that these studies were utilized by Giambattista for a dog that appears in the *Marriage of Barbarossa* fresco in the Kaisersaal at Würzburg.

PROVENANCE: Johann Dominik Bossi; Karl Christian Friedrich Beyerlen; sale, Stuttgart, Gutekunst, March 27, 1882; Dr. Hans Wendland, Lugano; de Vries, Amsterdam; sale, Paris, Hôtel Drouot, 1930, no. 66; Marquis de Biron, Paris and Geneva; purchased by the Metropolitan Museum in Geneva, 1937.

BIBLIOGRAPHY: Hadeln, *Tiepolo Drawings*, pl. 135 (as Giambattista); Freeden and Lamb, *Würzburger Residenz*, p. 105, pl. 45 (as Giambattista); George Knox, "The Paintings by G. B. Tiepolo," *Burlington Magazine*, CV, 1963, pp. 327ff., fig. 59 (as Giambattista).

EXHIBITIONS: New York, Tiepolo Exhibition, 1938, no. 46, repr. (as Giambattista); New York, M. Knoedler & Co., "The Artist and the Animal," 1968, no. 46, repr. (as Giambattista); Fogg, Tiepolo Exhibition, 1970, no. 32, repr. (as Giambattista).

*The Metropolitan Museum of Art
Rogers Fund, 37.165.53*

154 *Study of an Eagle*

Black chalk, heightened with white chalk, on blue paper. $9\frac{7}{8} \times 13\frac{3}{4}$ inches (25.1 × 34.9 cm.). Margins irregular; vertical creases at center. Watermark: letters RO SA (see watermark no. 36).

Inscribed in pen and brown ink on verso, *24 X no. 2938*.

George Knox, who attributes this drawing to Giambattista Tiepolo, suggests that it is a study for the eagle that appears hovering in the sky in a ceiling decoration in the Palazzo Pisani-Moretta, Venice, dated by Morassi about 1742 (Morassi, 1962, fig. 259). The correspondence is indeed close, closer perhaps than to the eagle at the top of a standard in the *Marriage of Barbarossa* in the Kaisersaal, Würzburg. The connection with Würzburg had been suggested by Hadeln and was accepted by Freeden and Lamb.

PROVENANCE: Johann Dominik Bossi; Karl Christian Friedrich Beyerlen; sale, Stuttgart, Gutekunst, March 27, 1882; Dr. Hans Wendland, Lugano; de Vries, Amsterdam; Marquis de Biron, Paris and Geneva; purchased by the Metropolitan Museum in Geneva, 1937.

BIBLIOGRAPHY: Hadeln, *Tiepolo Drawings*, pl. 136 (as Giambattista); Metropolitan Museum, *European Drawings*, no. 46, repr. (as Giambattista); Tietze, *European Master Drawings*, no. 90, repr.; Freeden and Lamb, *Würzburger Residenz*, p. 105, pl. 45 (as Giambattista); George Knox, "The Paintings by G. B. Tiepolo," *Burlington Magazine*, CV, 1963, pp. 327ff., fig. 56 (as Giambattista).

EXHIBITIONS: Venice, Palazzo del Esposizione, "Il Settecento italiano," 1929, p. 29; New York, Tiepolo Exhibition, 1938, no. 47, repr. (as Giambattista); Fogg, Tiepolo Exhibition, 1970, no. 31, repr. (as Giambattista).

The Metropolitan Museum of Art Rogers Fund, 37.165.109

Antonio Canal, called Canaletto

Venice 1697–Venice 1768

155 *Lagoon Capriccio*

Pen and brown ink, gray wash. Faint architectural sketch in black chalk barely visible at left of sheet. $10\frac{3}{16} \times 16\frac{3}{16}$ inches (25.8 × 41.1 cm.). Foxing.

Verso: Black chalk view of a Venetian canal.

This Venetian landscape is imaginary; Canaletto has combined in a capriccio a number of elements—a church, a farmhouse, a bridge, a ruined tower—that he may have seen and studied separately. Constable points out that the same church, campanile, and house appear in reverse in a painted capriccio in the Uffizi, which otherwise differs considerably from this drawing. The Uffizi picture, datable to the early 1740s, was once attributed to Bernardo Bellotto, but can be established as Canaletto's on the basis of the inscription on Berardi's engraving after the picture (see Constable, no. 485). On the verso of the drawing is a chalk sketch of a canal in Venice, possibly the Rio S. Barnaba.

PROVENANCE: Baron Dominique Vivant Denon (Lugt 779); Lady Sybil Grant; Miss Lucy Cohen; Earl of Rosebery; sale, London, Sotheby's, May 28, 1941, no. 83; purchased by the Metropolitan Museum in New York, 1943.

BIBLIOGRAPHY: Amaury Duval, *Monuments des arts du dessin ... recueillis par le baron Vivant Denon*, II, Paris, 1829, pl. 148 (reversed); Josephine L. Allen, "Capriccio by Canaletto," *Metropolitan Museum of Art Bulletin*, January 1946, pp. 124–125, repr. (recto and verso); Benesch, *Venetian Drawings*, no. 52, repr.; Constable, *Canaletto*, nos. 797 (recto), 608 (verso), repr.; Bean, *100 European Drawings*, no. 44 (recto), repr.

The Metropolitan Museum of Art Rogers Fund, 43.61

156 *Houses along a River*

Pen and brown ink, over red chalk. $5\frac{5}{8} \times 15\frac{1}{4}$ inches (14.1 × 38.7 cm.). Watermark: small circle with letters A C below at left, fragment of a fleur-de-lis at right (see watermark no. 35).

Inscribed in red chalk at left center, *chiaro*; at center, *scuro tuto*; at right, *1/2 squasi*; scattered letters, *B* and *R*.

This drawing and one in the Fogg Art Museum, Cambridge, which together form a continuous view of houses and gardens along the edge of a river, most likely the Brenta at Padua, show Canaletto as a topographer working directly on the scene. Very possibly he sketched in red chalk while working on the spot and later reaffirmed the preliminary chalk outlines in pen. The pen work is clearly revisory in certain passages: the rooftop indicated twice in red chalk at the upper left edge was let into the composition at the extreme left in pen, the artist having used two short parallels to remind himself of the point of insertion; the adjoining tall house was then shifted considerably to the right of its original chalk outlines; at the far right, in the pen work, the last rooftop and its chimney were shifted to the left. The scattered letters *B* and *R* are color notations: *B* for *bianco*; *R* for *rosso*. The notation *chiaro* and *scuro tuto* are indications of lighted and shaded areas, which, like the color notations, were precisely followed in the painting.

From this true working sketch and its companion at the Fogg the artist developed the painting owned by Mark Oliver, London (Constable, fig. 377), and an etching (De Vesme 9), the latter being in reverse of the panorama formed by the two drawings. The scene of the Morgan drawing constitutes the left half of the painting. The approximate date of all these various works is established by the Fogg drawing, which is signed and dated on the verso 1742.

At Windsor, there are two more elaborately worked drawings that include the major features of the Morgan composition, the footbridge, the tall house, and the mill, but with an extension of the foreground showing the river and its opposite bank (repr., Parker, nos. 87 and 88).

PROVENANCE: William Bates (Lugt 2604); Charles Fairfax Murray; purchased by J. Pierpont Morgan in London, 1910.

BIBLIOGRAPHY: Agnes Mongan, "Notes on Canaletto Drawings in the Fogg Art Museum," *Old Master Drawings*, XIII, 1938, pp. 34–36, pl. 38 (reversed); Mongan and Sachs, *Drawings in the Fogg Museum*, no. 307; Rodolfo Pallucchini and G. F. Guarnati, *Le Acqueforti del Canaletto*, Venice, 1945, pp. 22–23; K. T. Parker, *The Drawings of Antonio Canaletto in the Collection of His Majesty the King at Windsor Castle*, Oxford and London, 1948, under no. 88; *Eighteenth Century Venice*, London, Whitechapel Art Gallery, 1951, p. 13, no. 10; Vittorio Moschini, *Canaletto*, Milan, [1954], no. 171, repr.; Terisio Pignatti, *Il Quaderno di Disegni del Canaletto alle gallerie di Venezia*, Venice, 1958, pp. 14–15; Constable, *Canaletto*, I, pp. 132, note 1, 133, 135; II, no. 695, repr., also under no. 697; Gregory Martin, *Canaletto*, London, 1967, pl. 52.

EXHIBITIONS: New York, Tiepolo Exhibition, 1938, no. 55, repr.; Toronto, Ottawa, and Montreal, "Canaletto," 1964–1965, no. 90, repr.

The Pierpont Morgan Library
No. IV, 141a

157 *The East Front of Warwick Castle*

Pen and brown ink, gray wash. 12 $\frac{7}{16}$ × 22$\frac{1}{8}$ inches (31.6 × 56.2 cm.). Vertical crease at center; slight foxing. Watermark: coat of arms (see watermark no. 8). Lined.

Constable suggests that this particularly brilliant drawn *veduta* probably dates from 1749, fairly early in Canaletto's stay in England. The east front of Warwick Castle is seen from the exterior: at the left is Caesar's Tower; at center the gateway, and behind it the Chalk Tower; at right is Guy's Tower. A pendant drawing with approximately the same provenance and representing the interior of the east front seen from the courtyard was formerly in the collection of Sir George Leon, Bt. (repr. Constable, no. 760). It seems probable that the Lehman drawing served as a basis for the painting at Warwick Castle (repr. Constable. no. 446), though there are variations between the two.

PROVENANCE: Possibly Hon. Charles Greville; Paul Sandby (Lugt 2112); Lady Eva Dugdale, Royal Lodge, Windsor Great Park; sale, London, Sotheby's, November 18, 1920, no. 427; Adrien Fauchier-Magnan, Neuilly-sur-Seine; Fauchier-Magnan sale, London, Sotheby's, December 4, 1935, no. 5, repr.; Philip Hofer, Cambridge, Mass.

BIBLIOGRAPHY: H. F. Finberg, "Canaletto in England," *The Walpole Society*, IX, 1920–1921, p. 68, pl. XXVIIIa, repr.; Benesch, *Venetian Drawings*, no. 53, repr.; Constable, *Canaletto*, no. 759, repr.

EXHIBITIONS: New York, Pierpont Morgan Library, "Landscape Drawings and Watercolors, Breugel to Cézanne," 1953, no. 18, pl. X; Paris, Lehman Exhibition, 1957, no. 89; Cincinnati, Lehman Exhibition, 1959, no. 228.

Robert Lehman Collection

158 *View of Padua from the East*

Pen and brown ink, gray wash. 7$\frac{1}{4}$ × 10$\frac{7}{8}$ inches (18.4 × 27.6 cm.). Vertical crease at lower margin.

Conspicuous on the horizon in this drawn view are the church of S. Francesco on the left and to the right in the distance the Salone, Padua's enormous civic meeting house. A similar view in pen but without the wash that so successfully unifies the present composition is in the Queen's collection at Windsor Castle (repr. Constable, no. 686). The composition was engraved in reverse with some additions and changes by Berardi. A free copy of this drawing by Antonio Canal's nephew Bernardo Bellotto, also called Canaletto, is in the present exhibition (No. 215).

PROVENANCE: William Benoni White (Lugt 2592).

BIBLIOGRAPHY: Constable, *Canaletto*, no. 681, repr.

EXHIBITIONS: Wellesley College, Jewett Arts Center, "Eighteenth Century Italian Drawings," 1960, no. 11, pl. 4.

Mrs. Douglas Williams

159 *The South Pulpit in S. Marco*

Pen and brown ink, over black chalk. $11^{1}/_{2} \times 7^{1}/_{2}$ inches (29.2 × 19.1 cm.). Watermark: graduated triple crescents (see watermark no. 19).

Inscribed in pen and brown ink at lower right, *21*; in black chalk on verso, *Schizzo . . . original, di Anto, Canal, detto il Canaletto. V8V* [?].

Constable pointed out that this is a preliminary sketch for the south pulpit as seen in the diagrammatic *View of the Interior of S. Marco* in the Victoria and Albert Museum, London, and in the very elaborate drawing of the same view in Hamburg (repr. Constable, nos. 559 and 558 respectively). This rapid notation made, no doubt, on the spot, may well be a page from one of Canaletto's sketchbooks.

PROVENANCE: Italico Brass, Venice.

BIBLIOGRAPHY: Constable, *Canaletto*, no. 560, repr.

EXHIBITIONS: Venice, Scholz Exhibition, 1957, no. 79, repr.; Oakland, Scholz Exhibition, 1960, no. 5.

Janos Scholz

160 *Architectural Capriccio*

Pen and brown ink, gray wash, over black chalk. $9^{15}/_{16} \times 13^{9}/_{16}$ inches (25.2 × 34.5 cm.). Vertical crease at center.

In his mature years Canaletto made a specialty of such architectural capricci, in which he crowded together buildings of the most disparate nature, transforming monuments he had seen in Venice, Rome, and England. Here the buildings are largely of Venetian inspiration, though the triumphal column at right is surely a Roman recollection.

This drawing was presumably not known by W. G. Constable at the time of the publication of his *catalogue raisonné* of Canaletto's work, for the drawing seems perfectly authentic and indeed entirely typical.

An architectural capriccio in the Metropolitan Museum (Constable, *Canaletto*, fig. 807) with Roman and Gothic elements is executed in the same broken, curly line and involves the same contrast of luminous gray wash with warm brown pen line.

Private Collection

161 *Architectural Capriccio*

Pen and brown ink, gray wash, over traces of black chalk. $11^{1}/_{4} \times 8$ inches (28.6 × 20.3 cm.). Several losses and creases at margins. Illegible watermark.

Inscribed, presumably in the hand of MacGowan, in pen and brown ink on verso, *Canaletto / presented me by J. Hayes.*

Verso: Black chalk architectural sketch.

Canaletto in his views of Venice was sometimes tempted to group together monuments that were actually situated far from one another. These capricci were very much to the taste of the time. Here he has given us a fairly accurate view of the Rio della Pietà in Venice, with the apse of the church of S. Lorenzo at the right. But to the left he has added an imaginary campanile and closed the composition with a nonexistent bridge.

What appears to be an old copy of the drawing was in the Oppenheimer collection (sale, London, Christie's, July 10–14, 1936, no. 45A; repr. *The Vasari Society for the Reproduction of Drawings by Old Masters*, London, Part IX, 1913–1914, no. 11). There is a signed copy by Thomas Sandby in the British Museum (1944-10-14-174).

PROVENANCE: J. Hayes; John MacGowan (Lugt 1496); Count Antoine Seilern, London.

BIBLIOGRAPHY: Benesch, *Venetian Drawings*, no. 51, repr.; Tietze, *European Master Drawings*, no. 93, repr.; Constable, *Canaletto*, no. 772, repr.; "Italian Drawings from the Collection of Janos Scholz," *Metropolitan Museum of Art Bulletin*, May 1965, Part II, p. 342, repr.

EXHIBITIONS: Cambridge, Mass., Fogg Art Museum, "Venice in the Eighteenth Century," 1948, no. 7; Oberlin College, Drawings of the 18th Century, 1950–1951, no. 4, repr.; Minneapolis, Detroit, Indianapolis, "Venice 1700–1800," 1952, no. 15; Venice, Scholz Exhibition, 1957, no. 78, repr.; Oakland, Scholz Exhibition, 1960, no. 4, repr.; Hamburg, Scholz Exhibition, 1963, no. 27, pl. 90; New Haven, Scholz Exhibition, 1964, no. 76, fig. 13; Toronto, Ottawa, Montreal, "Canaletto," 1964–1965, no. 78, repr.; London, Scholz Exhibition, 1968, no. 17, pl. 21.

Janos Scholz

162 Man Smoking a Pipe
Verso: *Standing Gentleman and Two Studies of His Head*

Pen and brown ink, over black chalk (recto and verso). $11\frac{5}{8} \times 6\frac{3}{8}$ inches (29.5 × 16.2 cm.).

Inscribed in pen and the same ink as drawing at upper right of both recto and verso, *40/volta*.

Very few preparatory drawings for the figures that stroll through Canaletto's Venetian *vedute* have survived, and the male figures sketched on the recto and verso of this sheet are not immediately identifiable in any extant picture. However, a very similar drawing at the Courtauld Institute in London, numbered in the same fashion as this drawing and possibly from the same dismembered sketchbook, bears a figure that occurs in a view of S. Giacomo di Rialto, datable about 1746, now in the National Gallery of Canada at Ottawa (repr. Constable, no. 839 for the Courtauld drawing, no. 298 for the Ottawa picture). Like the London drawing, this study is drawn in Canaletto's most supple and meandering pen line.

PROVENANCE: Purchased by the Metropolitan Museum in New York, 1939.

BIBLIOGRAPHY: Metropolitan Museum, *European Drawings*, no. 35, repr. (recto); K. T. Parker, *The Drawings of Canaletto in the Collection of His Majesty the King at Windsor Castle*, Oxford and London, 1948, p. 26, note 37; Constable, *Canaletto*, p. 865, no. 840, repr. (recto and verso); Bean, *100 European Drawings*, no. 45, repr. (recto).

The Metropolitan Museum of Art
Purchase, Joseph Pulitzer Bequest, 39.79

Corrado Giaquinto
Molfetta 1699–Naples 1765

163 St. Joseph Presented by the Virgin to the Holy Trinity

Pen and brown ink, brown wash, heightened with white, over red chalk, on brownish paper. $10\frac{5}{16} \times 15\frac{13}{16}$ inches (26.2 × 40.2 cm.). Several spots at right margin. Partially lined.

Inscribed in pen and brown ink at lower right, *Corrado*; in a different hand, *Giaquinto*; in pen and brown ink on verso, *fatto p Il Re di Sardegnia di palmi 43 – 28*; numbered on verso, *100*.

A study, as Anthony Clark pointed out, for the fresco that ornaments the vault of a chapel designed by the architect Filippo Juvara in the church of S. Teresa in Turin. Giaquinto also supplied lateral canvases for this chapel representing the Rest on the Flight and the Death of St. Joseph (the three compositions repr. by Mario d'Orsi, *Corrado Giaquinto*, Rome, 1958, figs. 33–35). The work for this chapel dates from Giaquinto's second visit to Turin, sometime between 1735 and 1739. The artist's fluid style as a draughtsman reveals his considerable debt to his master Solimena.

PROVENANCE: Purchased by the Metropolitan Museum in London, 1965.

BIBLIOGRAPHY: *Le Dessin à Naples du XVIe siècle au XVIIIe siècle* (exhibition catalogue by Walter Vitzthum), Paris, Musée du Louvre, 1967, mentioned p. 51.

EXHIBITIONS: London, P. & D. Colnaghi, "Old Master Drawings," 1965, no. 77.

The Metropolitan Museum of Art
Rogers Fund, 65.131.7

164 The Relics of St. Acutius and St. Eutychetes Transported to Naples

Pen and black ink, gray wash, heightened with a little white, on pink paper. $17\frac{3}{8} \times 11\frac{1}{4}$ inches (44.2 × 28.7 cm.).

Anthony Clark identified this drawing as a preparatory study for Giaquinto's large canvas on the left wall of the apse of the Duomo in Naples, representing the transport from Pozzuoli to Naples of the relics of two of the six companions martyred at

Pozzuoli with St. Januarius, patron of Naples. The drawing differs in many details from both the preparatory oil sketch in the Museo Nazionale in Palermo (Mario d'Orsi, *Corrado Giaquinto*, Rome, 1958, fig. 72) and the finished picture, which was painted in 1744–1745 on the commission of the Cardinal Archbishop Giuseppe Spinelli. In comparison with the loose pictorial treatment of the previous Giaquinto drawing (No. 163), the present sheet is elaborately linear; both manners hark back to the example of Giaquinto's teacher Solimena.

EXHIBITIONS: A.F.A., 17th and 18th Century Drawings, 1966–1967, no. 33, repr.; Minneapolis Institute of Arts and four other cities, "Selections from the Drawing Collection of David Daniels," 1968, no. 18, repr.

David Daniels

Giovanni Antonio Guardi
Vienna 1699–Venice 1760

165 *The Good Samaritan*

Pen and brown ink, brown wash, over black chalk; squared for transfer in black chalk. $13^5/_8 \times 9^{15}/_{16}$ inches (34.6 × 25.2 cm.).

Inscribed in pen and brown ink at lower right, *Guardi*; in pen and brown ink on verso, *E [?] Ant° Guardi*.

A fine, newly rediscovered example of Gianantonio's idiosyncratic draughtsmanship. The light moves over the surface, animating the composition but not defining the forms. Byam Shaw suggests that the inscription *Ant° Guardi* on the verso of the sheet is the artist's signature.

PROVENANCE: Sale, London, Christie's, March 25, 1969, no. 27, repr.; purchased by the Metropolitan Museum in London, 1969.

EXHIBITIONS: London, P. & D. Colnaghi, "Old Master Drawings," 1969, no. 23.

The Metropolitan Museum of Art
Rogers Fund, 69.171.2

166 *The Taking of Padua*

Pen and point of brush, brown ink, brown wash. $21^1/_4 \times 30^3/_8$ inches (54.5 × 76.5 cm.). Watermark: large trefoil, letters A C.

Inscribed in pen and black ink at upper corner on verso, *13*.

This exceptionally large sheet belongs to a series of drawings, all of similar scale, of Venetian historical subjects, once in the Morosini-Gatterburg collection but now scattered in various European and American collections. The largest group (37) is in the possession of Count Vittorio Cini of Venice; there is one drawing in the Cleveland Museum; and others are to be found in private ownership in Berlin, Milan, Paris, and elsewhere. The drawings are numbered on the verso in the order of their original sequence, the Morgan sheet bearing no. 13. The highest number known, according to Alessandro Bettagno (*Disegni veneti del Settecento della Fondazione Giorgio Cini e delle collezioni venete*, 1963, no. 37) is 58.

As was pointed out by Giuseppe Fiocco, in *Le tre Venezie*, 1944, the drawings are not Gianantonio Guardi's original compositions but are based, for the most part, on paintings in the Ducal Palace in Venice or on canvases in the S. Marco cycle decorating the Scuola del Santo. (See also Antonio Morassi, "A Signed Drawing by Antonio Guardi and the Problem of the Guardi Brothers," *Burlington Magazine*, XCV, 1953, p. 267, note 19.) The Morgan drawing records the *Taking of Padua* by Francesco Bassano, one of the oval panels in the ceiling of the Sala dello Scrutinio in the Palazzo Ducale in Venice, usually dated 1583–1584. The conquest took place in 1405.

PROVENANCE: Richard S. Davis; purchased by the Morgan Library in Boston, 1969.

BIBLIOGRAPHY: Pignatti, *Disegni veneziani*, under no. 21; Pignatti, *Disegni dei Guardi*, under no. IX.

EXHIBITIONS: Houston, Guardi Family, 1958, no. 28, repr.

The Pierpont Morgan Library
Gift of the Fellows, 1969.5

167 *The Martyrdom of St. Clement*

Brush and brown wash, over black chalk. $16^5/_8 \times 10^7/_{16}$ inches (42.2 × 26.5 cm.). Vertical and horizontal creases at center; various spots and stains. Watermark: single crescent.

Numbered in pen and black ink on verso, *2548*. Collector's mark of Janos Scholz on verso (Lugt S. 2933b).

The name of Gianantonio Guardi was first associated with this drawing by Otto Benesch, who published it in 1947; in the Platt collection it had been attributed to Domenico Tiepolo. Benesch, however, hesitated between Gianantonio and the young Francesco Guardi. Pallucchini sustained the attribution to Gianantonio and pointed out as well that this drawing is a free copy of a lost picture by Giovanni Battista Pittoni, known today through a *bozzetto* preserved at the University of Upsala. Gianantonio was eclectic in his borrowing, and he dissolved the more solid forms that he imitated by the light that flickers over the surface of the composition.

PROVENANCE: Dan Fellows Platt (Lugt S. 750a).

BIBLIOGRAPHY: Benesch, *Venetian Drawings*, no. 55, repr.; Rodolfo Pallucchini, "Disegni veneziani del Settecento in America," *Arte Veneta*, II, 1948, p. 158, fig. 173, the Upsala *bozzetto* fig. 174; Antonio Morassi, "A Signed Drawing by Antonio Guardi and the Problem of the Guardi Brothers," *Burlington Magazine*, XCV, 1953, p. 264, fig. 9; Terisio Pignatti, "Nuovi Disegni di figura dei Guardi," *Critica d'Arte*, XI, 1964, nos. 67–68, pp. 57–72, fig. 92; Pignatti, *Disegni dei Guardi*, no. v, repr.

EXHIBITIONS: Venice, Scholz Exhibition, 1957, no. 90, repr.; Houston, Guardi Family, 1958, no. 27, repr.; Oakland, Scholz Exhibition, 1960, no. 41; Hamburg, Scholz Exhibition, 1963, no. 77, pl. 81; London, Scholz Exhibition, 1968, no. 50.

Janos Scholz

168 *The Education of the Virgin*

Red chalk. $16\frac{1}{8} \times 10\frac{3}{8}$ inches (41×26.4 cm.). Lower left corner replaced; paper yellowed at edges; some yellow and gray stains at upper left.

Inscribed in pen and brown ink at lower left, [da] *Giambatista Tiepolo Veneziano*.

Verso: Sketch in red chalk of draped seated figure.

Here the draughtsman, very plausibly identified by Pignatti as Gianantonio Guardi, has freely copied Giambattista Tiepolo's early altarpiece of the Chiesa della Fava, Venice (Morassi, 1955, pl. 16). The inscription on the sheet in the "Reliable Venetian Hand," which seems to attribute the drawing to Giambattista himself, is incomplete; the lower left corner of the sheet has been cut off, and it is safe to assume that the missing word was *da* (from or after). The knowledgeable Venetian collector, who possessed a number of copies of pictures and drawings, surely realized that this drawing was

after, rather than for Giambattista's picture. Recently Fernanda de' Maffei has made the rather fanciful suggestion that the drawing is by the Austrian painter Franz Anton Maulbertsch.

PROVENANCE: "Reliable Venetian Hand" (Lugt 3005c–d); Sir Robert Mond; Mrs. David Thomas, New York.

BIBLIOGRAPHY: Tancred Borenius and Rudolf Wittkower, *Catalogue of the Collection of Drawings by the Old Masters formed by Sir Robert Mond*, London, n.d., p. 62, no. 252 (as a copy after Giambattista Tiepolo); Terisio Pignatti, "Nuovi Disegni di figura dei Guardi," *Critica d'Arte*, XI, 1964, no. 67–72, pp. 57–67, fig. 96; Fernanda de' Maffei, "La Questione Guardi: precisazioni e aggriunte," *Arte in Europa. Scritti di storia dell' arte in onore di Edoardo Arslan*, Pavia, 1966, pp. 852–855, fig. 577; *Disegni di una collezione veneziana del Settecento*, Venice, 1966, no. 107, repr., though not exhibited; Pignatti, *Disegni dei Guardi*, no. 1, repr.

EXHIBITIONS: Venice, Guardi Exhibition, 1965, no. 8, repr.

Dr. Donald Tapley

Bartolomeo Nazari

Clusone (near Bergamo)1699–Milan 1758

169 *Portrait of Giovanni Paolo Rovillio*

Black and white chalk, brush and black wash, on dark brown paper. $11\frac{1}{8} \times 8\frac{1}{4}$ inches (28.6×21 cm.). Horizontal piece cut and reattached to sheet near lower margin; slight crease at upper right corner.

Inscribed in pen and black ink on frame surrounding portrait, *IOH. PETRUS ROUILLIO ACAD. 1743.6. JUNII TRANSFORMAT. RESTIT.*

One of nine portrait drawings in the Scholz collection that come from an album bearing the proprietary inscription *Familia Agudia e Sormani*, indicating a Lombard provenance. Nazari was successfully active as a portrait painter and draughtsman in Venice and throughout north Italy; his portraits have a realistic directness that reflects his early training with his fellow Bergamask Fra Galgario. These portrait drawings had been attributed by a previous owner to Pietro Longhi, and it was Mr. Scholz who in 1947 correctly identified the artist as Nazari. A chalk portrait head of a man, from the same source, is in the collection of Walter C. Baker, New York.

PROVENANCE: Ferruccio Asta (Lugt S. 116a).

EXHIBITIONS: Oakland, Scholz Exhibition, 1960, no. 50.

Janos Scholz

Pietro Bracci

Rome 1700–Rome 1773

170 *Project for a Tomb*

Pen and brown ink, brown and gray wash, heightened with a little white, over black chalk. 15¾ × 10⅝ inches (40 × 27 cm.). Slight foxing.

Signed in pen and brown ink at lower left, *Petrus Bracci Rom. F.*; inscribed in pen and red ink at base of tomb, *Scala di Palmi Sei.*

In this and the following drawing Bracci, one of the most inventive official sculptors in eighteenth-century Rome, proposes alternative solutions for the tomb of Cardinal Carlo Leopoldo Calcagnini, erected in 1746 in the church of S. Andrea delle Fratte, Rome, on the commission of the cardinal's nephew and heir, Teofilo. No. 171 comes closest to the tomb as executed, where an allegorical female figure of History writes the cardinal's name on an obelisk supported by two lions and ornamented by a painted portrait of the deceased (Rudolf Wittkower, *Art and Architecture in Italy, 1600–1750*, second rev. ed., Baltimore, 1965, pl. 168A).

PROVENANCE: Archivio di Palazzo Bracci, Rome; Arturo Pini di San Miniato, New York; purchased by the Metropolitan Museum in New York, 1966.

BIBLIOGRAPHY: Costanza Gradara, *Pietro Bracci Scultore Romano*, Milan, n.d., p. 55, pl. XVI; *Metropolitan Museum of Art Bulletin*, October 1967, p. 58, repr. p. 59.

The Metropolitan Museum of Art Purchase, Florence and Carl Selden Foundation Gift, 66.139.2

171 *Project for a Tomb*

Pen and brown ink, gray wash, over traces of black chalk. 15¾ × 10⅝ inches (40 × 27 cm.). Slightly foxed.

Signed in pen and brown ink at lower left, *Petrus Bracci Rom. F.*; inscribed in pen and red ink at base of tomb, *Scala di Palmi Otto Romani.*

See No. 170.

PROVENANCE: Archivio di Palazzo Bracci, Rome; Arturo Pini di San Miniato, New York; purchased by the Metropolitan Museum in New York, 1966.

The Metropolitan Museum of Art Purchase, Florence and Carl Selden Foundation Gift, 66.139.1

Luigi Vanvitelli

Naples 1700–Caserta 1773

172 *Stage Design: Architectural Perspective with an Obelisk*

Pen and gray ink, gray wash, over traces of black chalk. 9⅛ × 10⅜ inches (23.2 × 26.4 cm.). Foxing; hole at upper right; pen sketch on verso visible at upper right of recto.

Verso: Sketch in pen and brown ink of columns; black chalk sketch of columns and niche figures.

Luigi Vanvitelli, architect son of the Dutch-born painter of Italian views Gaspar van Wittel, was the designer of the palace of the Bourbon kings of the Two Sicilies at Caserta near Naples, a vast structure intended to rival Versailles in scale and magnificence. He not only was responsible for the overall exterior design of the palace but undertook the decoration of a number of interior areas, such as the splendid staircase and the interior of the theater. The present spirited sketch is a design for a stage set to be used in this theater. The identification is made possible by a drawing in the Metropolitan Museum that shows the proscenium arch of the theater framing a stage setting that involves the same obelisk at the end of a perspective view. The Metropolitan Print Department drawing (64.669.4) is inscribed: *Coupe sur la Largeur D C du petit Théâtre du Palais de Caserte qui fait voir la Scène;* it is one of four drawings in the Museum, probably from the hand of a studio assistant, recording Vanvitelli's schemes for the interior architecture of the theater. If the drawings in the Metropolitan reveal, in their rather dry correctness, the hand of a studio assistant, Mr. Oenslager's design for the stage setting is dashed off with a speed and authority that identify it as the work of Vanvitelli himself.

PROVENANCE: Edmond Fatio, Geneva (his mark at lower right).

EXHIBITIONS: Zurich, Eidgenössische Technische Hochschule, "Architektur-Dekorations-Zeichnungen der Barockzeit aus der Sammlung Edmond Fatio, Genf," 1946, no. 78, repr.; "Four Centuries of Theater Design: Drawings from the Donald Oenslager Collection," circulated by the American Federation of Arts, 1963, no. 43.

Donald Oenslager

Carlo Marchionni

Rome 1702–Rome 1786

173 *Doorway Surmounted by the Albani Arms*

Pen and brown ink, gray and brown wash, over black chalk. 15 15/16 × 7 5/8 inches (40.7 × 19.6 cm.). Watermark: letters I V.

Between 1746 and 1763 the architect Carlo Marchionni erected for Cardinal Alessandro Albani, the greatest art patron of his day, a sumptuous villa outside the Porta Salaria in Rome, intended principally to house the cardinal's remarkable collection of ancient sculpture. Rudolf Berliner has identified the drawing, one of twelve projects by Marchionni for the villa in the Cooper-Hewitt Museum, as a design for a doorway to the Grand Gallery of the villa—a splendid room on the ceiling of which Mengs painted his celebrated *Parnassus*.

The Albani arms, three monticules surmounted by a star, are conspicuously present above the door, where two figures have been introduced in order to suggest scale.

PROVENANCE: Giovanni Piancastelli (no mark, see Lugt S. 2078a); Mr. and Mrs. Edward Brandegee (no mark, see Lugt S. 1860c).

BIBLIOGRAPHY: Rudolf Berliner, "Zeichnungen von Carlo und Filippo Marchionni," *Münchner Jahrbuch der Bildenden Kunst*, IX–X, 1958–1959, p. 308, fig. 57; Wunder, *Extravagant Drawings*, no. 22, repr.

EXHIBITIONS: Cleveland, Museum of Art, "Neo-Classicism: Style and Motif," 1964, no. 30, repr.

Cooper-Hewitt Museum, Smithsonian Institution
1938–88–486

Pietro Longhi

Venice 1702–Venice 1783

174 *Venetian Senator*

Black and white chalk, on brown paper. 13 × 8 11/16 inches (33.1 × 22.1 cm.). Lined.

Inscribed in graphite at lower left corner, *Longi f*; at lower center on verso, *3*.

With one exception, students of eighteenth-century Venetian art have been generally inclined to classify this drawing as the work of Pietro Longhi,

to whom it was assigned by Fairfax Murray at the beginning of the century. Vittorio Moschini, in a dissenting opinion, suggests that it is from the hand of Pietro's son Alessandro, doubtless having in mind, in addition to the Pisani portrait, that of Angelo Memmo I dated 1770, in the Museo Correr (repr. Pignatti, *Il Museo Correr a Venezia*, no. 1399). While it is true that certain similarities in costume and pose are to be observed, the fact remains that so little is known of Alessandro's style as a draughtsman that it seems desirable to retain the drawing under the name of Pietro, with whose general handling of black and white chalks on brown paper it is compatible. Curiously, the figure also displays the somewhat diminutive stature that one observes in many of the personages of Pietro's paintings, although as a rule the related preparatory drawings tend to show the figures in taller guise. The Library's Venetian senator in his periwig and robes, with his stole or "flappe" over his left shoulder, does not seem to bear any relation to the drawing of two senators in the Museo Correr (Pignatti, *Longhi*, p. 127, pl. 140).

PROVENANCE: Charles Fairfax Murray; purchased by J. Pierpont Morgan in London, 1910.

BIBLIOGRAPHY: Fairfax Murray, IV, 142; Benesch, *Venetian Drawings*, no. 47, repr.; Rodolfo Pallucchini, *L'Arte Veneta*, 1948–1949, p. 158; Vittorio Moschini, *Pietro Longhi*, Milan, 1956, p. 56; Terisio Pignatti, *Il Museo Correr a Venezia*, Venice, 1960, no. 1399; Terisio Pignatti, *Pietro Longhi* [Venice, 1968], p. 119, fig. 310.

EXHIBITIONS: New York, Tiepolo Exhibition, 1938, no. 58.

The Pierpont Morgan Library
No. IV, 142

175 *Pastoral Landscape*

Red chalk, red wash. 10 5/8 × 15 1/2 inches (27 × 39.2 cm.). Watermark: three graduated crescents.

Inscribed in pen and black ink at lower right in an eighteenth-century hand, *Petri Longhi Auctographum*; in black chalk at lower center, *dal pier. . . .*

Verso: Landscape with cart disappearing over a hill, in black chalk.

Without the presence of the eighteenth-century inscription at the lower right edge of the sheet,

Pietro Longhi might not readily have come to mind as its designer. But given this clue, the student realizes that the types and groups are not inconsistent with the early phase of Longhi's development, when he painted a series of rustic genre scenes under the influence of his master, Giuseppe Maria Crespi; in *Le Lavandaie* of the Ca' Rezzonico, Venice, for example, the girl wearing a hat suggests the young maid in the central group of the Morgan composition. The identical inscription occurs on a number of entirely characteristic drawings, in the Print Room at Berlin (Pignatti, *Longhi*, figs. 301–307), which are executed in black and white chalk like those in the Museo Correr, where by far the largest single collection of Longhi's drawings is preserved. The same inscription is also found on a Longhi drawing owned by Mr. Brinsley Ford (Pignatti, *Longhi*, fig. 308), and the same hand inscribed a number of Tiepolo drawings as *autographum* (see Fogg, Tiepolo Exhibition, 1970, nos. 1 and 2). Further evidence for Pietro's authorship of this bucolic scene is afforded by the rapid compositional sketch outlined in black chalk on the verso, which offers a kind of stylistic bridge to his usual manner of drawing.

Such compositional studies are rare in Longhi's surviving oeuvre; another, a *Woman at the Bed of Her Husband*, is illustrated by Pignatti in his 1968 monograph as fig. 56.

PROVENANCE: Purchased by the Morgan Library in London, 1950.

BIBLIOGRAPHY: Morgan Library, *First Fellows Report, 1950*, pp. 51–52, repr.; Michelangelo Muraro, "Figure di Francesco Guardi," *Emporium*, CXXX, 1959, pp. 244, 252, note 6; Pignatti, *Disegni veneziani*, pp. 207–208, pl. 107; Terisio Pignatti, "Les Dessins de Pietro Longhi," *L'Oeil*, October 1968, no. 166, pp. 14–23; Terisio Pignatti, *Pietro Longhi* [Venice, 1968], p. 119, fig. 311; Morgan Library, *A Review of Acquisitions, 1949–1968*, p. 154.

EXHIBITIONS: New York, Staten Island Museum, "Italian Drawings and Sculpture from the Renaissance to the Present," 1958–1959, no. 27; Minneapolis, University of Minnesota Gallery, "The Eighteenth Century, One Hundred Drawings by One Hundred Artists," 1961, no. 52.

*The Pierpont Morgan Library
Gift of the Fellows, 1950.10*

Francesco Zuccarelli
Pitigliano (Tuscany) 1702–Florence 1788

176 *Landscape with a Lake and Horseman*

Pen and brown ink, brown and gray wash, heightened with white, over black chalk. $11\frac{5}{8} \times 18\frac{3}{16}$ inches (29.5 × 46.2 cm.). Lined.

Inscribed in pen and brown ink on mount, *Zucharelli*; in pen and brown ink on verso, *C.A.S. from LS. 1855*; numbered in pen and brown ink on verso, *No. 19–4–1–6, Lot 10–4.*

Zuccarelli, Tuscan by birth and Florentine and Roman in training, was in Venice by about 1730. There he set up as a specialist in idyllic, pastoral landscapes, either painted or drawn. The drawn landscapes, like the present fine example, were clearly produced as works of art in themselves, not as preparatory studies for paintings. Zuccarelli's European reputation was considerable, and he spent off and on some fifteen years in England, becoming a founding member of the Royal Academy in 1768.

Other similar wash landscapes by Zuccarelli are in the Metropolitan Museum and in the collection of Mr. and Mrs. Arnold Whitridge.

EXHIBITIONS: Venice, Scholz Exhibition, 1957, no. 83, repr.; Oakland, Scholz Exhibition, 1960, no. 99; London, Scholz Exhibition, 1968, no. 111.

Janos Scholz

177 *Country Party with Girl in a Swing*

Pen and brown ink, brown and a little gray wash. $15\frac{3}{8} \times 14\frac{1}{16}$ inches (39.1 × 35.7 cm.). Horizontal creases at center; several spots of gray wash. Letters that do not form words stamped in black ink at lower margin.

Numbered in pen and brown ink on verso, *g. 200 no. 32*; various other numbers and inscriptions on verso.

Verso: Tracing in pen and brown ink of pipe-smoking figure at left on recto.

Zuccarelli, who was eclectic in his borrowings from Italian and Northern examples, here does an exercise in a Netherlandish vein. The figures might have stepped out of a picture by Adriaen Brouwer, but Zuccarelli invests the scene with eighteenth-century pastoral poetry.

EXHIBITIONS: Oakland, Scholz Exhibition, 1960, no. 100, repr.; Hamburg, Scholz Exhibition, 1963, no. 177, pl. 85; London, Scholz Exhibition, 1968, no. 112.

Janos Scholz

178 *Landscape*

Pen and brown ink, brown wash, over black chalk. 10¾ × 16 11/16 inches (27.3 × 42.3 cm.). Several small stains.

In such a landscape with its familiar components of castle, arched bridge, distant mountains, and pastoral staffage, Zuccarelli registers the influence of Marco Ricci in light, dilute form. There are also examples of Zuccarelli's less well known figure style in the Morgan collection (Inv. IV, 143a).

PROVENANCE: Charles Fairfax Murray; purchased by J. Pierpont Morgan in London, 1910.

EXHIBITIONS: New York, Tiepolo Exhibition, 1938, no. 60; New Haven, Yale University Gallery of Fine Arts, "Exhibition of Eighteenth-Century Italian Landscape Painting and its Influence in England," 1940, no. 34, repr.

The Pierpont Morgan Library
No. IV, 143b

Pompeo Girolamo Batoni

Lucca 1708–Rome 1787

179 *Studies for the "Fall of Simon Magus"*

Red chalk with faint traces of white chalk, squared in red chalk. 12 1/16 × 8 7/16 inches (30.7 × 22.2 cm.). Cut and re-attached at lower right; oil stain along lower edge. Watermark: fleur-de-lis in a circle, surmounted by the letter A.

Signed at lower right in pen and brown ink, *Pompeo Batoni*; inscribed at upper left in pen and red ink, *N2581.*

The largest and perhaps most important painting produced by Batoni—Mengs's chief rival in Rome —who is probably best known for his portraits of princes and grand tourists, is the *Fall of Simon Magus* (Hermann Voss, *Die Malerei des Barock in Rom*, Berlin, 1924, pl. 411), which he completed in 1761. The painting was originally intended for St. Peter's, where it was to have been translated into mosaic, but, despite repeated revisions by the artist, it was declared unsuitable and assigned to S. Maria degli Angeli, where it still remains. The present

sheet, a study for St. Paul and another figure on the left of the painting, demonstrates the painstaking manner in which the artist prepared his pictures. In many instances he devoted a study to each figure and in addition separately worked out details of anatomy in the manner of the great Renaissance draughtsmen, notably Raphael, whom he particularly admired. Another drawing in the Morgan Library, which Fairfax Murray assigned to Domenichino (Inv. IV, 166), was identified some years ago by Anthony Clark as Batoni's study for the head of the frightened woman at the far right of the middle ground of the same painting. Clark states that the numbers in red ink at the upper left are frequently found on Batoni's drawings.

PROVENANCE: Walter Bürki; purchased by the Morgan Library in New York, 1965.

BIBLIOGRAPHY: Morgan Library, *Fourteenth Fellows Report, 1965–1966*, p. 127; Morgan Library, *A Review of Acquisitions, 1949–1968*, p. 130.

The Pierpont Morgan Library
Gift of the Fellows, 1965.20

Paolo Posi

Siena 1708–Rome 1776

180 *Design for the Chinea of 1760: Chinoiserie*

Pen and brown ink, brown, gray, and pinkish-brown wash. 16⅛ × 22¼ inches (40.9 × 56.5 cm.). Lined.

Signed in pen and brown ink at lower right of border, *Paolo Posi Architetto*; inscribed in pen and brown ink in border, *Prospetto della Seconda Machina rappresentante una Deliziosa all'uso cinese. Eretta per commando di Sua Eccellenza il Sig. DON LORENZO COLONNA Gran | Contestabile del Regno di Napoli & &. come Ambasciatore straordinario di S. M. il RE' delle due Sicilie &.&.&. la Sera delli 29. Giugno 1760. Festa di Gloriosi Santi | Apostoli PIETRO, e PAOLO in occasione d'aver presentata la Chinea alla Santità di Nostro Signore PAPA CLEMENTE XIII.*

Up to 1855, the festival known as the Chinea was celebrated each year in Rome on June 29, the day of the feast of the Apostles Peter and Paul. The Chinea itself was the white mule annually presented to the pope in the name of the king of Naples by the Grand Constable of Naples, always a member of the Colonna family. This ceremonial observance originated in the thirteenth century, when Charles of Anjou accepted the kingdom of the Two Sicilies as a fief of the Church. To mark the occasion a great pyrotechnical machine was set up in the Piazza dei SS. Apostoli in front of the Palazzo Colonna. After the display of fireworks, the machine, an elaborate construction of wood, canvas, and stucco, was itself consumed in a final blaze to the accompaniment of recitations and music.

In the decades of the 1750s and 1760s, the architect Paolo Posi was one of the most fertile inventors of the machines for the Chinea fête. This *deliziosa all'uso cinese* represents the *seconda machina* erected for the celebration on June 29, 1760, when Don Lorenzo Colonna presented his tribute to Pope Clement XIII; the drawing showing the *prima machina*, *The Temple of Neptune*, is also in the Morgan Library. Both drawings were engraved by Giuseppe Vasi.

PROVENANCE: Purchased by the Morgan Library in London, 1962.

BIBLIOGRAPHY: Morgan Library, *Twelfth Fellows Report*, 1962, pp. 88–89, repr.; Morgan Library, *A Review of Acquisitions, 1949–1968*, p. 161.

EXHIBITIONS: San Francisco, California Palace of the Legion of Honor, "Cathay Invoked: Chinoiserie, a Celestial Empire in the West," 1966, no. 16, pl. IV.

The Pierpont Morgan Library
Gift of the Fellows, 1962.8

Francesco Salvator Fontebasso
Venice 1709–Venice 1768/1769

181 *Two Standing Male Figures and Seated Woman with a Child*

Pen and brown ink, brown and gray wash, over black chalk. 14³/₄ × 10¹⁵/₁₆ inches (37.5 × 26.2 cm.). Vertical ruled lines at left and right.

Numbered in pen and brown ink at upper right, *41*.

This sheet comes from a now dismembered album, the pages of which bear vertical lines traced with a stylus, probably indicating that it was originally intended to be an account book. The album was broken up some time before 1924, and pages from it are now in the collection of David Daniels, New York, at Princeton University, in the British Museum, and elsewhere.

In this page the figure style is typical of Fontebasso, whose drawings have been studied by J. Byam Shaw (*Arte Veneta*, VIII, 1954, pp. 317–325). The figures here are heavy and Piazzettesque, with large clumsy hands and feet, while the rather brittle pen line comes out of Sebastiano Ricci.

The attribution of the drawings from this album to Fontebasso is not accepted by Janos Scholz ("Italian Drawings in the Art Museum of Princeton University," *Burlington Magazine*, CIX, 1967, p. 296).

PROVENANCE: Henry Scipio Reitlinger (Lugt S. 2274a); purchased by the Metropolitan Museum in London, 1961.

BIBLIOGRAPHY: *Italian Drawings in the Art Museum, Princeton University*, Princeton, 1966, under no. 98.

The Metropolitan Museum of Art
Rogers Fund, 61.56.2

Giuseppe Valeriani
Rome 1708–St. Petersburg 1762

182 *Design for the Decoration of a Dome with God the Father in a Trompe-l'Oeil Opening; Three Virtues in Panels*

Pen and brown ink, gray wash, and watercolor, over lead. 12⁹/₁₆ × 8¹⁵/₁₆ inches (31.9 × 22.7 cm.). Slight foxing; vertical crease in center. Watermark: graduated triple crescents (Heawood 867).

Inscribed on verso, in pen, *No 58* and in lead, *di Giuseppe Valeriani Roub*, followed by figure *4* in pen.

This bright watercolor rendering and two others for the same project come from the Leuchtenberg album of architectural and theatrical drawings belonging to the late Edmond Fatio, which was broken up following the sale of his collection in Geneva in 1959. The album, consisting chiefly of drawings by the Italian painter Giuseppe Valeriani, seems to have been compiled in the late eighteenth century in Russia where Valeriani—along with his brother Domenico—settled in 1742 to become the favorite painter and theatrical designer of the Empress Elisabeth Petrovna. The Library's drawings were apparently part of a program for the decoration of a church dome, one solution envisioning, according to the inscriptions, a division of the dome into eight sections and another a scheme for twelve sections. Romans by birth, the brothers Valeriani were also active in Venice and Turin at an early date; in this connection it is interesting to note that this sheet bears the familiar Venetian triple crescent watermark. The Library also owns a fourth drawing from the Leuchtenberg album, the *Mars and Venus*, given by David E. Rust in 1961. For the location of the drawings and letters of the artist in Russia, see *Disegni veneti del Museo di Leningrado* (exhibition catalogue by Larissa Salmina), Venice, Fondazione Giorgio Cini, 1964, under no. 85. The inscription on the verso, *Roub*, may refer to roubles.

PROVENANCE: Duc G. N. de Leuchtenberg; Edmond Fatio; purchased by the Morgan Library in London, 1959.

BIBLIOGRAPHY: Morgan Library, *Tenth Fellows Report, 1960*, pp. 57–59; Morgan Library, *A Review of Acquisitions, 1949–1968*, pp. 173–174.

The Pierpont Morgan Library
Gift of the Fellows, 1959.20

Giovanni Battista Marcola
Verona 1711–Verona 1780

183 *The Head of Pompey Brought to Caesar*

Pen and brown ink, brown wash, over black chalk. 11 15/16 × 17 9/16 inches (30.3 × 44.6 cm.). Several spots; small creases at corners and margins.

Unidentified collector's mark, *AG*, stamped in red at lower right.

Verso: Red chalk study of standing female figure.

A spirited example of the drawing style of this vigorous provincial master. G. B. Marcola often signed his drawings on the reverse of the sheet; here the signature is absent, but the draughtsmanship is characteristically his. The sharp, beaklike noses of the figures are almost a signature.

Mr. Scholz possesses a further drawing by G. B. Marcola, and another typical sheet is in the Metropolitan Museum.

EXHIBITIONS: Venice, Scholz Exhibition, 1957, no. 88, repr.; Oakland, Scholz Exhibition, 1960, no. 46.

Janos Scholz

Giuseppe Zocchi
Florence 1711–Florence 1767

184 *View of Florence along the Arno from the Porta a S. Niccolò*

Pen and black ink, gray wash, over black chalk. 19 3/8 × 26 1/2 inches (46.6 × 67.5 cm.). Watermark: coat of arms (fleur-de-lis in a shield, surmounted by a crown [Heawood 1803]).

Inscribed on mount, in pen and brown ink, *Veduta di una parte di Firenze presa fuori della Porta à S. Niccolò presso al Fiume Arno.*

Less well known and more modestly gifted than the great vedutists of Venice and Rome, Zocchi nevertheless pleasingly recorded the image of eighteenth-century Florence and its environs at the same time that Canaletto and Guardi were painting the celebrated vistas of their native city and Piranesi was glorifying the Rome of his adoption in his etchings. At the commission of the Marchese Andrea Gerini, Zocchi produced the designs for two series of etchings, one devoted to views of the city of Florence and the other to the Tuscan villas. Both the *Scelte di XXIV vedute delle principali contrade, piazze, chiese, e palazzi della città di Firenze* and the *Vedute delle ville e d'altri luoghi della Toscana* were first published in 1744 and reissued in 1754. The preparatory drawings, both series of which are in the Morgan Library, are executed on the full scale of the prints and in the same direction, with painstaking rendering of all details. Zocchi himself etched only two plates in their entirety, although he was responsible for the figures in a number of others; the rest were divided among numerous Italian graphic artists and several Germans.

As might be expected, six of the twenty-four Florentine views are taken along the Arno's two-mile course through the city. Here the draughtsman views the north bank with the square tower of the Old Mint (now destroyed) at the far right and the procession of familiar landmarks, the dome of the Cathedral, the Campanile, the apse of S. Croce, the upper section of Orsanmichele, and the lofty spire of the Palazzo Vecchio. The passengers in the ferry boat have a view of the Ponte alle Grazie and beyond a glimpse of the Ponte Vecchio.

Zocchi was also active as a painter, and from 1754 to 1760 he was the official designer for the manufactory of Pietre Dure, the popular "Florentine mosaic."

PROVENANCE: Mrs. J. P. Morgan, d. 1925.

BIBLIOGRAPHY: Morgan Library, *Fourth Fellows Report*, *1953*, pp. 63–64; Giuseppe Zocchi, *Views of Florence*, facsimile of 1754 ed., New York, 1967, p. 13, pl. IV; Morgan Library, *A Review of Acquisitions, 1949–1968*, p. 178.

EXHIBITIONS: New York, Pierpont Morgan Library and elsewhere, "Views of Florence and Tuscany by Giuseppe Zocchi, 1711–1767," circulated by the International Exhibitions Foundation, 1968–1969, no. 6, repr.

The Pierpont Morgan Library
Gift of Junius S. Morgan and Henry S. Morgan, 1952.30:6

185 *Villa Poggio Imperiale, near Florence*

Pen and black ink, gray wash. 11 × 18⅞ inches (28 × 48 cm.). Watermark: coat of arms (fleur-de-lis in a shield, surmounted by a crown [Heawood 1803]).

Inscribed on mount, in pen and brown ink, *La Real Villa, detta il Poggio Imperiale.*

Now a school for girls, the villa was in centuries past a favorite residence of the Medici, beginning with the Grand Duchess Maria Maddalena, wife of Cosimo II. Under her, the villa was enlarged about 1620 by Giulio Parigi, who was responsible for the design of the façade Zocchi set down in such faithful detail here. The villa now bears a nineteenth-century neoclassical front, but the sculptures of Jupiter and Atlas by Vincenzo de' Rossi (1563) at the entrance of the circular wall are still to be seen. The drawing was etched by Zocchi as plate 1 of the *Vedute delle ville.*

PROVENANCE: Mrs. J. P. Morgan, d. 1925.

BIBLIOGRAPHY: Morgan Library, *Fourth Fellows Report*, *1953*, pp. 63–64; Morgan Library, *A Review of Acquisitions, 1949–1968*, p. 178.

EXHIBITIONS: New York, Pierpont Morgan Library and elsewhere, "Views of Florence and Tuscany by Giuseppe Zocchi, 1711–1767," circulated by the International Exhibitions Foundation, 1968–1969, no. 28, repr.

The Pierpont Morgan Library
Gift of Junius S. Morgan and Henry S. Morgan, 1952.30:28

186 *Villa Palmieri, near Florence*

Pen and black ink, over black chalk. 10¹⁵⁄₁₆ × 18⁹⁄₁₆ inches (27.8 × 47.1 cm.). Watermark: coat of arms (fleur-de-lis in a shield, surmounted by a crown [Heawood 1803]).

Inscribed on mount, in pen and brown ink, *Tre Visi Villa de SS:ri Palmieri al principio della Salita / di Fiesole.*

Sometimes thought to be the setting of Boccaccio's *Decameron*, this villa situated among fine gardens on a slope below S. Domenico in Fiesole takes its name from a fifteenth-century owner, the writer Matteo Palmieri. On her first visit to Florence, Queen Victoria was the guest of the then owner, the Earl of Crawford.

More often than not, Zocchi dispenses with wash in the drawings of the villa series, achieving his effects solely with the pen as here and so more nearly approximating the appearance of the final print. The drawing was etched by Giuseppe Filosi as plate 39 of the *Vedute delle ville.*

PROVENANCE: Mrs. J. P. Morgan, d. 1925.

BIBLIOGRAPHY: Morgan Library, *Fourth Fellows Report*, *1953*, pp. 63–64; Morgan Library, *A Review of Acquisitions, 1949–1968*, p. 178.

EXHIBITIONS: New York, Pierpont Morgan Library, and elsewhere, "Views of Florence and Tuscany by Giuseppe Zocchi, 1711–1767," circulated by the International Exhibitions Foundation, 1968–1969, no. 66, repr.

The Pierpont Morgan Library
Gift of Junius S. Morgan and Henry S. Morgan, 1952.30:66

Francesco Guardi
Venice 1712–Venice 1793

187 *Virgin and Child Seated on Clouds*

Red chalk, on gray paper. 5⅝ × 4⅝ inches (14.3 × 11.8 cm.). Oil stains at upper right.

Inscribed in pen and brown ink at lower right, *Ricci.*

The old inscription, *Ricci*, is not surprising, for the physical types of the Virgin and the angels do indeed derive from the example of Sebastiano. However, Muraro has convincingly proposed that the drawing is in fact a typical example of the figure drawing of Francesco. We see Francesco's debt to his older brother, Gianantonio, in the flickering lighting of this group, although it is more solidly constructed than was Gianantonio's wont. The chalk style here can be compared with that of a drawing of the Virgin and Child in the British Museum (Byam Shaw, *Guardi*, pl. 5).

PROVENANCE: James Jackson Jarves.

BIBLIOGRAPHY: Michelangelo Muraro, "An Altarpiece and Other Figure Paintings by Francesco Guardi," *Burlington Magazine*, C, 1958, p. 7, fig. 20.

EXHIBITIONS: New York, The Metropolitan Museum of Art, "Drawings, Watercolor Paintings, Photographs, and Etchings, Tapestries, etc.," 1895, no. 491 (as Murillo).

The Metropolitan Museum of Art
Gift of Cornelius Vanderbilt, 80.3.491

188 *Four Studies of Gentlemen with Cloaks and Tricornes*

Black chalk. Architectural details at top of the sheet are in pen and brown ink. $7\frac{1}{4} \times 9\frac{1}{2}$ inches (18.4×24.1 cm.), sight.

Inscribed in pen and brown ink at lower right, *Guardi*; in pen and brown ink on verso, *Guardi*.

Verso: Studies for figures along a canal and on a bridge; to the right, a curtain and a stool (?), all in black chalk.

The figures on the recto are more elaborate and larger in scale than those in the sheet of pen *macchiette* (here exhibited No. 189), but the sketches on both recto and verso of this sheet are characteristic of Guardi. Byam Shaw has pointed out that the two figures on the right appear in the Earl of Iveagh's painting, the *Grand Canal below the Rialto*.

PROVENANCE: Lady Harcourt, London.

BIBLIOGRAPHY: Byam Shaw, *Guardi*, no. 48, repr.; James Byam Shaw, "Guardi at the Royal Academy," *Burlington Magazine*, XCVII, 1955, p. 15, fig. 16 (the relevant detail of the Iveagh picture, fig. 17).

EXHIBITIONS: Springfield, Mass., Museum of Fine Arts, "Francesco Guardi, 1712–1793," 1937, nos. 32 (recto), 33 (verso), both repr.; Toledo, Ohio, Museum of Art, "Four Centuries of Venetian Painting," 1940, no. 80; Montreal, Museum of Fine Arts, "Five Centuries of Drawings," 1953, no. 72, repr.; Houston, Guardi Family, 1958, no. 36; Baltimore, Museum of Art, "Age of Elegance, The Rococo and its Effect," 1959, no. 211; Wellesley College, Jewett Arts Center, "Eighteenth Century Italian Drawings," 1960, no. 28, pl. 12; Venice, Guardi Exhibition, 1965, no. 24, repr.

Harry G. Sperling

189 *Figure Studies*

Pen and brown ink, brown wash, on blue paper. Faint black chalk sketch of a figure at lower left. $6\frac{3}{8} \times 8\frac{5}{8}$ inches (16.2×21.8 cm.).

Signed in pen and brown ink at lower left, *f.co Guardi*.

Francesco Guardi was in the habit of making rapid abbreviated sketches of accessory figures—*macchiette*, as they are called—which he used over and over again to animate his painted views, whether realistic or imaginary. Byam Shaw has pointed out that the lady and gentleman at the lower right and the family group above both appear in a view of the Piazzetta with a crowd of senators, formerly in the Gutekunst collection (repr. *Pantheon*, I, 1928, opp. p. 87). The lady with her high feathered headdress (a feature that dates the sheet in the last dozen years of the painter's activity) and her escort also appear in a picture at Bergamo and in another at the National Gallery in London. We encounter them again in another drawing at the Metropolitan Museum, a sketch for an architectural capriccio (37. 165.81; Goering, *Guardi*, pl. 113) and a drawing at the Victoria and Albert Museum (Byam Shaw, pl. 60). The present drawing is signed by the artist himself in characteristic fashion; a similar signature appears on another sheet of *macchiette* in the Metropolitan Museum (40.91.2; Byam Shaw, pl. 50).

PROVENANCE: Harold K. Hochschild, New York.

BIBLIOGRAPHY: *Metropolitan Museum of Art Bulletin*, August 1940, p. 156; Byam Shaw, *Guardi*, no. 51, repr.; Bean, *100 European Drawings*, no. 47, repr.

The Metropolitan Museum of Art
Gift of Harold K. Hochschild, 40.91.3

190 *The Grand Canal above the Rialto*
Verso: *Priest Celebrating Mass and St. Vincent Ferrer*

Pen and brown ink, brown wash, over black chalk (recto). Pen and brown ink, brown wash, over red chalk (verso). $16\frac{1}{8} \times 28\frac{9}{16}$ inches (41×72.5 cm.). Three vertical creases at center. Watermark: monogram at left, bow and arrow (?) at right (see watermark no. 42).

Inscribed in pen and brown ink at lower right, *Canal*.

The *veduta* on the recto is a painstakingly accurate

view of the Grand Canal from the Fabbriche Nuove on the extreme left to the Palazzo Pesaro in the distance and including the campanile of S. Cassiano left of center. It is generally agreed to date from the early 1760s, when Francesco Guardi, previously a figure painter working under the direction of his elder brother Gianantonio, had begun to make a specialty of Venetian views. Francesco here, and in other large drawings of the same period, emulates Canaletto, whose early *vedute* were the point of departure for Guardi's career as a painter of the Venetian scene. The drawing, minus the awning in the right foreground, served as the model for a picture in a private collection in London (R. Pallucchini, *La Pittura veneziana del Settecento*, Venice and Rome, 1960, fig. 637).

The two fine figure studies on the verso, which presumably also date from the early 1760s, testify to Francesco's continuing interest in figure subjects. The St. Vincent Ferrer on the right may have been inspired by Giambattista Tiepolo's representation of the saint (Morassi, 1962, fig. 173). A painted version of the St. Vincent as sketched on this sheet recently appeared on the London art market (Christie's, July 2, 1965, no. 118, repr.).

PROVENANCE: Mylius, Genoa (according to J. P. Richter); J. P. Richter, London; purchased by the Metropolitan Museum in London, 1912.

BIBLIOGRAPHY: Bryson Burroughs, *Metropolitan Museum of Art Bulletin*, May 1912, p. 100 (recto as Canaletto and verso as G. B. Tiepolo); Joseph Breck, "Paintings and Drawings by Tiepolo in the Metropolitan Museum," *Art in America*, I, 1913, pp. 16–17 (as G. B. Tiepolo); Bryan Holme, *Master Drawings*, 1943, pl. 84 (as Follower of F. Guardi); Goering, *Guardi*, no. 45, repr. (recto); Byam Shaw, *Guardi*, nos. 9 (verso), 10 (recto), both repr.; Denis Mahon, in *Problemi Guardeschi*, Venice, 1967, p. 129, note 203.

The Metropolitan Museum of Art Rogers Fund, 12.56.14

191 *Ballad Singer on the Piazzetta*

Pen and brownish-black ink, over black chalk, on gray-brown paper. 8⅜ × 15 3/16 inches (21.2 × 38.5 cm.).

Inscribed in an old hand in brown ink at lower left, *Parte della Piazzetta e punta di S. Giorgio Maggiore.*

The ballad singer has set up his standard in front of

Sansovino's Libreria, to the right of which a bit of the Campanile is visible. To command such a view of the Piazzetta with the column of the Lion of St. Mark on the left and that of St. Theodore on the right, the draughtsman must have located himself on or near the steps of St. Mark's. Two other drawings, one in the Albertina and one in the Louvre (Byam Shaw, *Guardi*, pls. 32, 33) show the Piazzetta from more or less the same vantage point but display different passersby. Here, the family groups of *macchiette*, gathered to watch the performance of the graceful singer, are highly expressive in the brevity of their execution, none more so than the fashionable woman in plumes standing with her child at the far right. For another representation of a ballad singer, see the painting from the Rohoncz collection attributed to the early Guardi by Max Goering (*Guardi*, pl. 34).

The inscription at the lower left is not, as Benesch stated, in the same ink as the drawing, and one is reluctant to regard it as more than a contemporary inscription when it is compared with the artist's notation on No. 208. Guardi is known to have used papers of various qualities, including rough-textured sheets like this one.

PROVENANCE: Charles Fairfax Murray; purchased by J. Pierpont Morgan in London, 1910.

BIBLIOGRAPHY: Benesch, *Venetian Drawings*, no. 57, repr.

EXHIBITIONS: Oberlin College, Drawings of the 18th Century, 1950–1951, p. 53, no. 9, repr.; Houston, Guardi Family, 1958, no. 38, repr.; Hartford, Wadsworth Atheneum, "The Pierpont Morgan Treasures," 1960, no. 83, pl. XI; Venice, Guardi Exhibition, 1965, no. 45, repr.

The Pierpont Morgan Library No. I, 78c

192 *View of S. Marco*

Pen and brown ink, brown wash. 9⅝ × 8½ inches (24.5 × 21.6 cm.). Slight foxing.

This view of the principal façade of S. Marco treats the most Venetian of all Venetian subjects. The same brittle pen work, contrasted with pale, transparent brown wash, more sparingly applied, is to be found in another more extensive view of the façade, now in the Ashmolean Museum (Byam Shaw, *Guardi*, pl. 34).

PROVENANCE: J. P. Richter, London; purchased by the Metropolitan Museum in London, 1912.

BIBLIOGRAPHY: Bryson Burroughs, *Metropolitan Museum of Art Bulletin*, May 1912, p. 100; George A. Simonson, "Guardi's Drawings and their Relation to his Paintings," *Art in America*, I, 1913, p. 268, fig. 25; G. S. Hellman, "Drawings by Italian Artists in the Metropolitan Museum of Art," *Print Collector's Quarterly*, VI, 1916, pp. 182–183, repr.; Goering, *Guardi*, no. 71, repr.; Benesch, *Venetian Drawings*, no. 58, repr.

The Metropolitan Museum of Art
Rogers Fund, 12.56.15

193 *Panorama from the Bacino di S. Marco*

Pen and brown ink, brown wash, over traces of black chalk. 13¾ × 26⅝ inches (34.9 × 67.6 cm.). Support composed of two sheets joined vertically at center; crease at lower right corner. Watermark: letter A at right, three stars above the letters F V at left (see watermark no. 44). Lined.

A remarkably extensive panorama, which, as Byam Shaw points out, is certainly wider than the artist's eye could have encompassed in a single focus. He suggests that it was based, as far as the architectural background is concerned, on three separate drawings, two of which have survived, one in the National Gallery of Canada, the other in the Fogg Museum of Art. These three views would have been drawn by the artist in a boat on the Bacino, in front of S. Giorgio Maggiore.

Guardi has animated the foreground with two sailing barges and several decorated festival gondolas (*bissone*), from which spectators watch gondolas race up the Giudecca Canal.

PROVENANCE: Lady Catherine Ashburnham, Battle, Sussex; Ashburnham sale, London, Sotheby's, June 24, 1953, no. 54, pl. 13.

BIBLIOGRAPHY: Byam Shaw, *Guardi*, no. 27, repr.; Pignatti, *Disegni dei Guardi*, no. LXII, repr.

EXHIBITIONS: Paris, Lehman Exhibition, 1957, no. 104; Cincinnati, Lehman Exhibition, 1959, no. 230, repr.; New Haven, Yale University Art Gallery, "Paintings, Drawings, and Sculpture Collected by Yale Alumni," 1960, no. 163, repr.

Robert Lehman Collection

194 *The Stairway of the Giants*

Pen and brown ink, brown wash, over red chalk. 10⅜ × 7 5⁄16 inches (26.4 × 18.6 cm.). Pricked for transfer.

Though this rapid and brilliant pen sketch has all the air of an architectural capriccio, it is a fairly accurate view—by Guardi's standards—of the Scala dei Giganti in the courtyard of the Palazzo Ducale in Venice. The principal architectural features of the staircase and of the arcaded courtyard have been recorded by the draughtsman, but Jacopo Sansovino's giant statues of Mars and Neptune at the top of the stairs have been transformed into twisting draped figures in a rococo manner. The cloaked figures ascending the staircase, jotted down in the most abbreviated fashion, add an even more decisively "contemporary" note to the scene. The style of the drawing suggests that it is a fairly late work by Guardi. A drawing of the Scala d'Oro in the Palazzo Ducale, again with variants to suit the taste of the draughtsman, is in the Museo Correr in Venice (Byam Shaw, *Guardi*, pl. 58), and the Metropolitan Museum has another drawing of figures on a staircase that seems to be entirely a creation of the artist's fantasy (37.165.72).

PROVENANCE: Marquis de Biron, Paris and Geneva; purchased by the Metropolitan Museum in Geneva, 1937.

BIBLIOGRAPHY: Benesch, *Venetian Drawings*, no. 59, repr.; Bean, *100 European Drawings*, no. 48, repr.

The Metropolitan Museum of Art
Rogers Fund, 37.165.85

195 *The Bucintoro off S. Niccolò di Lido*

Pen and brown ink, brown wash, over black chalk, on two sheets of paper, pasted together, the larger of which is the reverse of an engraving by Carlo Orsolini inscribed: *Sacrum Convivium*. Indistinct black chalk sketch of architecture in opposite direction at upper left corner. 14⅝ × 31⅞ inches (37.1 × 81 cm.). Foxing throughout sheet. Watermark: graduated triple crescents and the word MEZANA below (see watermark no. 17).

Verso: Sketch of street scene in pen and brown ink by Giacomo Guardi; black chalk sketches of gondoliers.

Among the fêtes of eighteenth-century Venice, none was more magnificent than the *Festa della "Sensa,"* the Festival of the Ascension, when the

Marriage of the City of Venice and the Adriatic was celebrated in commemoration of the conquest of Dalmatia by Doge Pietro Orseolo II about the year 1000. None recorded the spectacle more often nor more brilliantly than Guardi. This large compositional sketch for a painting of the early 1780s, in the possession of Alessandro Brass, Venice, shows the return of the doge from the Lido where, until 1789, he annually performed the traditional ceremony of tossing a consecrated ring into the sea.

Working swiftly with staccato pen and fluent brush, Guardi encompasses the full sweep of the picturesque marine fête. The doge's gilded state barge, Il Bucintoro, with a state galley and a cluster of gondolas, lies opposite the church of S. Niccolò di Lido, silhouetted in the center distance; far right, a man-of-war offers a salute of gunfire, and in the foreground a graceful two-masted state galley, flags flying, moves after the Bucintoro; from the left, comes a flotilla of decorated craft with the Island of S. Elena faintly distinguishable in its unfinished black chalk outlines in the distance.

The street scene on the verso is by Francesco's son Giacomo, who in several other instances is known to have sketched on the backs of his father's drawings. In fact, as Byam Shaw pointed out, there are even motifs connected with the Brass painting and the Morgan drawing on the backs of Francesco's drawings in Rotterdam and Vienna, suggesting that the father used his apprentice son to make such studies in completion of details like the Island of S. Elena.

Nos. 196 and 197 show other views of the famous marine spectacle.

PROVENANCE: Dubois; David David-Weill; purchased by the Morgan Library in New York, 1947.

BIBLIOGRAPHY: Gabriel Henriot, *Collection David Weill*, III, Paris, 1928, pp. 221–222, repr.; Byam Shaw, *Guardi*, pp. 28, 50, 75, 79, no. 45, repr.; Felice Stampfle, "The Progress of the Bucentaur by Francesco Guardi," *Gazette des Beaux-Arts*, XLIII, 1954, pp. 77–82, fig. 1; Pignatti, *Disegni dei Guardi*, under no. LX.

EXHIBITIONS: New York, Pierpont Morgan Library, "Treasures from the Pierpont Morgan Library, Fiftieth Anniversary Exhibition," 1957, no. 101, pl. 66; Venice, Guardi Exhibition, 1965, no. 36, repr.

The Pierpont Morgan Library
1947.2

196 *The Bucintoro on the Way to the Lido on Ascension Day*

Pen and brown ink, brown wash, over traces of black chalk. $16\frac{3}{4} \times 27\frac{5}{8}$ inches (42.6 × 70.2 cm.), sight. Foxing; vertical crease at center; stains at left margin.

Inscribed in pen and brown ink at lower left, *S. Nicolo de Lido D. 1 S. Servolo D⁰ 3 malamoco D⁰. 5 | S. Lasaro D⁰. 2 Chioza D⁰ 4 e.*

Unlike the preceding sheet, this broad panorama of the Ascension Day sea fête is finished in every detail as befits the independent work of art it was designed to be. It shows the Bucintoro somewhat more distant from S. Niccolò di Lido, which is at the far left. A topographical key at the lower left margin enables the spectator to identify the islands silhouetted along the horizon.

Byam Shaw remarked that although the drawing corresponds very closely to one of a pair of paintings, formerly in the collection of Lord Shuttleworth but now belonging to Senatore Mario Crespi, Milan, its relationship is not that of a preparatory study but of the repetition of a composition. He suggested that if it was not made for the portfolio of an amateur, it may have been done with an engraving in mind, hence the inclusion of the topographical key. The drawing is a late work.

BIBLIOGRAPHY: J. Byam Shaw, "Unpublished Guardi Drawings, II," *Art Quarterly*, XVII, 1954, p. 165, no. 8, fig. 6.

Mrs. Herbert N. Straus

197 *The Bucintoro*

Pen and brown ink, brown and red-brown wash. $4\frac{11}{16} \times 9\frac{7}{16}$ inches (11.9 × 24 cm.). Slight foxing. Watermark: crescent (see watermark no. 12).

Verso: Pen sketch of the same subject.

The lively immediacy of this small sketch is such that one feels it could have been done as Guardi watched the great state barge row by, with flashing oars, in all its golden splendor. On the verso, he made another swift notation of the Bucintoro moving to the right in the midst of a swarm of gondolas (repr. Benesch, no. 67). There is another sketch of the Bucintoro's progress in the same stenographic style in the Fogg Art Museum. Both sheets may have come from a sketchbook as they are the same size. The Bucintoro that Guardi drew was the last of its kind; launched in 1729, it was destroyed by the French for its gold after the fall of the Venetian Republic in 1797.

PROVENANCE: Purchased by the Metropolitan Museum in London, 1919.

BIBLIOGRAPHY: Mongan and Sachs, *Drawings in the Fogg Museum*, under no. 317; Benesch, *Venetian Drawings*, no. 67, repr. (verso); Byam Shaw, *Guardi*, no. 52, repr.; Moschini, *Guardi*, pl. 181 (verso); Carlo L. Ragghianti, "Epiloghi Guardeschi," *Annali della Scuola Normale Superiore di Pisa*, XXII, 1953, no. 31, repr. (verso); Pignatti, *Disegni dei Guardi*, under no. LX.

The Metropolitan Museum of Art Rogers Fund, 19.151.2

198 *Dice Players in a Venetian Square*

Pen and brown ink, brown wash, over traces of black chalk. 14 13/16 × 10 9/16 inches (37.6 × 26.8 cm.). Watermark: graduated triple crescents (see watermark no. 14).

A street scene in a rather deserted part of the city with two figures involved in what may be a dice game. In the background is a typical, if unidentifiable, Venetian Gothic church. The composition was used almost exactly by Francesco in a picture now in the Loyd Collection at Lockinge, Berkshire, as Leslie Parris has pointed out.

PROVENANCE: Alfred Beurdeley (Lugt 421); Marquis de Biron, Paris and Geneva; purchased by the Metropolitan Museum in Geneva, 1937.

BIBLIOGRAPHY: Goering, *Guardi*, no. 122, repr.; Moschini, *Guardi*, pl. 183; *The Loyd Collection of Paintings and Drawings at Betterton House, Lockinge. . .*, London, 1967, p. 22, the Loyd picture repr. pl. 29.

EXHIBITIONS: New York, Tiepolo Exhibition, 1938, no. 64, repr.

The Metropolitan Museum of Art Rogers Fund, 37.165.70

199 *Architectural Capriccio: Courtyard of a Palace*

Pen and brown ink, brown wash, over red chalk. 10 3/4 × 7 3/8 inches (27.3 × 18.7 cm.). Watermark: coat of arms (see watermark no. 7).

Verso: A letter in pen and brown ink from a certain Domenico Tosti dated from Caprarola in 1761.

This capriccio, like No. 200 and a third drawing in the Metropolitan Museum (37.165.80; repr. New York, Tiepolo Exhibition, 1938, no. 62) all represent palace courtyards that differ conspicuously from the great courtyard of the Palazzo Ducale in Venice. The first two drawings include flights of stairs inspired by the Scala dei Giganti, the most conspicuous feature of that courtyard, but the architectural details and the proportions of the court are conspicuously altered. This is typical of what can be justly called Guardi's capriccio method. He transforms and charges with a new poetry the standard monuments of Venice.

The three drawings are related to painted architectural capriccios with similar palace courtyard views; one is in the Accademia Carrara at Bergamo (repr. Moschini, *Guardi*, pl. 178), a second in the National Gallery, London (no. 2519), and a third in the Wallace Collection, London (no. 647).

The letter on the verso dated 1761 has nothing to do with the drawing and is not in Guardi's hand. The sheet must have been seized by Guardi at random, and the date simply serves as a *terminus post quem*. Both Goering and Levey date the National Gallery picture 1770. This is not an improbable date for all three drawings. A rather dry copy of this sheet was on the New York market in 1950 (repr. *Country Life*, December 3, 1927, p. 861).

PROVENANCE: Marquis de Biron, Paris and Geneva; purchased by the Metropolitan Museum in Geneva, 1937.

BIBLIOGRAPHY: Herman W. Williams, "Drawings and Related Paintings by Francesco Guardi," *Art Quarterly*, II, 1939, p. 271, fig. 2; Goering, *Guardi*, no. 72, repr.; Byam Shaw, *Guardi*, p. 40, note 2; Michael Levey, *National Gallery Catalogues. The Eighteenth Century Italian Schools*, London, 1956, pp. 53–54 (the National Gallery picture repr. p. 34 of plate volume).

The Metropolitan Museum of Art Rogers Fund, 37.165.71

200 *Architectural Capriccio: Courtyard of a Palace*

Pen and brown ink, brown wash, over traces of black chalk. 10 7/8 × 7 3/16 inches (27.6 × 18.3 cm.). Watermark: coat of arms (see watermark no. 6).

Verso: List of figures in pounds in pen and brown ink.

84

See No. 199.

PROVENANCE: Possibly Earl of Warwick; sale, London, Christie's, May 20, 1896, no. 167; Edouard Warneck, Paris; Warneck sale, Paris, Hôtel Drouot, May 10–11, 1905, no. 179; Marquis de Biron, Paris and Geneva; purchased by the Metropolitan Museum in Geneva, 1937.

BIBLIOGRAPHY: Herman W. Williams, "Drawings and Related Paintings by Francesco Guardi," *Art Quarterly*, II, 1939, p. 271; Goering, *Guardi*, no. 74, repr.; Michael Levey, *National Gallery Catalogues. The Eighteenth Century Italian Schools*, London, 1956, pp. 53–54.

The Metropolitan Museum of Art
Rogers Fund, 37.165.87

201 *Architectural Capriccio: Vaulted Colonnade of a Palace*

Pen and brown ink, over red chalk. $7\frac{1}{8} \times 9\frac{15}{16}$ inches (18.1 ×25.2 cm.). Watermark: coat of arms (see watermark no. 11).

Signed in pen and brown ink at lower left, *f.ᶜᵒ Guardi*.

Once again Guardi transforms architectural elements from the Ducal Palace and other buildings on the Piazza S. Marco and the Piazzetta into quite new and original constructions. Here he supplies a glimpse of mountains at the left. The extensive use of red chalk underneath the pen design gives a particular coloristic charm to this sheet.

PROVENANCE: Marquis de Biron, Paris and Geneva; purchased by the Metropolitan Museum in Geneva, 1937.

BIBLIOGRAPHY: Mongan and Sachs, *Drawings in the Fogg Museum*, I, p. 162.

The Metropolitan Museum of Art
Rogers Fund, 37.165.88

202 *Architectural Capriccio: View Through an Archway*

Pen and brown ink, brown wash, over black chalk. $13\frac{11}{16} \times 11\frac{1}{16}$ inches (34.8 ×28.1 cm.). Slight foxing. Watermark: monogram (see watermark no. 39).

Guardi here makes another imaginative assemblage of Venetian monuments. Michael Levey has pointed out that the archway in the foreground is that of the Torre dell' Orologio, while the building is a free adaptation of the inside façade of the Doge's Palace and the Scala dei Giganti, without its giants. The drawing corresponds with only minor differences to a small picture in the National Gallery, London (Inv. 2523), and it may well have served as a model for the picture, which Levey, on documentary grounds, suggests was painted before August 1777. A free copy of this drawing, by a dull hand, is in the Berlin Print Room (no. 14013; *Arte Veneta*, III, 1949, fig. 151, as Giacomo Guardi); an even feebler copy is in the Victoria and Albert Museum (D. 1047–1900, Gernsheim photograph 54,588).

PROVENANCE: Lucy Cohen, London (according to Biron Inventory); Marquis de Biron, Paris and Geneva; purchased by the Metropolitan Museum in Geneva, 1937.

BIBLIOGRAPHY: Herman W. Williams, "Drawings and Related Paintings by Francesco Guardi," *Art Quarterly*, II, 1939, pp. 266, 271, fig. 1; Metropolitan Museum, *European Drawings*, no. 48, repr.; Goering, *Guardi*, no. 96, repr.; Agnes Mongan, *One Hundred Master Drawings*, Cambridge, Mass., 1949, p. 104, repr.; Rodolfo Pallucchini, "Nota per Giacomo Guardi," *Arte Veneta*, III, 1949, pp. 132–133, fig. 150; Michael Levey, *National Gallery Catalogues, The Eighteenth Century Italian Schools*, London, 1956, pp. 58–59 (the National Gallery picture repr. p. 38 of plate volume).

EXHIBITIONS: New York, Tiepolo Exhibition, 1938, no. 61, repr.

The Metropolitan Museum of Art
Rogers Fund, 37.165.79

203 *Capriccio with Ruins*

Pen and brown ink, over black chalk. $12\frac{3}{4} \times 8\frac{3}{4}$ inches (32.4 ×22.2 cm.). Several stains and spots of wash throughout sheet; repaired tear at lower left margin and at center of sheet. Watermark: coat of arms (see watermark no. 9).

Inscribed in black chalk on verso, *Francesco Guardi*.

Unusual in its heavily hatched surfaces that create a somewhat Riccesque effect, this composition in its main outlines was utilized for the painting in the North Carolina Museum of Art at Raleigh (repr. Venice, Guardi Exhibition, 1965, no. 92). In the latter, the staffage is different, and the mountains at the right of the drawing give way to a harbor scene. The drawing is probably not too far in date from the painting, which has been placed about 1765–1770.

PROVENANCE: Hippolyte-Alexandre-Gabriel-Walter Destailleur (Lugt 740).

BIBLIOGRAPHY: Janos Scholz, "Visiting Venetian Drawings at the National Gallery," *Art Quarterly*, XXVII, 1964, pp. 192, 195, note 10, fig. 5.

EXHIBITIONS: Geneva, Nicholas Rauch, "Dessins anciens et modernes," 1960, p. 70, no. 211, repr.

Mr. and Mrs. Eugene Victor Thaw

204 *Capriccio with a Tower*

Pen and brown ink, brown wash, over black chalk. $9\frac{3}{8} \times 13\frac{3}{4}$ inches (23.8 × 34.9 cm.), sight. Slight foxing; some spots of brown wash.

Guardi no doubt followed his fancy in creating this atmospheric caprice of a small inlet along the Lagoon, with its picturesque loading tower and the motif of entwined or crossed trees that he used more than once in other late capricci. Its composition seems to have found favor, as Simonson in his 1904 monograph recorded two paintings of a similar subject (nos. 122 and 139) plus a variant drawing (no. 283); a third painting from the Musée de Picardie, Amiens (no. 3), was exhibited with the present drawing at Cailleux in Paris in 1952. A weak copy with a few variations is in the Detroit Institute of Arts (repr. Detroit Institute of Arts, "Loan Exhibition of Old Master Drawings from Midwestern Museums," 1950, no. 19).

EXHIBITIONS: Cailleux, Tiepolo et Guardi, 1952, no. 106, pl. 61.

Christian Humann

205 *Capriccio with a Squall on the Lagoon*

Pen and brown ink, brown wash, over a little black chalk. $10\frac{1}{4} \times 15\frac{1}{8}$ inches (26 × 38.4 cm.). Slight foxing. Watermark: letter W below medallion (see watermark no. 38). Partially lined.

Byam Shaw noted that the composition of this late capriccio was used and reused with variations in format and figures in a number of Guardi's pictures, notably that formerly in the Alfred de Rothschild collection, one sold at Colnaghi's many years ago,

another sold in Paris in 1939 with the Gentile di Giuseppe collection, and still another in the Chiesa collection, Milan. The latter was one of a pair of small paintings made by Guardi for his friend Dr. Felice de Manfroni in 1782. A variant drawing was exhibited by Cailleux in 1952 (no. 108).

PROVENANCE: Donop de Monchy; Vitale Bloch, Paris.

BIBLIOGRAPHY: Byam Shaw, *Guardi*, p. 78, no. 72, repr.; Moschini, *Guardi*, fig. 184.

EXHIBITIONS: Cailleux, Tiepolo et Guardi, 1952, no. 107, repr.

Mr. and Mrs. Eugene Victor Thaw

206 *Gardens of the Villa Correr, near Strà*

Pen and brown ink, brown wash, over black chalk. $9\frac{1}{8} \times 15\frac{11}{16}$ inches (23.2 × 39.8 cm.). Watermark: medallion at left, letters F A at right (see watermark no. 37).

Inscribed in pen and brown ink at lower right, *Guardi F.*; in black chalk on verso, *Villa di Correr a Fiesso vicino a Stra*.

Verso: Study of St. Theresa and study of hands in black chalk.

This is a view of the elaborate gardens of the Villa Correr at Fiesso d'Artico near Strà. Another view of these gardens with hedges clipped into architectural forms and taken from a different point of view is in the Museo Correr (Pallucchini, *Disegni del Guardi al Correr*, fig. 91). Francesco must have been acquainted with the Correr family, and we know from old records that Count Teodoro Correr purchased drawings by Francesco from his son Giacomo Guardi, thus forming the nucleus of the large group of Guardi drawings conserved in the Correr Museum in Venice.

PROVENANCE: Baron Mathey (according to Biron Inventory); Marquis de Biron, Paris and Geneva; purchased by the Metropolitan Museum in Geneva, 1937.

BIBLIOGRAPHY: Benesch, *Venetian Drawings*, no. 61, repr.; Michelangelo Muraro, "An Altarpiece and Other Figure Paintings by Francesco Guardi," *Burlington Magazine*, C, 1958, p. 8, fig. 15 (verso).

The Metropolitan Museum of Art
Rogers Fund, 37.165.77

207 *The Villa Loredan, near Treviso*

Pen and brown ink, brown wash, over black chalk. $15\frac{3}{4} \times 29\frac{15}{16}$ inches (40×76 cm.). Vertical crease at center. Watermark: FAUSTINO CALCINARDI (see watermark no. 43).

This large view of the gate and the façade of a Venetian villa was used by Guardi in a picture of approximately the same dimensions, now in a private collection in London (Antonio Morassi, *Arte Veneta*, no. 4, 1950, p. 53, fig. 49). In the picture figures have been added; they stand outside the villa and on the road in the foreground. A fairly exact copy after the picture, drawn by Francesco himself or by his son Giacomo, is in the Ashmolean Museum at Oxford. This copy bears an inscription that identifies the now destroyed villa: *View of the Seat of S. E. Loredano at Paese near Treviso at present in the possession of John Strange Esqr. N. B. grass ground within the Fence; without the post road from Treviso to Bassan.* John Strange was British Resident in Venice from 1773 to 1790 and a patron of Francesco Guardi.

The artist made several drawings at the Villa Loredan. A smaller freer sketch of the entrance gate and façade is at the Rhode Island School of Design in Providence (*Master Drawings Selected from the Museums and Private Collections in America*, Buffalo, Albright Art Gallery, 1935, pl. 73). A view from the front windows of the villa is at the Fodor Museum in Amsterdam, and a view from the back windows in the Ashmolean Museum. The painted view of the façade corresponding to the present drawing is one of a series of four pictures formerly in Lord Rothermere's collection. The other pictures represent the garden façade of the Villa Loredan (now in the collection of Mr. and Mrs. Charles Wrightsman, New York), the façade and garden of the neighboring Villa dal "Timpano Arcuato," and the gardens of the Palazzo Contarini dal Zaffo in Venice. There are drawings for these last two pictures at Rotterdam, Oxford, and Lille. Byam Shaw has suggested that Guardi's drawings of the Villa Loredan probably date from 1778, when the painter undertook a journey from Venice to his family home in the Val di Sole.

PROVENANCE: Marquis de Biron, Paris and Geneva; purchased by the Metropolitan Museum in Geneva, 1937.

BIBLIOGRAPHY: Byam Shaw, *Guardi*, p. 65, no. 30, repr.; K. T. Parker, *Catalogue of the Drawings in the Ashmolean Museum*, II, *Italian Schools*, Oxford, 1956, pp. 510–511 (the copy after the painted view of the façade of the villa is pl. CCXIX); *Disegni veneti di Oxford* (exhibition catalogue by K. T. Parker), Venice, Fondazione Giorgio Cini, 1958, mentioned p. 74; *Canaletto e Guardi* (exhibition catalogue by K. T. Parker and J. Byam Shaw), Venice, Fondazione Giorgio Cini, 1962, mentioned pp. 76–77; Bean, *100 European Drawings*, no. 46, repr.

EXHIBITIONS: New York, Tiepolo Exhibition, 1938, no. 66, repr.; New York, Pierpont Morgan Library, "Landscape Drawings and Watercolors, Bruegel to Cézanne," 1953, no. 20.

The Metropolitan Museum of Art Rogers Fund, 37.165.69

208 *View of Lévico in the Valsugana*

Pen, brown and black ink, brown wash, over black chalk. $16\frac{3}{4} \times 25\frac{1}{8}$ inches (42.6×63.8 cm.). Vertical crease at center.

Inscribed in pen and brown ink in the artist's hand at lower left, *Levego verso il Borgo ci Valsugana dove la Brenta nazze*; illegible inscription in black chalk at lower right.

Verso: Landscape view in pen and brown ink, brown wash, over black chalk.

The inscription in Francesco Guardi's own hand identifies this splendid large view after nature; the village seen at the left is Lévico in the Valsugana. We know that the aging Francesco made a journey to this mountainous region near Trento in the autumn of 1778. Two other large landscape drawings record places seen by the artist in the Valsugana: a view of Borgo di Valsugana, formerly in the Jean Dubois collection (Byam Shaw, pl. 31) and a view of Borgo seen from a greater distance in the collection of J. Byam Shaw (*Canaletto e Guardi*, 1962, pl. 109).

PROVENANCE: Marius Paulme (Lugt 1910); sale, Paris, Galerie Georges Petit, May 13, 1929, no. 101, pl. 69; Mrs. C. I. Stralem.

BIBLIOGRAPHY: Benesch, *Venetian Drawings*, no. 66, repr.; Byam Shaw, *Guardi*, pp. 35, 43, 65–66; *Canaletto e Guardi* (exhibition catalogue by K. T. Parker and J. Byam Shaw), Venice, Fondazione Giorgio Cini, 1962, mentioned p. 78; Pignatti, *Disegni veneziani*, no. 135, repr.; Pignatti, *Disegni dei Guardi*, no. XXXIV, repr.

EXHIBITIONS: Buffalo, Albright Art Gallery, "Master Drawings Selected from Museums and Private Collections of America," 1935, no. 72, repr.; Springfield, Mass., Museum of Fine Arts, "Francesco Guardi, 1712–1793," 1937, in addendum to catalogue, no catalogue number; Boston, Museum of Fine Arts, "A Thousand Years of Landscape East and West," 1945, p. 9; Venice, Guardi Exhibition, 1965, no. 46, repr. (recto and verso).

Mr. and Mrs. Donald Stralem

209 *Bull Baiting in the Piazza S. Marco*

Pen and brown ink. $5\frac{1}{2} \times 13\frac{3}{16}$ inches (14×33.5 cm.).

Signed in pen and brown ink at lower left, *f.co Guardi.*

Guardi here records in a particularly abbreviated fashion the bull baiting that took place in the Piazza S. Marco on January 24, 1782, on the occasion of the visit of the Archduke Paul Pavlovitch of Russia and his Archduchess Maria Feodorovna, the "Conti del Nord." Guardi painted several pictures to commemorate the event, but the bull baiting is not recorded in the painted series. Two further sketches for the bull baiting spectacle are in the collection of Count Antoine Seilern (Seilern, pls. XCIX, C).

PROVENANCE: Purchased by the Metropolitan Museum in London, 1911.

BIBLIOGRAPHY: George A. Simonson, "Guardi's Drawings and Their Relation to His Paintings," *Art in America*, I, 1913, p. 268, fig. 25; Goering, *Guardi*, no. 124, repr.; Byam Shaw, *Guardi*, p. 69, under no. 43; [Antoine Seilern], *Italian Paintings and Drawings at 56 Princes Gate, London*, London, 1959, p. 101, under no. 139.

EXHIBITIONS: Springfield, Mass., Museum of Fine Arts, "Francesco Guardi, 1712–1793," 1937, no. 40, repr.

The Metropolitan Museum of Art
Rogers Fund, 11.66.12

210 *The Fire at S. Marcuola, Venice*

Pen and brown ink, brown wash, over black chalk. $12\frac{5}{16} \times 17\frac{3}{4}$ inches (31.3×45.1 cm.). Vertical crease at center; small creases at left margin. Watermark: three crescents at upper right, letters G F at lower left (see watermark no. 21).

Verso: Study of Roman ruins in pen and brown ink, brown wash.

This is one of Francesco's most brilliant records of a contemporary Venetian event, very probably drawn on the spot by the aging artist in the quarter of S. Marcuola, where a fire broke out on November 27, 1789. Another version of this subject with important variations is in the Museo Corer. The figures in that sheet are in Francesco's hand, while the buildings in the background, drawn in a rather dry and awkward fashion, seem to have been added by the hand of the artist's son Giacomo. At the bottom of the Corer sheet is an inscription added by Giacomo reading, *Incendio di S. Marcuola L'anno 1789 28* [N?] *bre*, and *Guardi F.* (repr. Byam Shaw, no. 41, and Kultzen, p. 15). The present drawing was utilized by Francesco in a fine small painting formerly in the Alphonse de Rothschild collection and now in the Pinakothek at Munich (repr. Kultzen, p. 13).

Byam Shaw points out that the ruined Roman triumphal arch sketch on the verso of the sheet also appears on the verso of a lagoon capriccio in the collection of Mrs. F. L. Evans (Byam Shaw, pl. 75), and that the same arch appears in two paintings by Guardi.

PROVENANCE: Lucy Cohen, London (according to Biron Inventory); Marquis de Biron, Paris and Geneva; purchased by the Metropolitan Museum in Geneva, 1937.

BIBLIOGRAPHY: George Simonson, *Francesco Guardi*, London, 1904, p. 59; Herman H. Williams, "Drawings and Related Paintings by Francesco Guardi," *Art Quarterly*, II, 1939, p. 272, fig. 9; Metropolitan Museum, *European Drawings*, no. 47, repr.; Goering, *Guardi*, p. 59, pl. 128 (verso); Tietze, *European Master Drawings*, no. 96, repr.; Byam Shaw, *Guardi*, no. 40, repr.; Moschini, *Guardi*, no. 163, repr.; Carlo Ragghianti, "Epiloghi Guardeschi," *Annali della Scuola Normale Superiore di Pisa*, XXII, 1953, p. 24, no. 26, repr.; Pignatti, *Disegni nel Museo Corer*, mentioned p. 65; Pignatti, *Disegni dei Guardi*, no. LIII, repr.; Maurizio Bonicatti, in *Problemi Guardeschi*, Venice, 1967, pp. 34–35, note 62, fig. 146 (verso); Rolf Kultzen, *Francesco Guardi in der Alten Pinakothek München. Nachtrag zum Bildband*, Munich, 1968, pp. 10–11, repr. p. 14.

EXHIBITIONS: New York, Tiepolo Exhibition, 1938, no. 68, repr.; Venice, Guardi Exhibition, 1965, no. 69, repr.

The Metropolitan Museum of Art
Rogers Fund, 37.165.74

211 *The Fenice Theater in Venice*

Pen and brown ink, brown and gray wash. $7\frac{7}{8} \times 10\frac{3}{16}$ inches (20×27.5 cm.). Watermark: crescent above crown (part of Heawood 884; see watermark no. 22).

Verso: Fragment of a larger drawing representing part of a column and a cornice, in pen and brown ink, gray wash.

This view of the Teatro La Fenice is one of Guardi's last drawings. The Fenice, work of the architect Gian Antonio Selva, was begun in 1790 and opened in April 1792, less than a year before Francesco's death. A freer view of the same building seen from a different angle is in the Museo Correr (Pallucchini, *Disegni del Guardi al Correr*, fig. 87). The rapidly noted staffage figures in the foreground are typical and closely related to those on the sheets of *macchiette* in the Metropolitan Museum (see No. 189).

PROVENANCE: Baron Mathey (according to Biron Inventory); Marquis de Biron, Paris and Geneva; purchased by the Metropolitan Museum in Geneva, 1937.

BIBLIOGRAPHY: Goering, *Guardi*, no. 151, repr.; Benesch, *Venetian Drawings*, no. 68, repr.; Byam Shaw, *Guardi*, p. 72; Pignatti, *Disegni dei Guardi*, no. LXIII, repr.

EXHIBITIONS: Venice, Guardi Exhibition, 1965, no. 71, repr.

The Metropolitan Museum of Art
Rogers Fund, 37.165.73

212 *Decorative Cartouche with a Lagoon Capriccio*

Pen and black ink, watercolor, over black chalk. $16\frac{1}{2} \times 27\frac{1}{8}$ inches (41.9×68.8 cm.). Drawing composed of two sheets joined vertically at right of center; vertical crease to left of center. Partially lined.

Illegible inscription in pen and brown ink, partially covered by lining, on verso.

This large drawing, lavishly heightened with watercolor, is rightly celebrated as one of Francesco's finest surviving decorative designs. The rococo cartouche, perhaps intended for an overdoor, contains a lagoon capriccio freely inspired by Canaletto's large etching *La Torre di Marghera*, as is a drawing by Francesco at Hamburg (Byam Shaw, pl. 68). The somewhat dry addition at the right is possibly the work of a restorer, who has cleverly completed Guardi's design, which may have at

some point been damaged in this area. In any case, the addition antedates the drawing's presence in the collection of the Earl of Warwick (1812–1893), since that collector's mark appears in the lower right corner.

PROVENANCE: George Guy, Fourth Earl of Warwick (Lugt 2600); sale, London, Christie's, May 20–21, 1896, no. 164; Raimundo de Madrazo; Sarah Cooper and Erskine Hewitt.

BIBLIOGRAPHY: G. A. Simonson, "Skizzen und Zeichnungen des Francesco Guardi," *Zeitschrift für bildende Kunst*, XVIII, 1907, p. 268, repr.; *Chronicle of the Museum for the Arts of Decoration of Cooper Union*, I, 1939, p. 198, repr.; Benesch, *Venetian Drawings*, no. 62, repr.; Rudolf Berliner, "Two Contributions to Criticism of Drawings Related to Decorative Art–II," *Art Bulletin*, XXXIII, 1951, pp. 53–55, repr.; Byam Shaw, *Guardi*, p. 77, under no. 68; J. Byam Shaw, "A Sketch for a Ceiling by Francesco Guardi," *Burlington Magazine*, CIV, 1962, p. 73; Wunder, *Extravagant Drawings*, no. 46, repr.; Pignatti, *Disegni dei Guardi*, no. XLVI, repr.

EXHIBITIONS: Baltimore, Museum of Art, "Age of Elegance: The Rococo and its Effect," 1959, no. 212, repr.; New York, Cooper Union Museum, "Five Centuries of Drawing," circulated by the American Federation of Arts, 1959–1961, no. 30; Venice, Guardi Exhibition, 1965, no. 31; Washington, Smithsonian Institution, National Collection of Fine Arts, "Treasures from the Cooper Union Museum," 1967, no. 209.

Cooper-Hewitt Museum, Smithsonian Institution
Bequest of Erskine Hewitt, 1938–57–242

213 *Design for a Framing Motif*

Pen and brown ink, green wash, over traces of black chalk. $16\frac{7}{16} \times 17\frac{1}{8}$ inches (41.8×43.5 cm.). Horizontal and vertical creases; brown stain at lower margin. Lined.

A superb, hitherto unpublished ornament drawing enriched by applications of green watercolor, in which Francesco proposes alternative solutions for a sumptuous framing motif—revealing his considerable talent as a decorator. The drawing came to the Metropolitan Museum in 1937 with the correct attribution to Francesco Guardi. Shortly thereafter it was banished to the limbo of Italian anonymity, and, it was quite recently that Larissa Salmina Haskell recognized Francesco's authorship.

PROVENANCE: Marquis de Biron, Paris and Geneva; purchased by the Metropolitan Museum in Geneva, 1937.

The Metropolitan Museum of Art
Rogers Fund, 37.165.101

214 Seated Turk with a Leopard

Pen and brown ink, black chalk, heightened with white, on blue paper. $12\frac{7}{8} \times 14\frac{5}{8}$ inches (32.7×37.2 cm.), sight. Contours pricked for transfer; vertical crease at center; several horizontal creases.

Unidentified collector's mark at lower left corner.

Janos Scholz has suggested that the pricking of this design implies that the contours were transferred for some decorative purpose, perhaps for the ornamentation of doors or furniture. Such exotic figures often were utilized in Venetian decoration. Vestiges of a similar pricked ornamental design appear on the verso of a landscape capriccio by Francesco Guardi in the Metropolitan Museum (37.165.84); all that survives of the figure in this sheet is a pair of feet wearing Eastern-looking pointed slippers.

BIBLIOGRAPHY: Janos Scholz, "Drawings by Francesco and Gianantonio Guardi," *Art Quarterly*, XVII, 1954, p. 385, fig. 1.

EXHIBITIONS: Houston, Guardi Family, 1958, no. 39, repr.; Oakland, Scholz Exhibition, 1960, no. 37, repr.; New Haven, Scholz Exhibition, 1964, no. 77; Venice, Guardi Exhibition, 1965, no. 96, repr.; Hamburg, Scholz Exhibition, 1965, no. 73, pl. 87; London, Scholz Exhibition, 1968, no. 49.

Janos Scholz

Bernardo Bellotto, called Canaletto
Venice 1720–Warsaw 1780

215 *View of Padua from the East*

Pen and brown ink, over black chalk. $7\frac{1}{8} \times 10\frac{3}{8}$ inches (18.1×26.4 cm.), sight. Several spots and stains; repaired loss at lower left corner.

Bellotto owed all, artistically, to his uncle, Canaletto, and even used his uncle's name on occasion. Here we see him doing an exercise in his own rather dry but sympathetic penwork that is based upon, and indeed is a free copy of a drawing by Canaletto in this exhibition (see No. 158).

PROVENANCE: Von Bojanus, Russian Councillor of State, sold 1829; Hessisches Landesmuseum, Darmstadt; sale, Lucerne, Galerie Fischer, June 2, 1945, no. 10, pl. 2.

BIBLIOGRAPHY: H. A. Fritzsche, *Bernardo Belotto genannt Canaletto*, Leipzig, 1936, p. 130; K. T. Parker, *The Drawings of Antonio Canaletto in the Collection of His Majesty the King at Windsor Castle*, London and Oxford, 1948, p. 46, under no. 80; Virch, *Baker Collection*, no. 65; Constable, *Canaletto*, under no. 680.

Walter C. Baker

Giovanni Battista Piranesi
Mogliano Veneto 1720–Rome 1778

216 *Sheet of Sketches*

Pen and brown ink. $16\frac{7}{16} \times 11\frac{3}{8}$ inches (41.8×28.3 cm.). Watermark: fleur-de-lis in double circle.

Inscribed by the artist in pen and brown ink, above, *statua/di Giove—cochio con cavali—a buo[?]—tempio*; center, *tempio—trofei—dorico/senza/involtar/lita[?]—naumachia/naumachia/ovata con principali/palazzi alle parti e nel mezo e sopra frontespici li soliti ornamen/ti di trofei statue, e cavali, cochi tirati da cavali—cochio/con l'imperatore dentro/e fama sopra che l'/incorona—a sei elefanti—Apoleo—rose—vaso con due rechie/per manico*; below, *trofei—arco/arco—elefanti/con cochio—arco e pure/nella fronte—soldato—animal/egizio/virile/alla meta. Verso, colonna Trajana/serve per campanile—per castaldo—Pale a fette di/melon.*

Verso: Pen and brown ink layout of garden and other sketches.

It was possibly on Piranesi's trip to Rome (1740–1743) that Johann Bernhard Fischer von Erlach's *Entwurff einer historischen Architectur . . .* , Vienna, 1721, came to his attention, perhaps through the good offices of his friend Nicola Giobbe, the builder to whom he dedicated *La prima parte di architetture, e prospettive*, 1743. The famous Austrian architect's pictorial history of architecture obviously struck the young Venetian as a good source book for ideas. As he turned through its plates, he systematically sketched and annotated, beginning at the top of the sheet and repeatedly working across from left to right, selecting now a principal monument, for instance, the temple of Artemis at Ephesus (Fischer, I, pl. VII), now only a small detail, like the group of figures on top of the Arch of Septimius Severus (Fischer, II, pl. V, lower right), that took his fancy. On the verso, he noted a detail of the palace at Schönbrunn, one of Fischer's own buildings (Fischer, IV, pl. III). This is one of two similar sheets of studies in the Morgan Library. Their relationship to Fischer von Erlach was first noted some years ago by Willard O. Clifford.

PROVENANCE: Mrs. J. P. Morgan, d. 1925.

BIBLIOGRAPHY: Stampfle, *Art Bulletin*, 1948, p. 124, no. 17, fig. 5; Corfiato, *Piranesi Compositions*, pl. 56; Mayor, *Piranesi*, pp. 3–4; Thomas, *Piranesi*, no. 3; Morgan Library, *Fifteenth Fellows Report, 1967–1968*, pp. 118–119; Morgan Library, *A Review of Acquisitions, 1949–1968*, p. 160.

EXHIBITIONS: New York, Piranesi Exhibition, 1949, p. 8, no. 17, fig. 3; Smith College, Piranesi, 1961, p. 100, no. 22, pl. 47.

> *The Pierpont Morgan Library*
> *Bequest of the late Junius S. Morgan*
> *and Gift of Henry S. Morgan, 1966.11:17*

217 *Central View of a Church Interior*

Pen and brown ink, gray and brown wash, over black chalk, with revisions by the artist in pen and darker brown ink and wash, also red chalk. $7^3/_8 \times 9^{11}/_{16}$ inches (18.7 × 24.6 cm.). Lined.

Inscribed in brown ink by the artist across the architrave, *IMPERATOR | IOANES BTTA PIRANESIS | SEPULCRUM EREXIT*; signed at lower right, *Piranesi*.

Although this sheet has previously been described as a product of Piranesi's atelier reworked by the artist himself, it is an admirable autograph drawing. The differences in handling are due to the fact that the drawing was made in two stages. The precise, fine drawing done in large part with the ruling pen and compass, and delicately washed with gray, is typical of Piranesi's early style (cf. Morgan Inv. 1966.11:3, which is directly preparatory for one of the etchings of *La prima parte di architetture*, 1743). At a subsequent time, the drawing was revised in a bolder manner. The inscription in the center of the drawing shows that Piranesi dreamed of himself as the designer of an imperial tomb.

The inscription *Piranesi* at the lower right is in all probability a signature; it is found on a great many of the artist's drawings, most of them mounted, as this one is, on a heavy paper with a double-ruled border in brown. Occasionally it is written partly on the paper of the drawing, partly on the mount. It does not appear on any of the drawings in the collection formed by Mrs. J. P. Morgan and now in the Morgan Library.

PROVENANCE: Edmond Fatio (sale, Nicolas Rauch, Geneva, June 3–4, 1959, no. 203); purchased by the Morgan Library in Geneva, 1959.

BIBLIOGRAPHY: Morgan Library, *Tenth Fellows Report, 1960*, pp. 59–61; Fischer, *Münchner Jahrbuch*, 1968, pp. 222–223, fig. 14; Morgan Library, *A Review of Acquisitions, 1949–1968*, p. 160.

> *The Pierpont Morgan Library*
> *Gift of the Fellows, 1959.14*

218 *Prison Interior*

Pen and brown ink, gray and brown wash, over black chalk. $7^3/_{16} \times 9^{11}/_{16}$ inches (18.2 × 24.5 cm.).

In such a drawing Piranesi is dependent on the conventions of baroque stage design, as witness the projecting central angle and the divergent wings opening left and right. Its restrained line and neatly confined washes mark it as an early work, probably executed prior to the freer studies for the famous series of etchings of prisons, the *Invenzioni capric. di carceri*, which appeared about 1745.

PROVENANCE: Mrs. J. P. Morgan, d. 1925.

BIBLIOGRAPHY: Stampfle, *Art Bulletin*, 1948, p. 124, no. 16, fig. 1; Corfiato, *Piranesi Compositions*, pl. 50; Howard Daniel, *Devils, Monsters and Nightmares*, London, 1964, p. 66, fig. 282; Morgan Library, *Fifteenth Fellows Report, 1967–1968*, pp. 118–119; Morgan Library, *A Review of Acquisitions, 1949–1968*, p. 160.

EXHIBITIONS: New York, Piranesi Exhibition, 1949, pp. 8, 18, fig. 1; Stockholm, Nationalmuseum, "Pierpont Morgan Library gästra Nationalmuseum," 1970, no. 45.

> *The Pierpont Morgan Library*
> *Bequest of the late Junius S. Morgan*
> *and Gift of Henry S. Morgan, 1966.11:16*

219 *Gondola*

Pen and brown ink, brown wash, over black chalk. $11^5/_8 \times 26^7/_8$ inches (29.6 × 68.3 cm.). Watermark: bow and arrow (Briquet 738).

Verso: Black chalk ornament with sun and star motifs; pen and brown ink design for decorative frame; similar sketch in red chalk.

An unusual aspect of the Morgan Library's Piranesi collection is its preservation of an important group of drawings clearly demonstrating the artist's Venetian origin. None does so more explicitly than this sparkling design for a festal gondola, which is the peer of the drawings of similar ornamental craft by Tiepolo and Guardi. The *Gondola* and Nos. 220–224 were probably executed between late 1743 and 1745 during Piranesi's stay in Venice, whence he had returned from Rome because of lack of funds; it is at this period that he is said—and not without reason as these drawings bear witness—to have worked in the studio of Tiepolo.

PROVENANCE: Mrs. J. P. Morgan, d. 1925.

BIBLIOGRAPHY: Stampfle, *Art Bulletin*, 1948, pp. 123, 124, 129, no. 10, fig. 3; Mayor, *Piranesi*, pp. 6, 33, pl. 2 (detail); Thomas, *Piranesi*, pp. 16–17, 41, nos. 16–17, pls. 16, 17 (detail); Morgan Library, *Fifteenth Fellows Report, 1967–1968*, pp. 118–119; Morgan Library, *A Review of Acquisitions, 1949–1968*, p. 160.

EXHIBITIONS: New York, Piranesi Exhibition, 1949, pp. 6–8, 13, no. 10, figs. 6, 7 (detail); Oberlin College, Drawings of the 18th Century, 1950–1951, no. 16, repr.; New York, Pierpont Morgan Library, "Treasures from the Pierpont Morgan Library, Fiftieth Anniversary Exhibition," 1957, no. 102, pl. 67.

The Pierpont Morgan Library
Bequest of the late Junius S. Morgan
and Gift of Henry S. Morgan, 1966.11:10

220 *Design for a Title Page*

Pen and brown ink, brown wash, over black chalk; smudges of red chalk. $15\frac{1}{2} \times 20\frac{7}{16}$ inches (39.5×51.9 cm.). Watermark: fleur-de-lis in circle with letters C^AC above and letter F below.

Verso: Black chalk study of standing male nude.

Although they are of the lavish nature of the title pages or frontispieces that adorn Piranesi's etched works, neither the present design nor No. 221 was apparently carried any further.

The standing male nude that occupies the full length of the vertically oriented verso is probably Piranesi's largest figure study. The figure is the large-scale counterpart of the muscular *ignudi* indolently gracing the gondola of No. 219. The verso is reproduced in Stampfle, fig. 6.

PROVENANCE: Mrs. J. P. Morgan, d. 1925.

BIBLIOGRAPHY: Stampfle, *Art Bulletin*, 1948, pp. 124, 129, no. 7; Thomas, *Piranesi*, p. 17, no. 14, repr.; Morgan Library, *Fifteenth Fellows Report, 1967–1968*, pp. 118–119; Morgan Library, *A Review of Acquisitions, 1949–1968*, p. 160.

EXHIBITIONS: New York, Piranesi Exhibition, 1949, p. 7, no. 7, figs. 4, 8 (verso).

The Pierpont Morgan Library
Bequest of the late Junius S. Morgan
and Gift of Henry S. Morgan, 1966.11:7

221 *Design for a Title Page*

Pen and brown ink, brown wash, over black chalk; some red watercolor; pulpit pricked for transfer. $20 \times 29\frac{1}{2}$ inches (50.8×75 cm.). Watermark: bow and arrow (Briquet 738).

One is reluctant to follow the assumption of the late Professor Hylton A. Thomas that the delicately worked central design for a pulpit and its ground plan, with a touch of color at the left, are a part of the main composition, constituting a kind of trompe-l'oeil design on the representation of a large rippled and folded sheet that partly conceals the classical tablet. The fact that the pulpit alone is meticulously pricked for transfer would seem to work against such an assumption, but a bizarrerie of this kind was not beyond Piranesi. The facile flow of the golden brown washes in the broader passages is indicative of the immediacy of Tiepolo's influence in this sheet.

PROVENANCE: Mrs. J. P. Morgan, d. 1925.

BIBLIOGRAPHY: Stampfle, *Art Bulletin*, 1948, pp. 123, 124, no. 8, fig. 4; Morgan Library, *Fifteenth Fellows Report, 1967–1968*, pp. 118–119; Morgan Library, *A Review of Acquisitions, 1949–1968*, p. 160.

EXHIBITIONS: New York, Piranesi Exhibition, 1949, pp. 6, 7, no. 8.

The Pierpont Morgan Library
Bequest of the late Junius S. Morgan
and Gift of Henry S. Morgan, 1966.11:8

222 *Capriccio*

Pen and brown ink, brown wash, over black chalk. $14\frac{7}{16} \times 20\frac{1}{8}$ inches (36.7×51.1 cm.), upper margin. Trimmed unevenly along lower margin. Watermark: bow and arrow (Briquet 738).

Inscribed by the artist at lower left, *tronco | grande per terra | ò sia terreno*.

With its fountain, its jumble of fallen columns, and its mourning satyrs, this haunting drawing is related to the sequence of four large etchings in the *Opere varie di architettura*, 1750, known as the *Grotteschi*, in which a similar mood of brooding melancholy prevails. The Grotesques are the most Tiepolesque of all Piranesi's prints, and, like this drawing, were probably made at the time of his short stay in Venice in the early 1740s, although they were first published in 1750 in the *Opere varie di architettura*.

PROVENANCE: Mrs. J. P. Morgan, d. 1925.

BIBLIOGRAPHY: Stampfle, *Art Bulletin*, 1948, p. 124, no. 9, fig. 2; Thomas, *Piranesi*, under no. 14; Morgan Library, *Fifteenth Fellows Report, 1967–1968*, pp. 118–119; Morgan Library, *A Review of Acquisitions, 1949–1968*, p. 160.

EXHIBITIONS: Oberlin College, Drawings of the 18th Century, 1950–1951, no. 17; New York, Piranesi Exhibition, 1949, p. 8, no. 9, fig. 5; Stockholm, Nationalmuseum, "Pierpont Morgan Library gästra Nationalmuseum," 1970, no. 46, repr.

The Pierpont Morgan Library
Bequest of the late Junius S. Morgan
and Gift of Henry S. Morgan, 1966.11:9

223 *Design for a Wall Panel*

Pen and brown ink, gray-brown wash, over black chalk. 12 13/16 × 14 3/4 inches (32.5 × 37.4 cm.). Watermark: bow and arrow (Briquet 738).

Verso: Pen and brown ink sketch for a table.

Piranesi's biographer J. G. Legrand in his manuscript *Life* (1799) of the artist, preserved in the Bibliothèque Nationale, Paris (Nouv. acq. fr. 5968; folio 131 verso), makes brief mention of his activity as architect and decorator in Venice. No trace of work of this kind remains in the Venetian palaces, but drawings such as this and two other Morgan sheets in similar rococo vein (Inv. 1966.11:11 and 13) seem to support Legrand's passing reference.

PROVENANCE: Mrs. J. P. Morgan, d. 1925.

BIBLIOGRAPHY: Stampfle, *Art Bulletin*, 1948, p. 124, no. 12, fig. 7; Mayor, *Piranesi*, pp. 6, 33, pl. 3; Thomas, *Piranesi*, pp. 16–17, no. 15, repr.; Morgan Library, *Fifteenth Fellows Report, 1967–1968*, pp. 118–119; Morgan Library, *A Review of Acquisitions, 1949–1968*, p. 160.

EXHIBITIONS: New York, Piranesi Exhibition, 1949, pp. 6–8, no. 12; Kansas City, The Nelson Gallery and Atkins Museum, "The Century of Mozart," *Bulletin*, I, 1956, no. 1, p. 37, no. 163.

The Pierpont Morgan Library
Bequest of the late Junius S. Morgan
and Gift of Henry S. Morgan, 1966.11:12

224 *Design for a Wall Panel*

Pen and brown ink, brown wash, over black chalk. 11 5/16 × 11 1/8 inches (28.8 × 28.2 cm.).

This piece of airy Venetian rococo ornamentation,

which is seen in perspective, may be interestingly compared with Guardi's (see No. 212).

PROVENANCE: Mrs. J. P. Morgan, d. 1925.

BIBLIOGRAPHY: Stampfle, *Art Bulletin*, 1948, p. 124, no. 13; Thomas, *Piranesi*, under no. 15; Morgan Library, *Fifteenth Fellows Report, 1967–1968*, pp. 118–119; Morgan Library, *A Review of Acquisitions, 1949–1968*, p. 160.

EXHIBITIONS: New York, Piranesi Exhibition, 1949, pp. 6–8, no. 13.

The Pierpont Morgan Library
Bequest of the late Junius S. Morgan
and Gift of Henry S. Morgan, 1966.11:13

225 *Architectural Complex*

Pen and brown ink, brown wash, over black chalk. 10 1/16 × 7 1/16 inches (25.5 × 18 cm.).

Verso: Black chalk sketch of colonnade.

Such a drawing is conceived in the grandiose idiom of the imaginative architectural inventions of Piranesi's *Opere varie di architettura*, which appeared in 1750. It reminds one of Horace Walpole's words, "He piles palaces on bridges and temples on palaces, and scales Heaven with mountains of edifices" (*Anecdotes of Painting in England*, IV, 1771, p. VI).

PROVENANCE: Mrs. J. P. Morgan, d. 1925.

BIBLIOGRAPHY: Stampfle, *Art Bulletin*, 1948, pp. 123–124, no. 4; Mayor, *Piranesi*, pl. 40; Thomas, *Piranesi*, p. 18, no. 42, repr.; Morgan Library, *Fifteenth Fellows Report, 1967–1968*, pp. 118–119; Morgan Library, *A Review of Acquisitions, 1949–1968*, p. 160.

EXHIBITIONS: New York, Piranesi Exhibition, 1949, p. 7, no. 4, fig. 2; Waterville, Maine, Colby College, "An Exhibition of Drawings," 1956, no. 12; Newark, New Jersey, The Newark Museum, "Old Master Drawings," 1960, no. 51, repr.

The Pierpont Morgan Library
Bequest of the late Junius S. Morgan
and Gift of Henry S. Morgan, 1966.11:4

226 *Architectural Fantasy*

Pen and brown ink, brown wash. 12 15/16 × 19 5/16 inches (32.9 × 49.1 cm.), sight. Small creases and tears at all margins; lower right corner replaced.

Collector's mark of Janos Scholz at lower left (Lugt S. 2933b).

This imaginary architectural complex—with a triumphal arch, approached by a colossal stairway and set into a great two-story colonnade with circular wings surmounted by obelisks and trophies—owes something to Piranesi's perusal of Fischer von Erlach's *Entwurff einer historischen Architectur . . .*, Vienna, 1721, as well as to his studies of stage design. It was probably produced about 1745–1750.

BIBLIOGRAPHY: G. Freedley, *Theatrical Designs*, I, New York, 1940, pl. 9; Charles de Tolnay, *History and Technique of Old Master Drawings*, New York, 1943, no. 142, repr.; Tietze, *European Master Drawings*, p. 202, pl. 101; Janos Scholz, *Baroque and Romantic Stage Design*, New York, 1949, p. 14, pl. 68; Mayor, *Piranesi*, p. 38, pl. 24.

EXHIBITIONS: Venice, Scholz Exhibition, 1957, no. 98, repr.; Oakland, Scholz Exhibition, 1960, no. 62; Hamburg, Scholz Exhibition, 1963, no. 118, pl. 56; New Haven, Scholz Exhibition, 1964, no. 82, pl. 15; London, Scholz Exhibition, 1968, no. 71, pl. 24.

Janos Scholz

227 *S. Maria del Priorato, Rome: Design for the Central Panel of the Vault*

Pen and brown ink, gray wash, over black chalk. 20⅚ × 12½ inches (53.2 × 31.7 cm.). Design silhouetted at top.

Inscribed in pen and brown ink on plaque beneath the statue of St. John the Baptist, *S. IOANES / PROTECT.or.*

Piranesi, on the title pages of his etched works, was wont to style himself "architetto veneziano," but what is known of his limited activity as an architect is restricted to Rome in the 1760s. At least a baker's dozen of his drawings in the Morgan Library are architectural. Seven are connected with his restoration of the church of the Knights of Malta (variously known as S. Maria Aventina and S. Maria del Priorato) and the adjoining priory; four relate to his ideas for the rebuilding of the west end of S. Giovanni in Laterano; two others are merely exercises representing the Farnese Palace in ground plan and elevation.

Strictly speaking, the drawings related to the renovation of S. Maria del Priorato, the project undertaken in 1764–1765 at the commission of Piranesi's friend, patron, and fellow Venetian, Cardinal Giovanni Rezzonico, Grand Prior of the Order of Malta, are designs for elements of the decoration, both interior and exterior. The design

for the vault decoration is conceived as one continuous panel running the length of the church. It displays the emblems of the Knights of Malta framed by a border of laurel. The order's patron saint, John the Baptist, is represented in the lower section; above him are the Maltese cross, with its equal arms, and the galleys and shields symbolic of centuries of sea conquests; at the top is the shirt of humility worn by the knights in memory of the Baptist's camel-hair garments. The finished nature of the drawing suggests that it may have been intended for submission to the patron cardinal for his approval. In the main, the actual decoration as carried out by Tommaso Righi follows the drawing, although there were changes in such details as the disposition of the small angels and the pose of the figure of St. John.

PROVENANCE: Mrs. J. P. Morgan, d. 1925.

BIBLIOGRAPHY: Stampfle, *Art Bulletin*, 1948, pp. 125–126, no. 50, fig. 8; Corfiato, *Piranesi Compositions*, pl. 64; Mayor, *Piranesi*, pp. 18, 33, 40, pl. 94; Thomas, *Piranesi*, under no. 46; Morgan Library, *Fifteenth Fellows Report, 1967–1968*, pp. 118–119; Morgan Library, *A Review of Acquisitions, 1949–1968*, p. 160.

EXHIBITIONS: New York, Piranesi Exhibition, 1949, p. 9, no. 50; Kansas City, The Nelson Gallery and Atkins Museum, "The Century of Mozart," *Bulletin*, I, 1956, no. 1, p. 37, no. 164; Smith College, Piranesi, 1961, pp. 104–105, no. 63, pl. 52.

The Pierpont Morgan Library
Bequest of the late Junius S. Morgan
and Gift of Henry S. Morgan, 1966.11:50

228 *S. Maria del Priorato, Rome: Sketch for the High Altar*

Pen and brown ink. 4⅝ × 4⁹⁄₁₆ inches (11.8 × 11.7 cm.).

In this quick, preliminary sketch Piranesi's conception of the altar of S. Maria del Priorato had already crystallized. The two ancient sarcophagus forms, placed one on top of the other and surmounted by the figure of St. Basil, appear very much the same in the altar itself where, however, the several large flanking candelabra were not retained.

PROVENANCE: Purchased by the Morgan Library in New York, 1952.

BIBLIOGRAPHY: Mayor, *Piranesi*, p. 18, pl. 81; Morgan

Library, *Fourth Fellows Report, 1953*, p. 65; Fischer, *Münchner Jahrbuch*, 1968, pp. 208–209, fig. 4; Morgan Library, *A Review of Acquisitions, 1949–1968*, p. 160.

EXHIBITIONS: Smith College, Piranesi, 1961, p. 104, no. 58, pl. 49.

The Pierpont Morgan Library
1952.26

229 S. Maria del Priorato, Rome: Design for the Lower Part of the High Altar

Pen and brown ink, gray wash, over black chalk; additions in black chalk. 18 9/16 × 14 3/8 inches (47.1 × 36.6 cm.).

Watermark: fleur-de-lis in single circle with letter V above. Computations at upper left and right; scale at bottom.

The present drawing is a study for the lower section of the high altar (Mayor, pl. 93); the upper part of the finished work shows St. Basil borne heavenward above the globe behind the lamb. The execution of the design in gypsum and stucco was carried out by Tommaso Righi, who was responsible for the stucco work throughout the church. It will be remarked that after the drawing was more or less completed by the application of the gray wash, the artist worked over it again with black chalk to heighten the three-dimensional effect.

Piranesi is buried in S. Maria del Priorato.

PROVENANCE: Mrs. J. P. Morgan, d. 1925.

BIBLIOGRAPHY: Stampfle, *Art Bulletin*, 1948, p. 125, no. 51; Mayor, *Piranesi*, pp. 17–19, 33, pl. 92; Morgan Library, *Fifteenth Fellows Report, 1967–1968*, pp. 118–119; Morgan Library, *A Review of Acquisitions, 1949–1968*, p. 160.

EXHIBITIONS: New York, Piranesi Exhibition, 1949, pp. 8–9, 14, 20, no. 51, fig. 10; Kansas City, The Nelson Gallery and Atkins Museum, "The Century of Mozart," *Bulletin*, I, 1956, no. 1, p. 37, no. 165; Smith College, Piranesi, 1961, pp. 104–105, no. 59, pl. 50.

The Pierpont Morgan Library
Bequest of the late Junius S. Morgan
and Gift of Henry S. Morgan, 1966.11:51

230 S. Maria del Priorato, Rome: Vertical Wall Panel

Black chalk; right half outlined in pen and brown ink. 15 13/16 × 10 7/16 inches (40.3 × 26.6 cm.). Watermark: fleur-de-lis in double circle with letters C B above.

For the wall bordering the *piazzale* of the Priory of the Knights of Malta, Piranesi designed several ornamental stelae. The present working drawing, inscribed with measurements, is preparatory for the vertical panel or tablet set between two obelisks to the right of the central stele (Mayor, pl. 88). The panel combines two sets of musical pipes with the Maltese cross and the tower, the double-headed eagle, and the crescent of the Rezzonico arms. Another Morgan drawing incorporates the design for the horizontal panel below the central stele.

PROVENANCE: Mrs. J. P. Morgan, d. 1925.

BIBLIOGRAPHY: Stampfle, *Art Bulletin*, 1948, p. 125, no. 53; Mayor, *Piranesi*, pp. 17–18, pl. 87; Morgan Library, *Fifteenth Fellows Report, 1967–1968*, pp. 118–119; Morgan Library, *A Review of Acquisitions, 1949–1968*, p. 160.

EXHIBITIONS: New York, Piranesi Exhibition, 1949, pp. 9–10, no. 53; Smith College, Piranesi, 1961, pp. 104–105, no. 57, pl. 48.

The Pierpont Morgan Library
Bequest of the late Junius S. Morgan
and Gift of Henry S. Morgan, 1966.11:53

231 S. Giovanni in Laterano, Rome: Longitudinal Section of Proposed Alteration of West End

Pen and brown ink, brown wash, with traces of black chalk. 12 9/16 × 21 3/8 inches (32 × 54.5 cm.).

Inscribed in pen and brown ink on verso, *Ponte S. Angelo / Teatro di Marcello / Piramide Nuova / Foro di Nerva / Curia Ostilia / Tempio di Cibelle / S. Urbano / Arco di Titto / Portico d'Adriano / Interno.*

As Piranesi himself recorded in the dedication of his work *Diverse maniere d'adornare i cammini . . .*, 1769, addressed to Cardinal Giovanni Battista Rezzonico, it was at the commission of the cardinal's uncle, Pope Clement XIII, that he drew up plans for the rebuilding of the west end of the great basilica of S. Giovanni in Laterano. The death of the Venetian pope in February 1769, however, put an end to the project. This longitudinal section, which begins at the point of the transept, as it still exists today with Cavaliere d'Arpino's fresco of the Ascension, shows one of Piranesi's proposals for the alteration of the choir and apse. It features an ambulatory and a decorative system of alternating stars and medallions for the half dome, obviously designed to harmonize with Borromini's nave. Another scheme is preserved in Morgan drawing Inv. 1966.11:55. See also Nos. 232 and 233.

PROVENANCE: Mrs. J. P. Morgan, d. 1925.

BIBLIOGRAPHY: Stampfle, *Art Bulletin*, 1948, pp. 125–126, no. 56; Corfiato, *Piranesi Compositions*, pl. 62; Morgan Library, *Fifteenth Fellows Report, 1967–1968*, pp. 118–119; Fischer, *Münchner Jahrbuch*, 1968, pp. 209–211, fig. 5; Morgan Library, *A Review of Acquisitions, 1949–1968*, p. 160.

EXHIBITIONS: New York, Piranesi Exhibition, 1949, pp. 10–11, no. 56, fig. 11; Smith College, Piranesi, 1961, no. 66.

The Pierpont Morgan Library
Bequest of the late Junius S. Morgan
and Gift of Henry S. Morgan, 1966.11:56

232 S. Giovanni in Laterano, Rome: Sketch for Choir Wall; Putti

Pen and dark brown ink, gray wash, over black chalk. $13\frac{3}{4} \times 10\frac{1}{4}$ inches (34.9 × 26 cm.). Watermark: fleur-de-lis in double circle with letters C B above.

Verso: Sketch in black chalk for pedimented niche of choir wall; fragmentary ground plan of the choir.

As was recently recognized by Manfred F. Fischer, this sheet and No. 233 were once joined together. In the separation of the two sketches, each half was slightly trimmed so that they no longer fit together exactly. From the plans on the verso of each half, Dr. Fischer was able to reconstruct the ground plan of a portion of Piranesi's projected renovation of the choir. A slightly different solution for the choir wall is put forth in Morgan Inv. 1966.11:57.

PROVENANCE: Mrs. J. P. Morgan, d. 1925.

BIBLIOGRAPHY: Stampfle, *Art Bulletin*, 1948, pp. 126, 129, no. 58, fig. 11; Thomas, *Piranesi*, p. 19, no. 50, repr.; Morgan Library, *Fifteenth Fellows Report, 1967–1968*, pp. 118–119; Fischer, *Münchner Jahrbuch*, 1968, pp. 209–217, figs. 8b, 9b; Morgan Library, *A Review of Acquisitions, 1949–1968*, p. 160.

EXHIBITIONS: New York, Piranesi Exhibition, 1949, p. 10, no. 58, fig. 12.

The Pierpont Morgan Library
Bequest of the late Junius S. Morgan
and Gift of Henry S. Morgan, 1966.11:58

233 S. Giovanni in Laterano, Rome: Design for a Papal Monument

Pen and brown ink, gray wash, over black chalk. $13\frac{1}{4} \times 7\frac{3}{16}$ inches (33.6 × 18.3 cm.).

Verso: Black chalk fragment of ground plan.

No doubt this design, distinguished for the freedom and bravura of its execution, was also intended for some architectural feature of the choir of S. Giovanni in Laterano, since it was once a part of the same sheet as the above drawing. Presumably the oval was meant to frame a papal portrait as in the design for a papal wall monument in the Ashmolean Museum, Oxford (Thomas, pl. 45). The latter drawing and a similar one in the Ornamentstichsammlung of the Berlin Kunstgewerbemuseum (Box 3940, no. 138) appear to be works of the same period. If they do not relate, as Professor Thomas suggested, to Piranesi's presumably lost interior decorations for Pope Clement XIII at the Vatican or at Castelgandolfo, they might conceivably be a part of the Lateran project.

PROVENANCE: Mrs. J. P. Morgan, d. 1925.

BIBLIOGRAPHY: Stampfle, *Art Bulletin*, 1948, p. 123, no. 110; Thomas, *Piranesi*, under no. 45; Morgan Library, *Fifteenth Fellows Report, 1967–1968*, pp. 118–119; Fischer, *Münchner Jahrbuch*, 1968, p. 212, figs. 8a, 9a; Morgan Library, *A Review of Acquisitions, 1949–1968*, p. 160.

EXHIBITIONS: New York, Piranesi Exhibition, 1949, p. 6, no. 110, fig. 16.

The Pierpont Morgan Library
Bequest of the late Junius S. Morgan
and Gift of Henry S. Morgan, 1966.11:110

234 Design for Mantelpiece with Confronted Elephant Heads

Pen and brown ink, brown wash, over black chalk; smudges of red chalk at right. $8\frac{3}{8} \times 12\frac{5}{8}$ inches (21.3 × 32.1 cm.).

Inscribed in pen and brown ink at lower right, *Rotta de c . . . | Carioni* [?].

Verso: Fragment of Ottaviani etching after Guercino.

The designs for decoration constitute the largest single category of drawings in the Morgan Piranesi collection, their number running into the forties.

The majority are, like this sheet and the following one, ideas for mantelpieces of eccentric opulence, but there are also designs for chairs and tables, candelabra and sconces, even sedan chairs. A number were etched in Piranesi's influential publication *Diverse maniere d'adornare i cammini ed ogni altra parte degli edifizi*, 1769. Frequently, as in the present instance, they are drawn on the back of proofs or discarded sheets of his etched plates of earlier date. Several of the preliminary studies for etched mantelpieces are even executed on the verso of other plates from the *Diverse maniere d'adornare i cammini . . .* , indicating the various levels at which the artist was working at one period.

PROVENANCE: Mrs. J. P. Morgan, d. 1925.

BIBLIOGRAPHY: Stampfle, *Art Bulletin*, 1948, no. 61; Morgan Library, *Fifteenth Fellows Report, 1967–1968*, pp. 118–119; Morgan Library, *A Review of Acquisitions, 1949–1968*, p. 160.

EXHIBITIONS: New York, Piranesi Exhibition, 1949, no. 61, fig. 14; Smith College, Piranesi, 1961, no. 68.

The Pierpont Morgan Library
Bequest of the late Junius S. Morgan
and Gift of Henry S. Morgan, 1966.11:61

235 *Design for Mantlepiece*

Red chalk, some black chalk, additions in pen and brown ink. 9⅛ × 14 5/16 inches (23.2 × 36.4 cm.). Paper pieced together; loss at upper center.

Verso: Fragmentary sketch in pen and brown ink of wall decoration.

Six of the Morgan designs for mantelpieces were etched. This one is preparatory for the plate that is no. 893 in Henri Focillon's *G. B. Piranesi: Essai de catalogue raisonné de son oeuvre*, Paris, 1918.

PROVENANCE: Mrs. J. P. Morgan, d. 1925.

BIBLIOGRAPHY: Stampfle, *Art Bulletin*, 1948, p. 127, no. 63; Marianne Fischer, "Piranesis radiertes Oeuvre und die zugehörigen Entwürfe in der Kunstbibliothek," *Berliner Museen Berichte . . .* , XVI, 1966, no. 2, p. 23, note 10; Morgan Library, *Fifteenth Fellows Report, 1967–1968*, pp. 118–119; Morgan Library, *A Review of Acquisitions, 1949–1968*, p. 160.

EXHIBITIONS: New York, Piranesi Exhibition, 1949, pp. 11–12, no. 63.

The Pierpont Morgan Library
Bequest of the late Junius S. Morgan
and Gift of Henry S. Morgan, 1966.11:63

236 *Ruins at Pozzuoli*

Pen and brown-black ink, over black chalk, on a heavy light brown paper. 19 5/16 × 30 inches (49 × 76 cm.). Creased at the center. Watermark: animal inscribed in a circle, the letters R U S S below.

Inscribed at lower left margin in pen and gray-black ink, the letter *P* in a rough cartouche; fragment of a somewhat similar inscription on verso.

This monumental drawing is a product of the 1770s when Piranesi made numerous trips to the region of Pompeii and Herculaneum to study the Roman ruins. At first thought to be a view of Pompeian remains, it is now known to represent a site in Pozzuoli, another ancient city near Naples. The identification was made by Hylton A. Thomas on the basis of an engraving of the same ruins by Giuseppe Vasi (1710–1782), which he chanced upon in the New York art market immediately following his first glimpse of this drawing; he forthwith presented the print to the Morgan Library. The three columns are those of the Serapeum at Pozzuoli. The Library owns another late drawing of this kind, a view of the Temple of Isis at Pompeii.

PROVENANCE: Purchased by the Morgan Library in London, 1961.

BIBLIOGRAPHY: Morgan Library, *Eleventh Fellows Report, 1961*, pp. 93–95, repr. (as *Ruins of Pompeii*); Morgan Library, *Thirteenth Fellows Report, 1963–1964*, p. 103; Morgan Library, *A Review of Acquisitions, 1949–1968*, p. 160.

The Pierpont Morgan Library
Gift of the Fellows, 1961.1

237 *Figure Studies*

Pen and brown ink. 8⅞ × 5 5/16 inches (22.5 × 13.5 cm.), sight. Several creases and repairs.

Piranesi's figure drawings are not as rare as once thought, but their numbers are not large considering the myriads of personages who enliven his etchings. Usually they are free notations of men in lively movement or animated gesticulation as here and in the following drawing; only occasionally are there representations of women and children. Sometimes, as in examples in Milan, Paris, and Oxford (Thomas, pls. 67, 74, 77), as well as in the Morgan Library (Inv. 1950.53) and the collection of Count Seilern (*Italian Paintings and Drawings at 56 Princes Gate, London*, London, 1959, no. 144), Piranesi appears to have used his pressmen (or paper makers?) as models, but ordinarily the action of his figures goes unexplained.

PROVENANCE: J. A. Duval le Camus, Paris (Lugt 1441).

BIBLIOGRAPHY: Mayor, *Piranesi*, p. 39, pl. 41; Thomas, *Piranesi*, no. 70, repr.; "Italian Drawings from the Collection of Janos Scholz," *Metropolitan Museum of Art Bulletin*, May 1965, Part II, p. 343, repr.

EXHIBITIONS: Venice, Scholz Exhibition, 1957, no. 97, repr.; Oakland, Scholz Exhibition, 1960, no. 63; London, Scholz Exhibition, 1968, no. 72.

Janos Scholz

238 *Figure Studies*

Pen and brown ink, point of brush. $6\frac{1}{4} \times 8\frac{1}{4}$ inches (15.9×21 cm.), sight. Tear at upper margin; waterstains throughout sheet; diagonal crease in right half of sheet.

Illegible inscription in black chalk at lower right; unidentified collector's mark stamped in blue at lower left; mark of unidentified collector (Lugt S. 735a) stamped in red at center.

It is reported by Bianconi, a contemporary biographer of Piranesi, that the Senator Abbondio Rezzonico owned a group of Piranesi's drawings of beggars and still-life compositions (see Henri Focillon, *Giovanni Battista Piranesi*, Paris, 1928, p. 74). With this reference in mind, one might be persuaded to regard these figures, especially that on the right, as sketches of blind beggars. See No. 237.

BIBLIOGRAPHY: Virch, *Baker Collection*, no. 64.

Walter C. Baker

Giovanni Domenico Tiepolo
Venice 1727–Venice 1804

239 *Kneeling Woman with Two Children*

Red chalk on blue paper. $12\frac{13}{16} \times 10$ inches (32.5×25.4 cm.). Pen and brown ink inscription at lower margin of verso visible on recto. Lined.

The three figures correspond exactly to a group on the right in Giambattista's *Family of Darius before Alexander*, a picture painted during the Tiepolos' stay in Würzburg from 1750 to 1753 and now in the University Museum, Würzburg (Morassi, 1962, fig. 283). Morassi has suggested that Domenico collaborated with his father on this picture, but it would be risky to assume that this is Domenico's painstakingly exact study *for* part of a picture on which he worked with his father. Rather it is a record *after* a detail of the finished picture.

The present drawing is a particularly brilliant sample of the vast production of chalk record drawings made by the Tiepolo studio, especially during the Würzburg years. The best of these were formerly attributed by some scholars to Giambattista himself and thought to be studies for works executed in Würzburg. Recent scholarship, however, is fairly unanimous in giving many of the record drawings to Domenico, whose hand we feel is to be recognized here at its very best.

The complex question of the record drawings is discussed lucidly by Byam Shaw in the second chapter of his *Drawings of Domenico Tiepolo*.

Private Collection

240 *Two Angel Musicians on a Balustrade*

Red chalk, heightened with white chalk, on blue paper. $7\frac{15}{16} \times 13\frac{1}{2}$ inches (20.1×34.3 cm.). Small repaired losses at upper left and lower right corners.

Inscribed on verso in pen and brown ink, . . . *C. M. No. 3260*; in black ink, *743* and *178*.

In this characteristic red chalk record drawing, Domenico set down the figures of the cellist and lutist who appear in the very center of the lower edge of the *Triumph of Faith* in the central compartment of the ceiling of the Chiesa della Pietà, Venice, the large oval fresco painted by his father in 1754–1755. It is one of a considerable series of copies after details of the ceiling, many of which are preserved in Stuttgart. Among those illustrated by Hadeln (as Giambattista in *Tiepolo Drawings*), plates 175 and 176 show the other members of the celestial orchestra flanking the pair of the Morgan example. One is thereby enabled to follow Domenico's method of isolating groups and disregarding overlapping details, sometimes leaving off with an incomplete passage like that of the bagpipe at the far right, which he then picked up in the drawing formerly in the F. W. Boehler collection, Lucerne (Hadeln, *Tiepolo Drawings*, pl. 176). Byam Shaw speculates that such record drawings after the frescoes may have been made while the scaffolding was still in place. Since Domenico etched one of the smaller frescoes in the Pietà (De Vesme, 78), it is possible that he may have contemplated a more extensive graphic series for which the record drawings would have been useful. The inscription in brown ink on the verso may be a Bossi-Beyerlen code number.

PROVENANCE: Edward Habich, Cassel (according to Sack); Charles Fairfax Murray; purchased by J. Pierpont Morgan in London, 1910.

BIBLIOGRAPHY: Sack, *Tiepolo*, pp. 273–274, fig. 295.

The Pierpont Morgan Library
No. IV, 151f

241 Abraham Visited by the Angels

Pen and brown ink, brown wash, over black chalk; black chalk horizontal and vertical lines. 16 3/16 × 10 7/8 inches (42.7 × 27.6 cm.). Horizontal crease at center; repaired loss at upper left; foxing.

Verso: Black chalk tracings over contours of figure of Abraham on recto.

An early work of Domenico, who has freely copied a drawing by his father, now in the Museo Civico at Bassano (*Master Drawings*, III, 1965, no. 4, pl. 31). Both as a painter and draughtsman, Domenico's style is based on a close but not servile imitation of his father's work. The drawing that Domenico copies here was part of a series of highly finished compositions engraved by Pietro Monaco.

PROVENANCE: Marquis de Biron, Paris and Geneva; purchased by the Metropolitan Museum in Geneva, 1937.

BIBLIOGRAPHY: Metropolitan Museum, *European Drawings*, pl. 45; Bryan Holme, *Master Drawings*, New York, 1943, pl. 79 (as Giambattista); Byam Shaw, *Domenico Tiepolo*, p. 74, no. 12, repr.

The Metropolitan Museum of Art
Rogers Fund, 37.165.5

242 The Assumption of the Virgin

Pen and black ink, gray wash, over red chalk. 14 15/16 × 10 13/16 inches (37.9 × 27.5 cm.). Strips of gray-washed paper pasted to left and lower margins; repaired tear at upper margin.

Signed in pen and black ink at lower right, *Dom Tiepolo f.*

A good part of Domenico Tiepolo's vast production as a draughtsman is devoted to variations on religious themes: the Trinity, God the Father, Christ, the Virgin seen in glory, the Baptism of Christ, scenes from the Passion, St. Anthony with the Christ Child—long series discussed in detail by Byam Shaw. The present *Assumption of the Virgin* is a brilliant variation on the theme stated in 1759 by Giambattista in the ceiling fresco of the Chiesa della Purità, Udine (Morassi, 1955, fig. 53). Another variation in the Morgan Library (Byam Shaw, pl. 24), where the Virgin's hands are clasped, seems to have as point of departure Giambattista's representation of the Virgin in the somewhat earlier central ceiling fresco in the Church of the Pietà, Venice (Morassi, 1955, fig. 43).

PROVENANCE: Marquis de Biron, Paris and Geneva; purchased by the Metropolitan Museum in Geneva, 1937.

BIBLIOGRAPHY: Byam Shaw, *Domenico Tiepolo*, p. 33, pl. 25.

EXHIBITIONS: New York, Tiepolo Exhibition, 1938, no. 73, repr.

The Metropolitan Museum of Art
Rogers Fund, 37.165.65

243 The Baptism of Christ

Pen and brown ink, brown wash. 10 1/8 × 7 7/8 inches (26.7 × 20 cm.). Illegible watermark.

Signed in pen and brown ink at lower left, *Dom Tiepolo f.*

The Baptism of Christ is another religious subject that served Domenico as point of departure for a long series of hastily drawn but inventive variations. In New York the Robert Lehman Collection possesses six lively exercises on this theme.

PROVENANCE: Hamilton E. Field (Lugt S. 872a); purchased by the Metropolitan Museum in New York, 1918.

The Metropolitan Museum of Art
Rogers Fund, 18.144

244 Oriental Lancer Approaching a Town

Pen and brown ink, brown wash, over traces of black chalk. 11¼ × 16⅛ inches (28.6 × 41 cm.).

Signed in pen and brown ink at lower left, *Dom.º Tiepolo f.*

The turbaned Oriental lancer is an exotic visitor to the typical north Italian town seen at the left, and this bizarre combination of the familiar and unfamiliar is an excellent example of Domenico's taste for the fantastic. Two further variations on this theme—Oriental horsemen in landscapes—are in the Metropolitan Museum (34.42.1 and 34.42.2; the former repr. Byam Shaw, pl. 42); others are in collections abroad.

PROVENANCE: Baron Louis-Auguste de Schwiter (Lugt 1768); Schwiter sale, Paris, Hôtel Drouot, April 20–21, 1883, no. 149.

BIBLIOGRAPHY: Sack, *Tiepolo*, p. 322, no. 143; Byam Shaw, *Domenico Tiepolo*, p. 40.

The Metropolitan Museum of Art
Rogers Fund, 37.165.67

245 Two Families of Satyrs

Pen and brown ink, brown wash, over a little black chalk. 7⅝ × 10⅞ inches (19.4 × 27.6 cm.). Lined.

Signed in pen and brown ink at lower left, *Dom.º Tiepolo f.*

A favorite fanciful theme of Domenico was the representation of tenderly humorous scenes involving the family life of satyrs and centaurs. Four further compositions of this kind are in the Robert Lehman Collection.

Robert Lehman Collection

246 Satyr Leading a Centauress

Pen and brown ink, brown and gray wash, over black chalk. 7½ × 10¾ inches (19.1 × 27.3 cm.). Slight foxing.

Signed in pen and brown ink at lower left, *Dom.º Tiepolo f*; inscribed in pen and brown ink on old mount, . . . *fotogra . . . |da Val . . . | . . . fotografato dal . . . | . . . Raccolta di 100 disegni originali. . . .*

Domenico was amused to depict happy marriages between centauresses and satyrs or satyresses and centaurs. Here the offspring has the attributes of a satyr. The exotic pair moves across a typical northern Italian landscape. Eleven further drawings of such subjects from the Biron collection are in the Metropolitan Museum.

PROVENANCE: Baron Louis-Auguste de Schwiter (Lugt 1768); Schwiter sale, Paris, Hôtel Drouot, April 20–21, 1883, no. 142; Marquis de Biron, Paris and Geneva; purchased by the Metropolitan Museum in Geneva, 1937.

The Metropolitan Museum of Art
Rogers Fund, 37.165.61

247 Caricature of a Gentleman and Other Studies

Pen and brown ink, brown wash, over a little black chalk. 10⅝ × 7 5/16 inches (27 × 18.6 cm.). Lined.

Signed in pen and brown ink at lower right, *Dom.º Tiepolo f.*

Giambattista's and Domenico's proficiency as caricaturists is well exemplified in this spirited sheet, which if it were not signed by the son might easily be taken for the work of the father. Above the standing gentleman appears a bouquet of the character heads that appear in many of Domenico's paintings and etchings; at the left border there are sketches of a hand and the tip of a quiver.

PROVENANCE: Marquis de Biron, Paris and Geneva; purchased by the Metropolitan Museum in Geneva, 1937.

BIBLIOGRAPHY: Metropolitan Museum, *European Drawings*, no. 60, repr.; Giorgio Vigni, "Note su Giambattista e Giandomenico Tiepolo," *Emporium*, XCVIII, 1943, p. 23, fig. 10; Max Kozloff, "The Caricatures of Giambattista Tiepolo," *Marsyas*, X, 1961, p. 22, fig. 33; Byam Shaw, *Domenico Tiepolo*, p. 90, no. 78, repr.; Bean, *100 European Drawings*, no. 49, repr.; Pignatti, *Disegni veneziani*, no. 118, repr.

EXHIBITIONS: Chicago, Tiepolo Exhibition, 1938, no. 114; New York, Tiepolo Exhibition, 1938, no. 74, repr.

The Metropolitan Museum of Art
Rogers Fund, 37.165.68

248 Monkey Swinging on a Parapet and Two Monkey Skeletons

Pen and brown ink, brown wash. 10 × 7½ inches (25.4 × 19.1 cm.).

Signed in pen and brown ink at lower right, *Dom.º Tiepolo.*

The monkey swinging from the parapet is copied

after a detail in the Africa section of Giambattista's fresco in the staircase of the Würzburg Residenz; there the monkey plucks a feather from the tail of an ostrich (Freeden and Lamb, *Würzburger Residenz*, pl. 93). This monkey also appears a good deal later in the ceiling of the Throne Room in the Royal Palace at Madrid (Morassi, 1955, pl. 83).

Though Domenico has copied his father here, the sheet can hardly be called a record drawing. He has added two lively monkey skeletons of his own invention, and given us an entertaining scherzo.

PROVENANCE: F. A. C. Prestel; Prestel sale, Frankfurt-am-Main, November 12–13, 1918, no. 227, pl. 38; Tomas Harris, London.

BIBLIOGRAPHY: Byam Shaw, *Domenico Tiepolo*, no. 47, repr.

EXHIBITIONS: London, Arts Council, Tiepolo Exhibition, 1955, no. 64, pl. VIII.

Dr. and Mrs. Rudolf Heinemann

249 *Figures Around a Sacrificial Altar*

Pen and brown ink, over a little black chalk. 11 15/16 × 18 1/8 inches (30.3 × 46 cm.). Several stains and spots; inscription at lower right scraped away and now illegible.

Several numbers in pen and brown ink on verso; collector's mark of Janos Scholz at lower left (Lugt S. 2933b).

This drawing, executed in a rather angular, forceful pen line without heightening in wash, is one of a quite considerable group of drawings representing mysterious, perhaps biblical, subjects. Many of these were in the past attributed to Giambattista, but Giorgio Vigni pointed out that they can be grouped around a drawing in Trieste that is signed by Domenico (*Emporium*, XCVIII, 1943, pp. 14–24, and Byam Shaw, *Domenico Tiepolo*, pp. 80–81). Most of these figure compositions are arranged in a flat, friezelike fashion, without much indication of depth—and this becomes characteristic of Domenico's mature work. Mr. Scholz has suggested that the subject is Moses Breaking the Tablets of the Law, though there are, of course, recollections of the mysterious scenes that Giambattista etched in the *Scherzi di Fantasia*. Two drawings similar in technique and composition are in the Robert Leh-

man Collection (repr. Venice, Wallraf Exhibition, 1959, nos. 90–91).

PROVENANCE: Dan Fellows Platt (Lugt S. 750a).

EXHIBITIONS: Venice, Scholz Exhibition, 1957, no. 72, repr.; Oakland, Scholz Exhibition, 1960, no. 86.

Janos Scholz

250 *Studies of Two Orientals*

Brush and brown wash. 9 5/8 × 7 1/2 inches (24.5 × 19.1 cm.). Corners cut.

A number of similar drawings executed with great brio with the point of a brush and lavish applications of dark brown wash have survived. They were clearly produced in the Tiepolo studio, and in the past were attributed without hesitation to Giambattista. Byam Shaw was the first to counsel caution, and he now convincingly attributes this group, which in at least one case involves records of Würzburg motifs, to Domenico (see Byam Shaw, *Domenico Tiepolo*, p. 66).

PROVENANCE: Sir Gilbert Lewis; H. Duff Gordon; Tomas Harris, London.

BIBLIOGRAPHY: A. P. Oppé, "A Fresh Group of Tiepolo Drawings," *Old Master Drawings*, V, September 1930, p. 31, pl. 11 (as Giambattista).

EXHIBITIONS: London, Arts Council, Tiepolo Exhibition, 1955, no. 28.

Dr. and Mrs. Rudolf Heinemann

251 *The Trinity in Glory*

Pen and brown ink, brown and orange wash, over red chalk, on blue-gray paper. 10 3/4 × 12 1/16 inches (27.3 × 30.6 cm.). Illegible erased inscription at upper right corner. Watermark: letters T G B (see watermark no. 26).

Numbered in black chalk on verso, 4.

Verso: Sketches in pen and brown ink of flying figures.

A study, as Knox pointed out in his catalogue of the Fogg Museum Tiepolo exhibition, for the ceiling of the parish church of Casale sul Sile, datable about 1773–1778 (*Arte Veneta*, XXI, 1967, p. 230, fig. 293). Given the great rarity of composition drawings by Domenico that can be related to specific commissions, this is an important document, and as well, a specially luminous example of the mature Domenico's draughtsmanship.

PROVENANCE: Monsignor Antidicola, Rome.

BIBLIOGRAPHY: James Byam Shaw, "A Sketch for a Ceiling by Domenico Tiepolo," *Burlington Magazine*, CI, 1959, p. 448, fig. 46.

EXHIBITIONS: Venice, Scholz Exhibition, 1957, no. 75, repr.; Oakland, Scholz Exhibition, 1960, no. 88; Hamburg, Scholz Exhibition, 1963, no. 157, pl. 83; New Haven, Scholz Exhibition, 1964, no. 86; London, Scholz Exhibition, 1968, no. 98, pl. 23; Fogg, Tiepolo Exhibition, 1970, no. 100, repr.

Janos Scholz

252 *Joachim's Offering Refused*

Pen and brown ink, brown, gray, and ochre wash, over black chalk. 18 × 13 15/16 inches (45.7 × 35.4 cm.). Watermark: bow and arrow (or crossbow) over letters A M (see watermark no. 2).

Signed at upper left in pen and brown ink on plaque, *Domenico Tiepolo f*, and in pen and brown ink at left center, *Tiepolo*.

Byam Shaw estimates that after his return from Spain, Domenico produced at least two hundred and fifty drawings in the large format of this fine example and its fellows in the exhibition, most likely as independent "album drawings," the kind of work to which he turned his attention as he painted less and less. The largest single group of the Large Biblical Series is the Recueil Fayet, the 138 sheets bound in the folio volume in the Cabinet des Dessins at the Louvre. In the former collection of M. Cormier of Tours, there were an additional 82.

As related in the Book of James in the Apocryphal New Testament, Joachim's offering was refused because of his childlessness, following which he sojourned in the wilderness in prayer until the Lord hearkened, and he and Anna became the parents of the Virgin Mary.

This sheet provides a classic example of Domenico's technique of covering his entire sheet with a progression of graded washes, reserving only the most strongly highlighted passages that are left in the white of the paper in effects of remarkable brilliance.

PROVENANCE: Charles Fairfax Murray; purchased by J. Pierpont Morgan in London, 1910.

BIBLIOGRAPHY: Fairfax Murray, IV, 145; Otto Benesch, "Domenico Tiepolo, Draughtsman and Painter," *Art Quarterly*, X, 1947, pp. 13 ff., pl. 12; Byam Shaw, *Domenico Tiepolo*, p. 36.

The Pierpont Morgan Library No. IV, 145

253 *The Betrothal of the Virgin*

Pen and brown ink, brown wash, over black chalk. 19 × 15 3/16 inches (48.3 × 38.6 cm.). Slight foxing. Watermark: graduated triple crescents (see watermark no. 18).

Signed in pen and brown ink on column at right of center, *Dom.º Tiepolo f*.

Joseph is here singled out as Mary's successful suitor by the miraculous flowering of his branch while those of the younger men of the House of David remain barren; the Holy Dove hovers above the branch as Joseph clasps the arm of the Virgin in a gesture of espousal.

PROVENANCE: Luzarches, Tours; Roger Cormier, Tours; Cormier sale, Paris, Galerie Georges Petit, April 30, 1921, no. 44; Adrien Fauchier-Magnan, Neuilly-sur-Seine; Fauchier-Magnan sale, London, Sotheby's, December 4, 1935, no. 61.

BIBLIOGRAPHY: Henri Guerlin, *Au Temps du Christ, Giovanni Domenico Tiepolo*, Tours, 1921, p. 94, repr.

EXHIBITIONS: Amsterdam, Rijksmuseum, "Tentoonstelling Van Oude Kunst, Uit Het Bezit Van den Internationalen Handel," 1936, no. 216.

Robert Lehman Collection

254 *The Arrival of the Virgin in Bethlehem*

Pen and brown ink, brown wash, over black chalk. 18 15/16 × 15 inches (48.1 × 38.1 cm.). Several spots. Watermark: graduated triple crescents (see watermark no. 18). Lined.

Signed in pen and brown ink at lower left, *Dom.º Tiepolo f*.

Since the Virgin carries a staff and there is no sign of the Holy Infant, one assumes that the angel has appeared to assist Mary and Joseph in the last stage of their journey to Bethlehem rather than in their flight from the city. The Oriental horseman is one of Domenico's stock figures.

EXHIBITIONS: Cincinnati, Lehman Exhibition, 1959, no. 232.

Robert Lehman Collection

255 *The Flight into Egypt: The Holy Family Leaving Bethlehem*

Pen and brown ink, brown wash, over black chalk. 18 $\frac{7}{16}$ × 14$\frac{1}{4}$ inches (46.8 × 36.2 cm.). Stained at center left. Watermark: bow and arrow (or crossbow) over letters M A (Heawood 878; see watermark no. 3).

Signed in pen and brown ink at lower left, *Dom.º Tiepolo f.*

The story is told that Domenico etched his twenty-four variations on the theme of the Flight into Egypt for the express purpose of demonstrating his originality, which had been called into question by a presumptuous patron (see Byam Shaw, *Domenico Tiepolo*, p. 31). The same subject inspired a number of drawings as well, including ten in the Louvre's Recueil Fayet and three in the Morgan Library.

Joseph still carries his flowering branch or staff as the Holy Family moves through a wooden gate beyond which one glimpses a wellhead and an ordinary Italian farmhouse. The Virgin and her mount are exact repetitions from Domenico's etching De Vesme 7.

PROVENANCE: Charles Fairfax Murray; purchased by J. Pierpont Morgan in London, 1910.

BIBLIOGRAPHY: Fairfax Murray, IV, 146; Benesch, *Venetian Drawings*, no. 43.

EXHIBITIONS: Detroit, Institute of Arts, "Venice 1700–1800, An Exhibition of Venice and the Eighteenth Century," 1952, no. 83.

The Pierpont Morgan Library
No. IV, 146

256 *The Flight into Egypt: The Holy Family Passing a Flock of Sheep*

Pen and brown ink, brown wash, over black chalk. 18$\frac{1}{4}$ × 14$\frac{3}{16}$ inches (46.5 × 36 cm.). Watermark: crowned eagle over letter A (see watermark no. 24).

Signed in pen and brown ink at lower left, *Dom.º Tiepolo f.*

In contrast to the preceding representation in which the setting is an everyday Italian scene, Domenico here introduces as somewhat more exotic notes befitting the subject, a palm tree and a truncated pyramid, the latter also figuring in the etching De Vesme 20 and in the following drawing.

PROVENANCE: Charles Fairfax Murray; purchased by J. Pierpont Morgan in London, 1910.

BIBLIOGRAPHY: Fairfax Murray, IV, 147; Byam Shaw, *Domenico Tiepolo*, p. 36.

EXHIBITIONS: Ames, Iowa, State University of Iowa, "Six Centuries of Master Drawings," 1951, no. 109, repr.

The Pierpont Morgan Library
No. IV, 147

257 *The Flight into Egypt: The Rest*

Pen and brown ink, brown wash, over black chalk. 18$\frac{1}{2}$ × 14$\frac{15}{16}$ inches (47 × 37.9 cm.). Slight foxing. Watermark: letter W below hand holding sword (see watermark no. 45).

Signed in pen and brown ink at lower left, *Dom.º Tiepolo f.*

The scene is that of the Angel bending the branches of the date palm so that the Child may partake of its fruit. The dotted halo is a not infrequent feature in Domenico's religious scenes; it also occurs in triangular form.

PROVENANCE: Luzarches, Tours; Roger Cormier, Tours; Cormier sale, Paris, Galerie Georges Petit, April 30, 1921, possibly no. 54.

Robert Lehman Collection

258 *The Death of St. Joseph*

Pen and brown ink, brown wash, over black chalk. 18$\frac{1}{4}$ × 14$\frac{1}{4}$ inches (46.4 × 36.2 cm.), sight. Repaired tear at left margin; hole above center at left margin; slight foxing.

Signed in pen and brown ink at lower left, *Domo / Tiepolo f.*

In scenes where brick or masonry is used as in this interior, Domenico has no hesitation in lightening his task by extensive use of the ruler.

PROVENANCE: Luzarches, Tours; Roger Cormier, Tours; Cormier sale, Paris, Galerie Georges Petit, April 30, 1921, possibly no. 68.

Dr. and Mrs. Rudolf Heinemann

259 *St. Peter Healing the Lame Man at the Beautiful Gate*

Pen and brown ink, brown wash, over black chalk. 18$\frac{1}{8}$ × 14$\frac{1}{16}$ inches (46 × 35.7 cm.). Watermark: letter W below hand holding sword (see watermark no. 45).

Inscribed by the artist on plaque at right, *Porta / Spetiosa.*

The friezelike arrangement of a crowd of figures in the lower two-fifths of the sheet, leaving a lofty space above, is a compositional device often favored by Domenico in the Large Biblical Series (cf. No. 253). The story of the healing of the lame man is recounted in Acts 3: 1–7.

PROVENANCE: Charles Fairfax Murray; purchased by J. Pierpont Morgan in London, 1910.

BIBLIOGRAPHY: Fairfax Murray, IV, 150; Otto Benesch, "Domenico Tiepolo, Draughtsman and Painter of Architecture," *Art Quarterly*, X, 1947, pp. 13 ff., fig. 2; Byam Shaw, *Domenico Tiepolo*, p. 36.

EXHIBITIONS: New York, Tiepolo Exhibition, 1938, no. 71.

The Pierpont Morgan Library
No. IV, 150

tional wash, almost apricot in hue, to vary the customary browns and grays.

PROVENANCE: Alfred Beurdeley, Paris; sale, London, Sotheby's, July 6, 1967, no. 41, repr.

BIBLIOGRAPHY: Henry de Chennevières, *Les Tiepolos*, Paris, 1898, p. 133; Oswald Kutschera-Woborsky, "Die Fresken der Puritàkapelle in Udine und die Kunst Domenico Tiepolos," *Jahrbuch der Preussischen Kunstsammlungen*, XLI, 1920, p. 183, fig. 19 (wrongly stated to be in the Louvre); Antonio Morassi, "Domenico Tiepolo," *Emporium*, XCIII, 1941, p. 280, repr. (wrongly stated to be in the École des Beaux-Arts, Paris); Byam Shaw, *Domenico Tiepolo*, no. 68, repr.; Morgan Library, *Fifteenth Fellows Report, 1967–1968*, pp. 120–121, repr.; Morgan Library, *A Review of Acquisitions, 1949–1968*, p. 173, repr.

The Pierpont Morgan Library
Gift of the Fellows, 1967.22

260 *Scene of Contemporary Life: At the Dressmaker's*

Pen and brown ink, gray-brown, gray, and ochre wash, over black chalk. 11 5/16 × 16 7/16 inches (28.8 × 41.8 cm.). Watermark: monogram (see watermark no. 40).

Signed in pen and brown ink at lower left, *Dom.⁰ Tiepolo / f. 1791.*

It is in his genre subjects that Domenico, both as painter and as draughtsman, makes his distinctive contribution to the art of eighteenth-century Venice. This diverting composition and the following seven belong to the considerable sequence of finished independent drawings of similar format that mirror the contemporary Venetian scene with delightful wit and an occasional twist of caricature. Some twenty of these contemporary life drawings, like this one and Nos. 261 and 262, are dated 1791, and it seems clear that most of the others were produced in the last decades of the eighteenth century and the first years of the nineteenth.

The fact that the dressmaker's assistant stands by holding a large bundle of what one supposes might be samples of materials suggests that the modiste has come to the house of her client rather than that the tousled young hoyden and her chaperon have traveled to the dressmaker's. Like the more elaborate companion subject, *At the Milliner's* in the Museum of Fine Arts, Boston, the drawing has been given a charming lightness through the use of an addi-

261 *Scene of Contemporary Life: A Visit to a Lawyer*

Pen and brown ink, gray-brown and gray wash, over black chalk. 11 5/16 × 16 1/2 inches (28.7 × 41.9 cm.). Watermark: monogram (see watermark no. 40).

Signed and dated in pen and brown ink at upper left, *. . . om Tiepolo f. / 1791;* variously inscribed by the artist on the papers, books, and folios.

The older man and woman sitting at opposite ends of the document-strewn table, she in the company of a foppish young gentleman, are clearly parties to a dispute involving their private life. The inscription on a document held by the clerk on the left would seem to indicate that the matter will be settled out of court to the advantage of the complacent young man. In any event, the rakish lawyer, informally attired in dressing gown and cap, does not stand to lose whatever the outcome.

As a part of the setting, Domenico shows a framed representation of the Virgin and Child similar to the compositions he and his father used in their paintings. The spatial ambiguity in the right background suggests that the draughtsman laid down his pen before he had completed the window at the right through which one is intended to glimpse the large building outside.

PROVENANCE: Alfred Beurdeley, Paris; sale, London, Sotheby's, July 6, 1967, no. 52, repr.

BIBLIOGRAPHY: Byam Shaw, *Domenico Tiepolo*, p. 48; Morgan Library, *Fifteenth Fellows Report, 1967–1968*, pp. 120–121; Morgan Library, *A Review of Acquisitions, 1949–1968*, p. 173.

The Pierpont Morgan Library
Gift of the Fellows, 1967.23

262 *Scene of Contemporary Life: A School*

Pen and brown ink, brown and gray wash, over black chalk. $14\frac{1}{2} \times 19\frac{3}{4}$ inches (36.8 × 50.2 cm.). Small stains. Watermark: graduated triple crescents over letters IM . . . RIAL (see watermark no. 20).

Signed and dated in pen and light brown ink at upper right, *Tiepolo 1791*; signed again in pen and dark brown ink at upper right, *Dom.º Tiepolo f.*

On a raised platform at the left, the aged reading master hears the lesson of a young disciple while another less successful reader kneels beside him wearing a dunce's cap. Across the room, older pupils sit at a table practising their penmanship under the supervision of the bespectacled writing master. Other pupils, some with their parents, await their turn in a sequence of amusing back views that may well have had their inspiration in Giovanni Battista's volumes of caricatures, from which Domenico openly lifted an occasional figure. As is sometimes the case, Domenico has here signed twice.

PROVENANCE: Henry Oppenheimer, London; Granville Tyser, London.

BIBLIOGRAPHY: K. T. Parker, "Giovanni Domenico Tiepolo," *Old Master Drawings*, VI, December 1931, p. 49, pl. 42; Byam Shaw, *Domenico Tiepolo*, p. 63, note 6.

EXHIBITIONS: London, Royal Academy, 1953, no. 190; London, P. & D. Colnaghi, "Old Master Drawings," 1960, no. 15, pl. X.

Robert Lehman Collection

263 *Scene of Contemporary Life: The Acrobats*

Pen and brown ink, brown wash, over slight traces of black chalk. $16\frac{3}{8} \times 11\frac{3}{8}$ inches (41.6 × 28.9 cm.).

Unidentified collector's mark stamped in red at lower right of verso.

Byam Shaw points out that the two men turning somersaults, the plumed leading lady holding a fan, and two of the spectators in the background recur almost exactly in a similar scene painted by Domenico in the Villa Tiepolo at Zianigo and now in the

Ca' Rezzonico, Venice (G. Lorenzetti, *Ca' Rezzonico*, Venice, 1938, pl. 75). The drawing, though not dated, may be assigned like the other Scenes of Contemporary Life to 1791; the fresco probably dates from 1793.

PROVENANCE: Alfred Beurdeley, Paris; M. Fauchier-Magnan, Paris (according to Byam Shaw); purchased in London by the Metropolitan Museum, 1968.

BIBLIOGRAPHY: Byam Shaw, *Domenico Tiepolo*, p. 86, no. 65, repr.; *Metropolitan Museum Bulletin*, February 1969, p. 318, repr.

The Metropolitan Museum of Art
Rogers Fund, 68.54.4

264 *Scene of Contemporary Life: The Presentation of the Fiancée*

Pen and brown ink, gray wash, over black chalk. $11\frac{5}{16} \times 16$ inches (28.7 × 40.6 cm.), sight.

The charms of the young lady on display here obviously meet with the unqualified approval of the large woman seated with a small boy at her side. Presumably, she is the young lady's prospective mother-in-law. The subject—which has also been described as The Matchmaker—provides an interesting and perhaps intentional contrast with the mood of the following drawing in which there is a less cordial reception for the fiancé. The squat figure of the maid on the left, perhaps a hunchback, is a replica of Domenico's red and white chalk drawing from the Gatteri sketchbook in the Correr Museum, Venice (repr. G. Lorenzetti, *Quaderno dei Tiepolo . . .*, Venice, 1946, no. 75).

PROVENANCE: Martin Wilson.

Dr. and Mrs. Rudolf Heinemann

265 *Scene of Contemporary Life: The Presentation of the Fiancé*

Pen and gray-brown ink, gray wash, over black chalk. $14\frac{5}{8} \times 19\frac{3}{4}$ inches (37.2 × 50.2 cm.). Some spots of wash in upper half of sheet; brown spot at left margin. Watermark: crescent above crown and H F IMPERIAL (Heawood 884; see watermark no. 22).

Numbered in black chalk at upper left corner, *7 H* [?].

Neither the apparently enceinte woman nor her small spaniel appear to welcome the diffident suitor approaching, nosegay in hand, in the company of his young lady. The couple would seem to be considering the matrimonial experience, of which the pregnant woman's downturned mouth, just visible beneath the rim of her great bonnet, suggests a jaundiced view on her part.

PROVENANCE: Sale, London, Sotheby's, November 11, 1965, no. 26.

BIBLIOGRAPHY: "Quelques Tableaux et dessins vénitiens du XVIIIe siècle," *L'Oeil*, March 1967, no. 147, p. 12, repr.

Mr. and Mrs. Eugene Victor Thaw

266 *Scene of Contemporary Life: Two Ladies with Their Cavaliers before a Fountain*

Pen and brown ink, brown wash, over black chalk. $11\frac{1}{2} \times 16\frac{3}{8}$ inches (29.2 × 41.6 cm.), sight.

Signed in pen and brown ink at lower right, *Domo Tiepolo f.*

The two ladies seated in a sculpture garden before a modified version of Palladio's Villa Rotonda are, together with their cavaliers, almost exact counterparts of the spectators studying the sculptures in the *Actaeon Statue* (repr. Byam Shaw, *Domenico Tiepolo*, no. 69), a drawing Byam Shaw dates about 1800 on the basis of the ladies' costume. Indeed, the two drawings might be considered a pair. The same two ladies also appear in the *Café on the Quay-Side* (repr. Byam Shaw, *Domenico Tiepolo*, no. 71). Hercules' androgynous opponent in the fountain group is possibly meant to be the Queen of the Amazons, although there is no sign of the girdle the hero steals from her; if the opponent is regarded as Antaeus, it is strange that Hercules pins him to the earth, which is the source of his strength, rather than holds him aloft.

PROVENANCE: Sale, London, Sotheby's, November 11, 1965, no. 25, repr.

Mrs. Douglas Williams

267 *Scene of Contemporary Life: Bagpiper, with a Bear, Passing Peasants on a Mountain Road*

Pen and brown ink, brown wash, over black chalk. $11\frac{3}{4} \times 16\frac{9}{16}$ inches (29.8 × 42.1 cm.). Watermark: bow and arrow (or crossbow) above the letters M A (Heawood 878; see watermark no. 3).

Domenico's representations of the contemporary scene include subjects drawn from the life of the peasants or the gypsies on the Venetian mainland. He devoted several sheets to itinerant showmen like the present bagpiper leading a bear on a rope. The identical animal, in fact, occurs in *Dancing Bears and Monkeys*, formerly in the Beurdeley collection (repr. Byam Shaw, no. 64).

PROVENANCE: Tomas Harris, London.

BIBLIOGRAPHY: Byam Shaw, *Domenico Tiepolo*, p. 48.

EXHIBITIONS: London, Royal Academy, 1953, no. 172.

Robert Lehman Collection

268 *Resting Traveler Watching Dogs at Play*

Pen and brown ink, brown wash, over black chalk. $11\frac{7}{8} \times 16\frac{5}{8}$ inches (30.2 × 42.2 cm.). Watermark: monogram (see watermark no. 40).

Signed in pen and brown ink at lower right, *Dom. Tiepolo f.*

Verso: Black chalk tracing of barking dog at right on recto.

A surprisingly large number of Domenico's drawings are devoted to animal subjects that he usually drew, as Byam Shaw has demonstrated, not from life but from such sources as the prints of Stefano della Bella or of an animalier like Johann Elias Ridinger of Augsburg. Many are renderings of one or two individual animals, but there are, as well, large compositions with landscape backgrounds as in this assemblage of gamboling dogs. Domenico often depicted the whippet or Italian grayhound, which appears here in the coy group in the center foreground. The pair of dogs on the hillock at the top of the sheet also occurs in a drawing at the Ashmolean Museum, Oxford (Byam Shaw, *Domenico Tiepolo*, pl. 50).

Robert Lehman Collection

269 The Marriage Feast of Punchinello's Parents

Pen and brown ink, brown wash, over black chalk. $13\frac{7}{8}$ $\times 18\frac{9}{16}$ inches (35.2 $\times$ 47.2 cm.). No. 5 of the series. Foxing throughout sheet; creases and some abrasions at upper right. Watermark: monogram (see watermark no. 41).

Signed in pen and brown ink at lower right, *Dom.º Tiepolo f*; numbered in pen and brown ink at upper left, *5*.

The latest and most complete of all Domenico's various series of drawings is the celebrated Punchinello cycle of 104 drawings, which he entitled *Divertimento per li Regazzi (Entertainment for Children)*. The series was produced at the very end of the artist's life, probably just a few years before his death in 1804 when he was living in retirement in the family villa at Zianigo. There he had earlier (1793) frescoed the "Camera dei Pagliacci" with scenes of the daily life of Punchinello and his fellows. The hero of the drawing series is also this Italian comedy character, who was first introduced on the stage by the Neapolitan actor Silvio Fiorillo around 1600. His history as illustrated by Domenico follows no known text.

At some point, the drawings were numbered in the upper left margin, whether by Domenico or his heirs is not known, but Byam Shaw points out that the order of the original sequence was probably somewhat different. In several instances drawings that would appear to belong to one category of subjects sometimes have numbers that place them out of character. The drawings of the present exhibition are listed in the order of their old numbers in the series with three exceptions.

Byam Shaw suggests that this drawing, which as no. 5 comes very early in the sequence, represents the wedding banquet, not of Punchinello himself, but of his parents. It looks back to the great feasts of Veronese. A drawing of the same subject, with the diners identically arranged but without the presence of the Punchinellos, was sold at Sotheby's in 1965 (repr. sale, November 11, 1965, no. 19).

PROVENANCE: Anonymous collection, London; sale, London, Sotheby's, July 6, 1920, part of lot 41; Richard Owen, Paris; W. W. Crocker; San Francisco Art Association.

BIBLIOGRAPHY: Byam Shaw, *Domenico Tiepolo*, p. 58; Janos Scholz, "Visiting Venetian Drawings at the National Gallery," *Art Quarterly*, XXVII, 1964, p. 195, fig. 1.

Mr. and Mrs. Eugene Victor Thaw

270 The Pregnancy of Punchinello's Mother

Pen and brown ink, brown wash, over black chalk. $13\frac{7}{8}$ $\times 18\frac{7}{16}$ inches (35.2 $\times$ 46.8 cm.). No. 15 of the series. Slight foxing. Watermark: crescent (see watermark no. 13).

Signed in pen and brown ink at lower left, *Dom.º Tiepolo f*; numbered in pen and brown ink at upper left corner, *15*.

This subject has also been identified as the Indisposition of Punchinello's Mistress, but its early number places it with the group of drawings Byam Shaw puts together under the heading "The Ancestry, Childhood and Youthful Amusements of Punchinello."

PROVENANCE: Anonymous collection, London; sale, London, Sotheby's, July 6, 1920, part of lot 41; Richard Owen, Paris.

BIBLIOGRAPHY: Antonio Morassi, "Domenico Tiepolo," *Emporium*, XCIII, 1941, p. 279, repr.; Byam Shaw, *Domenico Tiepolo*, p. 56, note 3.

EXHIBITIONS: Chicago, Tiepolo Exhibition, 1938, no. 104.

Robert Lehman Collection

271 Punchinello as a Baby in Bed with His Parents

Pen and brown ink, brown wash, over black chalk. $13\frac{13}{16}$ $\times 18\frac{3}{8}$ inches (35.1 $\times$ 46.7 cm.). No. 8 of the series. Foxing. Watermark: coat of arms (see watermark no. 10).

Numbered in pen and brown ink at upper left corner, *8*.

The presence of Punchinello's father in the bed is the only irregular note in this scene that harks back to traditional representations of biblical birth scenes. Punchinello begins life as an ordinary-looking infant, only his rather large nose indicating the shape of things to come. When he is wrapped in his swaddling clothes, apparently held here by the taller of the maidservants, he will be wearing a mask (see the *Nursing of Punchinello*, formerly in the Reitlinger collection, which Byam Shaw reproduces as plate 84). The figure of the veiled woman seated at the right is an instance of Domenico's numerous borrowings from himself; she occurs earlier as the duenna in *At the Dressmaker's*, 1791 (No. 260).

PROVENANCE: Anonymous collection, London; sale, London, Sotheby's, July 6, 1920, part of lot 41; Richard Owen, Paris.

BIBLIOGRAPHY: Byam Shaw, *Domenico Tiepolo*, indirect reference on p. 55.

Robert Lehman Collection

272 Punchinello Takes Part in a "Triumph of Flora"

Pen and brown ink, brown wash, over black chalk. 11½ × 16¼ inches (29.2 × 41.3 cm.). No. 26 of the series.

Domenico amused himself by parodying his father's *Triumph of Flora*, the painting commissioned in 1743 by Francesco Algarotti for Count Brühl, which is now in the M. H. de Young Memorial Museum, San Francisco (Morassi, 1962, fig. 354). He may have had before him the engraving by G. Leonardis (1766) after Algarotti's watercolor *ricordo* of the picture Giambattista had painted when Domenico was still in his teens.

PROVENANCE: Anonymous collection, London; sale, London, Sotheby's, July 6, 1920, part of lot 41; Richard Owen, Paris; Countess Wachtmeister; sale, London, Sotheby's, December 15, 1954, no. 107, repr.; Tomas Harris, London.

EXHIBITIONS: London, Arts Council, Tiepolo Exhibition, 1955, no. 67, pl. III.

Dr. and Mrs. Rudolf Heinemann

273 Punchinello Riding an Ass in a Procession of His Fellows

Pen and brown ink, brown and yellow-brown wash, over black chalk. 10¾ × 15⅞ inches (27.3 × 40.3 cm.), sight. No. 28 of the series. Crease at lower left margin; water stain at lower right.

Signed in pen and brown ink at lower left, *D. Tiepolo f.*

The presence of the antique altar at the left suggests some kind of mock ceremonial rite to which Punchinello either contributes—or from which he removes—the morsel he brandishes on a fork.

PROVENANCE: Anonymous collection, London; sale, London, Sotheby's, July 6, 1920, part of lot 41; Richard Owen, Paris; Brinsley Ford, London; sale, London, November 10, 1954, no. 40, repr.

EXHIBITIONS: London, Whitechapel Art Gallery / Birmingham, Museum and Art Gallery, "Eighteenth Century in Venice," 1951, no. 138e.

Dr. and Mrs. Rudolf Heinemann

274 Punchinello Felling a Tree

Pen and brown ink, brown wash, over black chalk. 13 15/16 × 18⅝ inches (35.4 × 47.3 cm.). No. 40 of the series. Watermark: graduated triple crescents (see watermark no. 19).

Signed in pen and brown ink at lower left, *Dom.º Tiepolo f*; numbered in pen and brown ink at upper left corner, *40*.

The drum in the foreground and the sprinkling of girls in the crowd of Punchinellos might indicate that the tree felling was an occasion for merrymaking as well as the gathering of wood. Punchinello, his axe on his shoulder, rests his foot on a neat bundle of faggots.

PROVENANCE: Anonymous collection, London; sale, London, Sotheby's, July 6, 1920, part of lot 41; Richard Owen, Paris; sale, Paris, Palais Galliéra, December 6, 1966, no. 11, repr.

Robert Lehman Collection

275 Punchinellos Resting Outside the Circus

Pen and brown ink, brown wash, over black chalk. 13¾ × 18¼ inches (34.9 × 46.4 cm.). No. 50 of the series. Water stain at upper left. Watermark: crescent (see watermark no. 13).

Signed in pen and brown ink on paper attached to fence, *Domº Tiepolo f*; numbered in pen and brown ink at upper left corner, *50*.

At least one of the spectators standing outside the circus is peering through a crack or knothole in the wooden barrier for a preliminary glimpse of the elephant advertised on the placard at the upper center and fully seen in the following drawing. Byam Shaw points out that the boy with the lantern on the left occurs earlier in two Contemporary Life scenes, the *Arrival by Gondola* in Rotterdam and the drawing sold at Sotheby's on July 6, 1967, as lot 43.

PROVENANCE: Anonymous collection, London; sale, London, Sotheby's, July 6, 1920, part of lot 41; Richard Owen, Paris; sale, Paris, Hôtel Drouot, March 19, 1965, no. 72, pl. VI.

BIBLIOGRAPHY: Byam Shaw, *Domenico Tiepolo*, p. 56.

EXHIBITIONS: Paris, Musée Carnavalet, "Chefs-d'oeuvre des collections parisiennes," 1950, no. 147.

Robert Lehman Collection

276 *Punchinello with an Elephant*

Pen and brown ink, brown and ochre wash, over black chalk. $11\frac{5}{8} \times 16\frac{3}{16}$ inches (29.4 × 41.1 cm.). Slight foxing. Watermark: graduated triple crescents (see watermark no. 16).

Signed in pen and brown ink on scroll at upper center, *Dom.º Tiepolo*; numbered in pen and brown ink on verso at lower left corner, *4*.

This drawing, which does not carry one of the old series numbers, came to the Morgan Library with the Fairfax Murray collection in 1910 and so was not, like the others exhibited here, among the series of 102 Punchinello drawings (plus the title page) sold at Sotheby's on July 6, 1920, as lot 41. The possibility remains, however, that originally it may have been a part of the series and was detached from the group some time prior to 1910. Although the title page of the series, which is now in the Nelson Gallery, Kansas City, specifies *Carte no. 104*, only 103 drawings, including the title page, were sold at Sotheby's in 1920. It is, in any case, a very logical companion for the preceding drawing and the others of circus scenes. According to Byam Shaw, the drawings numbered 38–39 and 45–46 of the series also depict circus subjects.

PROVENANCE: Charles Fairfax Murray; purchased by J. Pierpont Morgan in London, 1910.

BIBLIOGRAPHY: Helen B. Harkonen, *Circuses and Fairs in Art*, Minneapolis, 1965, pp. 24–25, repr.; Byam Shaw, *Domenico Tiepolo*, pp. 52, note 1, 56.

EXHIBITIONS: Chicago, Tiepolo Exhibition, 1938, no. 113.

The Pierpont Morgan Library
No. IV, 151b

277 *Punchinello as a Tailor's Assistant*

Pen and brown ink, brown wash, over black chalk. $13\frac{7}{8} \times 18\frac{9}{16}$ inches (35.2 × 47.2 cm.). No. 55 of the series. Slight foxing. Watermark: graduated triple crescents (see watermark no. 19).

Signed in pen and brown ink at lower left, *Domº Tiepolo f*; numbered in pen and brown ink at upper left corner, *55*.

This and the two following drawings belong to the group that Byam Shaw entitles "Punchinello's Var-

ious Trades and Occupations." He also appears as peddler, barber, carpenter, tavern keeper, and schoolmaster. Here he tries his hand at measuring and cutting a length of cloth.

PROVENANCE: Anonymous collection, London; sale, London, Sotheby's, July 6, 1920, part of lot 41; Richard Owen, Paris.

BIBLIOGRAPHY: Byam Shaw, *Domenico Tiepolo*, no. 88, repr.

Robert Lehman Collection

278 *Punchinello as a Dressmaker*

Pen and brown ink, brown wash, over black chalk. $13\frac{7}{8} \times 18\frac{7}{16}$ inches (35.2 × 46.8 cm.). No. 12 of the series. Watermark: graduated triple crescents (close to watermark no. 18).

Numbered in pen and brown ink at upper left corner, *12*.

While Punchinello fits the new dress on his stocky client in a rococo interior, his assistant carries off the old garments made of the familiar striped Venetian stuff, of which Domenico seldom fails to include a length as a skirt, a waistcoat, a jacket, hose, a scarf, an Oriental's robe, or camel's saddle cloth. This and Nos. 259 and 271 are among the few instances in which Domenico neglected to sign his finished work.

PROVENANCE: Anonymous collection, London; sale, London, Sotheby's, July 6, 1920, part of lot 41; Richard Owen, Paris.

BIBLIOGRAPHY: Byam Shaw, *Domenico Tiepolo*, p. 56.

Robert Lehman Collection

279 *Punchinello as a Portrait Painter*

Pen and brown ink, brown and yellow-brown wash, over black chalk. $12 \times 16\frac{3}{4}$ inches (30.5 × 42.6 cm.). No. 70 of the series. Slight foxing; dark brown stain on easel.

Signed in pen and brown ink at lower left, *Domo Tiepolo f*.

In a composition blending faint reminiscences of his father's paintings of Alexander and Campaspe in the Studio of Apelles (Morassi, 1955, colorplate II; 1962, fig. 284), Domenico shows Punchinello taking the measure of a sitter who seems to be identical with the "Flora" of No. 272. At the right, his assistant grinds the colors. In no. 71 of the series Punchinello appears as a painter of histories.

PROVENANCE: Anonymous collection, London; sale, London, Sotheby's, July 6, 1920, part of lot 41; Richard Owen, Paris; Robert Goelet, New York; sale, London, Sotheby's, July 6, 1967, no. 38, repr.

BIBLIOGRAPHY: Byam Shaw, *Domenico Tiepolo*, under no. 89.

Mr. and Mrs. Jacob M. Kaplan

280 *Punchinello Retrieving Dead Fowl from a Well*

Pen and brown ink, brown wash, over black chalk. 13 13⁄16 ×18 7⁄16 inches (35.1×46.8 cm.). No. 83 of the series. Watermark: graduated triple crescents (see watermark no. 19).

Signed in pen and brown ink at lower right, *Dom⁰ Tiepolo f.*; numbered in pen and brown ink at upper left corner, *83*.

The miscreant responsible for this incident may well be the small Punchinello who is being unceremoniously removed from the scene at the right. The gesture of the young woman suggests that the fowl have been in the well for some time.

PROVENANCE: Anonymous collection, London; sale, London, Sotheby's, July 6, 1920, part of lot 41; Richard Owen, Paris.

BIBLIOGRAPHY: Tancred Borenius, "Illustrierte Berichte," *Pantheon*, III, 1929, p. 194, repr.; Antonio Morassi, "Domenico Tiepolo," *Emporium*, XCIII, 1941, p. 280, repr. p. 277.

EXHIBITIONS: Chicago, Tiepolo Exhibition, 1938, no. 112; Cincinnati, Lehman Exhibition, 1959, no. 233, repr.

Robert Lehman Collection

281 *Punchinello at a Flogging*

Pen and brown ink, brown wash, over black chalk; several of the masks touched in yellow-brown wash. 13 15⁄16× 18½ inches (35.4×47 cm.). No. 85 of the series. Watermark: crowned eagle above letters G F A (see watermark no. 23).

Signed in pen and brown ink at lower right, *Dom⁰ Tiepolo f*; numbered in pen and brown ink at upper left corner, *85*.

Since its old number closely follows that of the preceding drawing, it is logical to assume that the

punishment meted out here is a consequence of the action there. The Punchinello being publicly flogged, however, is clearly not the small personage of the other drawing. The figure at the far right is identically posed in No. 275.

PROVENANCE: Anonymous collection, London; sale, London, Sotheby's, July 6, 1920, part of lot 41; Richard Owen, Paris; sale, Paris, Palais Galliéra, December 6, 1966, no. 10, repr.

Robert Lehman Collection

282 *Punchinellos Picking Fruit and Quarreling in a Garden*

Pen and brown ink, brown wash, over black chalk. 11½ ×16 inches (29.2×40.6 cm.), sight. No. 88 of the series. Light foxing in upper half of the sheet.

Signed in pen and brown ink at lower right, *Dom.⁰ Tiepolo f.*

This scene of pilfering at the edge of a charming villa garden is notably fresh in its preservation.

PROVENANCE: Anonymous collection, London; sale, London, Sotheby's, July 6, 1920, part of lot 41; Richard Owen, Paris.

EXHIBITIONS: Poughkeepsie, New York, Vassar College, "Drawings and Watercolors from Alumnae and Their Families," 1961, no. 69, repr.

Mr. and Mrs. E. Powis Jones

283 *Burial of Punchinello*

Pen and brown ink, brown wash, over black chalk; several of the masks touched in yellow-brown wash. 13 15⁄16× 18⅝ inches (35.4×47.3 cm.). No. 103 of the series. Slight foxing. Watermark: graduated triple crescents (see watermark no. 18).

Signed in pen and brown ink at lower left, *Dom.⁰ Tiepolo f.*; numbered in pen and brown ink at upper left, *103*.

The end of Punchinello's story is heralded in the drawing numbered 82, formerly in the collection of Sir Osbert Sitwell, in which he suffers a seizure. Thenceforth, he declines until he is seen on his death bed attended by doctors with asses' ears and then by priests administering the Sacrament. In the drawing numbered 100, his coffin is placed on the funeral gondola for transport to the place of burial represented here.

PROVENANCE: Anonymous collection, London; sale, London, Sotheby's, July 6, 1920, part of lot 41; Richard Owen, Paris; Léon Suzor, Paris; sale, Paris, Hôtel Drouot, March 19, 1965, no. 70, repr.

EXHIBITIONS: Paris, Musée Carnavalet, "Chefs-d'oeuvre des collections parisiennes," 1950, no. 151.

Robert Lehman Collection

284 *Apparition of Punchinello's Skeleton at His Tomb*

Pen and brown ink, brown wash, over black chalk. 12 × 16⅞ inches (30.5 × 42.9 cm.), sight. No. 102 of the series.

Signed in pen and brown ink at lower right corner, *Do: Tiepolo f.*

Byam Shaw has recently noted in correspondence that in this scene of Punchinello's macabre curtain call, Domenico freely adapted the motif of the skeleton crawling up to the tomb from an engraving by Giorgio Ghisi after G. B. Bertano dated 1554 (Bartsch, XV, p. 413, no 69). The caryatid on the tomb corresponds exactly to that detail in the print.

PROVENANCE: Anonymous collection, London; sale, London, Sotheby's, July 6, 1920, part of lot 41; Richard Owen, Paris; Léon Suzor, Paris; sale, Paris, Hôtel Drouot, March 19, 1965, no. 71.

EXHIBITIONS: Paris, Musée Carnavalet, "Chefs-d'oeuvre des collections parisiennes," 1950, no. 152.

Mr. and Mrs. Jacob M. Kaplan

Francesco Casanova
London 1727–Brühl (Vienna) 1802

285 *Pastoral Landscape*

Brush and brown wash, over black chalk. 18⅝ × 23¹¹⁄₁₆ inches (47.3 × 60.2 cm.). The decorative border, washed in green, is drawn on the sheet itself. Several spots. Lined.

Francesco Casanova was nearly as peripatetic as his celebrated elder brother, the writer and adventurer Jacopo Casanova. Born in England of Italian parents, Francesco's first artistic training was Italian, but he worked in Dresden and in Paris, where he was admitted to the Académie Royale in 1763. His specialties were many, but he is best known for his battle and genre scenes, in which the influence of Jacques Courtois matches that of Dutch painting of the seventeenth century. In the present drawing the example of Nicolaes Berchem is apparent in the feathery chalk line that contrasts so happily with transparent, atmospheric brown wash.

The green wash bordering band surrounding the drawing was drawn by the artist himself on the original sheet, and the presence of this autograph "mount" testifies that the landscape was executed as an end in itself rather than as a preparatory study for a picture, a custom that becomes increasingly current as the eighteenth century goes on.

Robert and Bertina Suida Manning

Ubaldo Gandolfi
S. Matteo della Decima 1728–Ravenna 1781

286 *Design for a Door Knocker*

Pen and brown ink, brown wash, over black chalk. 11⅝ × 8¼ inches (29.5 × 21 cm.). Several stains; small tears at margins; slight foxing. Watermark: anchor in a circle with letters B M below.

Inscribed in red chalk at lower right, *G. Bologna*; on verso in pen and brown ink, *Gand:*.

The mistaken attribution of this ornamental design to the sixteenth-century sculptor Giambologna is understandable; the scheme, involving a male head biting the tails of two dolfins, who in turn bite the head of an anguished man below, might be considered a typically mannerist conceit. The draughtsmanship, however, has nothing to do with that of Giambologna, and it was J. Byam Shaw who recognized here the hand of the eighteenth-century Bolognese Ubaldo Gandolfi, himself a designer of amusing ornamental schemes. It is sometimes difficult to distinguish the pen drawings of Ubaldo from those of his younger brother Gaetano (see Nos. 289, 290, and 291), but those of Ubaldo often have the rather wiry elegance that characterizes this sheet.

EXHIBITIONS: Poughkeepsie, New York, Vassar College, "Drawings and Watercolors from Alumnae and Their Families," 1961, no. 19, repr. (as Giambologna).

Mr. and Mrs. A. Hyatt Mayor

Pier Antonio Novelli
Venice 1729–Venice 1804

287 *Bacchante with Two Infant Fauns*

Pen and brown ink. 15 5/16 × 9 13/16 inches (38.9 × 24.9 cm.). Lined.

Inscribed in pen and dark brown ink at center of lower margin: *Pierantonio Novelli Veneziano.*

Although Novelli's paintings are to be seen hanging in Venetian churches, and he worked diligently as a book illustrator, he appears nowhere to better advantage than in a finished drawing like this one vouched for by the "Reliable Venetian Hand" in the inscription at the lower center. He was a pupil of Diziani, but his extensive use of close parallel hatching in airy, rhythmic patterns recalls similar effects in Fontebasso's draughtsmanship.

PROVENANCE: "Reliable Venetian Hand" (Lugt 3005c–d); Charles Fairfax Murray; purchased by J. Pierpont Morgan in London, 1910.

BIBLIOGRAPHY: Fairfax Murray, IV, 153, repr. (as F. Novelli).

EXHIBITIONS: Venice, Disegni di una collezione veneziana del Settecento, 1966, no. 179, repr.

The Pierpont Morgan Library
No. IV, 153

Fedele Fischetti
Naples 1734–Naples 1789

288 *Design for a Ceiling: The Age of Gold*

Pen, black and gray ink, gray wash, over traces of black chalk. 13 5/8 × 18 1/8 inches (34.6 × 46 cm.). Rose-colored wash over inscription at lower left. Several spots and stains; upper margin cut to shape of arch.

Inscribed in pen and brown ink at lower left, *Volta dipinta nella stanza di Conversazione del Real Palazzo di Caserta: F.F. Inv.*

As the old inscription points out, this is a study for a ceiling fresco in one of the small rooms in the Queen's Apartments in the royal palace at Caserta, where Saturn is seen surrounded by festive nymphs and youths. Fischetti, a late eighteenth-century Neapolitan decorator who worked extensively at Caserta, verges on the neoclassical as painter and

draughtsman, but his pen line derives from the elegant example of Solimena.

BIBLIOGRAPHY: *Disegni napoletani del Sei e del Settecento nel Museo di Capodimonte* (exhibition catalogue by Walter Vitzthum), Naples, Museo di Capodimonte, 1966, mentioned p. 42.

EXHIBITIONS: New York, Finch College Museum of Art, "In the Shadow of Vesuvius, Neapolitan Drawings from the Collection of Janos Scholz," 1969, no. 57, repr.

Janos Scholz

Gaetano Gandolfi
S. Matteo della Decima 1734–Bologna 1802

289 *Noah*

Black chalk, stumped, heightened with white, on buff paper. 16 3/8 × 12 3/16 inches (41.6 × 30.8 cm.). Overall foxing; small losses at upper left edge, center left edge, and upper right corner; abrasion. Watermark: word PONTECCHIO on a banner.

This and the following drawing are typical of the felicitous chalk draughtsmanship with its easy control of the figure that marks Gaetano as the very last of the followers of the Carracci. Both drawings are studies for the fresco decoration of the cupola of S. Maria della Vita at Bologna, executed between 1776 and 1779.

PROVENANCE: Purchased by the Morgan Library in London, 1957.

BIBLIOGRAPHY: Morgan Library, *Ninth Fellows Report, 1958–1959*, p. 110; Morgan Library, *A Review of Acquisitions, 1949–1968*, p. 147.

EXHIBITIONS: London, P. & D. Colnaghi, "Old Master Drawings," 1957, no. 23.

The Pierpont Morgan Library
Gift of the Fellows, 1957.9

290 *Joshua*

Black chalk, heightened with white, on beige paper. 16 1/2 × 12 3/16 inches (41.9 × 31 cm.). Several creases; repairs at left and right margins. Lined.

See No. 289. Joshua is identified by the sun reflected in his shield, a reference to the day when the Lord fought for Israel and "the sun stood still and the moon stayed, until the people had avenged themselves upon their enemies" (Joshua 10: 12–14). Mr. Gurney also owns a further study for the cupola fresco of S. Maria della Vita, Bologna, the figure of a turbaned prophet, seen from behind, seated on clouds, and there is yet another of angels in the Morgan Library (Inv. 1957.8). Other drawings for the same project are in the Ashmolean Museum, Oxford.

Donald P. Gurney

291 *Apelles Painting Campaspe*

Black chalk, heightened with white, on brownish paper. 12 1/16 × 16 7/8 inches (30.6 × 42.9 cm.). Foxing. Watermark: anchor in a circle with a star above and the initials G L below.

Inscribed in black chalk on verso, *G. Gfi f. 1797.*

The figures here have a smooth, porcelainlike finish that gives them a suitably neoclassic air. Gandolfi simplified Bolognese academic methods of draughtsmanship that went back to the example of the Carracci, reducing these methods to a series of intelligent, attractive, if rather superficial conventions. The drawing was one of a series of four composition drawings, exhibited together in London in 1962. The others represent the Rape of the Sabines, the Death of Germanicus, and Tullia Driving over the Body of Her Father. An earlier representation, dated 1793, of the present subject with notable variants in the composition was in a private collection in Bologna (Lidia Bianchi, *I Gandolfi*, Rome, 1936, pl. XLVIII).

PROVENANCE: Purchased by the Metropolitan Museum in London, 1962.

EXHIBITIONS: London, P. & D. Colnaghi, "Old Master Drawings," 1962, no. 22.

The Metropolitan Museum of Art
Rogers Fund, 62.132.3

Lorenzo Baldissera Tiepolo
Venice 1736–Madrid 1776

292 *Head of a Bearded Man in a Turban*

Black and white chalk, on gray paper. 15 7/16 × 11 inches (39.2 × 27.9 cm.). Waterstains; losses at three corners. Lined.

Among the hundreds of chalk drawings surviving

from the studio of the Tiepolos, scholars have in recent years assigned a certain number to Giambattista's younger son Lorenzo. Usually these drawings are studies of heads, executed in varying combinations of red, black, and white chalks, sometimes with the addition of blue; some, like the *Head of St. Anne* in the Scholz collection, New York (repr. Fogg, Tiepolo Exhibition, 1970, no. 69), and a drawing in the Rasini collection, Milan, are inscribed with Lorenzo's name in an old hand. The Morgan drawing was assigned to Lorenzo by Terisio Pignatti on the basis of its relationship to two works: a painting of an Oriental he attributed to Lorenzo in the Ca' Rezzonico (repr., *Mostra del Tiepolo*, Venice, 1951, no. 71) and a superior drawing of the same subject at Weimar, presumably Lorenzo's model, which he attributes to Giambattista. For a second Morgan drawing attributed to Lorenzo (Inv. IV, 144) and various others in American and European collections, see Knox's catalogue of the 1970 Fogg exhibition (nos. 63–69).

PROVENANCE: See No. 64.

BIBLIOGRAPHY: Pignatti, *Disegni veneziani*, p. 214, pl. 121; Fogg, Tiepolo Exhibition, 1970, under nos. 66–67.

The Pierpont Morgan Library
No. IV, 144a

Jacopo Palmieri
Bologna 1737–Turin 1809

293 *Trompe-l'Oeil Exercise: A Group of Prints*

Pen and brown ink, brown wash. 16 1/4 × 22 1/16 inches (41.3 × 56 cm.).

Signed and dated in pen and brown ink left of center, *P. Palmieri Fece 1766*, at lower left, *Pietro Giacomo Palmieri Disegnò a Penna L'anno 1766*; various inscriptions by Palmieri identifying prints represented.

An amusing graphic tour de force by the Piedmontese Palmieri who, not surprisingly, was professor of draughtsmanship at the University of Turin. The prints that figure here, inscribed with the signatures of Berchem, Della Bella, Callot, and Jean Pesne, are in most cases not exact "reproductions." Palmieri has, for example, added an earring to Della Bella's mustachioed Turk, and the Jean

Pesne *View of a Lake with Bathers* is a pastiche of a reproductive print after Guercino. In No. 294 Palmieri includes for good measure three prints that he attributes, in their inscriptions, to himself.

PROVENANCE: Sir Bruce Ingram (Lugt S. 1405a on old mount); Carl Winter (his mark, *CWR*, at lower right); sale, London, Sotheby's, July 1, 1965, no. 82; purchased by the Metropolitan Museum in New York, 1969.

The Metropolitan Museum of Art
Rogers Fund, 69.14.1

294 *Trompe-l'Oeil Exercise: A Group of Prints*

Pen and brown ink, brown wash. 16 7/16 × 22 7/16 inches (41.8 × 57 cm.).

Signed and dated in pen and brown ink at left of center, *Pietro Giacomo Palmieri Inventò, e Fece a Penna 1766*; various inscriptions by Palmieri identifying prints represented.

See No. 293.

PROVENANCE: Sir Bruce Ingram (Lugt S. 1405a on old mount); Carl Winter (his mark, *CWR*, at lower right); sale, London, Sotheby's, July 1, 1965, no. 81; purchased by the Metropolitan Museum in New York, 1969.

The Metropolitan Museum of Art
Rogers Fund, 69.14.2

Giuseppe Cades
Rome 1750–Rome 1799

295 *The Virgin Immaculate*

Pen and brown ink, brown and a little gray wash, over black chalk. 17 5/8 × 12 1/8 inches (44.8 × 30.8 cm.).

Inscribed in pen and black ink on verso, *Cherubino Alberti (Borgheggiano)*; unidentified collector's mark at lower right.

The very linear character of this design is evidence of Cades's neoclassic partialities. The composition is no doubt studied for an altarpiece, but no such picture is recorded. That it was the subject of some study on Cades's part is made clear by the fact that, as Anthony Clark points out, there is a chalk study for the same composition among a large group of drawings by Cades in the Museu Nacional de Arte Antigua in Lisbon (No. 2093). In addition he calls attention to another version in pen with slight variations, which is recorded in a photograph in the Witt Library, London. The present whereabouts of this last drawing is unknown.

Cades represents the Virgin holding the Child, standing above a crescent moon, and attended by an angel on the right who offers a symbolic basket full of human hearts, while at the left a youth protected by the Virgin recoils before a dragon symbolizing evil.

PROVENANCE: Private collection, Vienna; purchased by the Metropolitan Museum in London, 1970.

EXHIBITIONS: London, Yvonne Tan Bunzl, "Old Master Paintings and Drawings," 1970, no. 13.

The Metropolitan Museum of Art
Rogers Fund, 1970.113.2

296 *Two Monks Kneeling before the Virgin*

Pen and gray ink, gray wash, colored chalks, over black chalk. 17 1/2 × 11 1/2 inches (44.5 × 29.2 cm.). Both lower corners cut; repaired tear at left margin; several spots of wash. Watermark: shield with crown above, letter W below.

Signed and dated in black chalk at lower right corner, *G. Cades 1791*; inscribed in pen and brown ink on separate sheet attached to verso, *Disegno di Giuseppe Cades eseguito nel quadro da esso fatto in S. Andrea delle Fratte Sua Parocchia.*

The old inscription on the verso of this sheet correctly identifies the drawing as Cades's study for an altarpiece in S. Andrea delle Fratte, Rome, representing, as Anthony Clark points out, the Virgin appearing to two members of the Order of Minims, the Blessed Caspar de Bono and the Blessed Nicolas Saggio da Longobardi. S. Andrea delle Fratte was and is the Roman church of the Minims, a Franciscan split-off group founded by St. Francis of Paola.

EXHIBITIONS: Providence, Rhode Island School of Design, "The Age of Canova," 1957, no. 46, repr.

Janos Scholz

Giuseppe Bernardino Bison

Palmanova (Friuli) 1762–Milan 1844

297 *Scene of Antique Sacrifice*

Pen and brown ink, brown and pink wash. $9\frac{1}{8} \times 13\frac{11}{16}$ inches (23.1 × 34.7 cm.).

Inscribed in pen and brown ink at lower left, *G. Bison Veneziano.*

Bison, a minor Venetian decorative painter who lived on well into the nineteenth century, was a virtuoso draughtsman who produced innumerable charming, if rather insignificant, pen sketches. The present example is a more elaborate exercise in a neoclassic vein, a pastiche of an antique relief, carried off with much brio.

PROVENANCE: Purchased by the Metropolitan Museum in London, 1970.

EXHIBITIONS: London, P. & D. Colnaghi, "Old Master and English Drawings," 1970, no. 46.

The Metropolitan Museum of Art
Rogers Fund, 1970.177

Francesco Tironi

Venice after 1750–Venice 1800

298 *The Meeting of Pius VI and the Doge on the Island of S. Giorgio in Alga*

Pen and brown and black inks, brown and gray wash, touched with white. $13\frac{3}{8} \times 18\frac{5}{8}$ inches (34 × 47.5 cm.).

Slight foxing; cleavage within support at lower left corner. Watermark: coat of arms enclosing fleur-de-lis (close to Heawood 1743).

Tironi, a lesser vedutist and imitator of Canaletto, is chiefly known through his twenty-four views of the islands of the Venetian Lagoon, which were engraved by Antonio Sandi and published in 1779, but ever since Hermann Voss's initial researches in the twenties ("Francesco Tironi...," *Zeitschrift für bildende Kunst*, LXI, 1927–1928, pp. 266–270), scholars have been adding to the number of his

somewhat prosaic but not uninteresting drawings. There are examples at the Museum of Fine Arts, Boston, the Albertina, the Victoria and Albert Museum, the Whitworth Art Gallery, and the Robert Lehman Collection. W. G. Constable first identified the present drawing and another in the Morgan Library as the work of Tironi. The drawing represents the meeting of Pius VI and the doge before the church of S. Maria di Nazareth on the island of S. Giorgio in Alga, so called because of the seaweed that accumulates on its shores. This event was also the subject of one of four paintings by Francesco Guardi (Moschini, *Guardi*, pl. 156) commemorating the Pope's sojourn at Venice in the spring of 1782 during the course of his trip to Vienna to see the Emperor Joseph II. The Library's second sheet likewise records an event of this visit, the benediction of Pius VI delivered from a loggia in the Campo SS. Giovanni e Paolo.

One of Sandi's engravings shows S. Maria di Nazareth from a slightly different viewpoint, without the religious gathering.

PROVENANCE: Charles Fairfax Murray; purchased by J. Pierpont Morgan in London, 1910.

BIBLIOGRAPHY: Pignatti, *Disegni veneziani*, p. 204.

The Pierpont Morgan Library
No. IV, 141c

Antonio Terreni, attributed to

Active Livorno after 1750

299 *A Ball at the Pitti Palace, May 31, 1785*

Pen and brown ink, brown wash, and tempera. $20\frac{3}{8} \times 29$ inches (51.7 × 73.7 cm.). Edges abraded; small repair at right-hand margin. Lined.

Inscribed in ornamental border in pen and brown ink, *Veduta della Festa di Ballo data da S. A. R. alle L. L. M. M.: il Re, e Regina delle due | Sicilie nel Cortile del Palazzo Pitti, e Giardino di Boboli annesso, la Sera del di 31: Mag:io 1785.*

The artist who left this sparkling record of an enchanted May evening at the Pitti Palace and Boboli

Gardens in Florence was tentatively identified almost a half century ago by Odoardo H. Giglioli as Antonio Terreni. There are a number of drawings by this artist at the Uffizi, and while they are sketches of an ornamental type for ceilings and related decorations, Dr. Anna Forlani Tempesti reports that, judging on the basis of a photograph, the handling is not unlike that of the present drawing.

In recent correspondence, Dr. Marco Chiarini suggested that the draughtsman might be the better-known Giuseppe Maria Terreni (1739–1811), the fresco ornament painter who was variously employed by the Grand Duke of Tuscany and members of his court. If it is indeed he, the border may represent the shade of green to which he gave his name. When there is an opportunity to compare the present sheet with his tempera works in the Museo Topografico Fiorentino, Florence, it may be possible to establish its attribution more firmly.

His Royal Highness who was the host on this colorful occasion was Leopold, first Grand Duke of Tuscany and brother of Queen Marie-Antoinette of France; the royal guests whom he honored were his sister Queen Marie-Caroline and her husband, King Ferdinand of the Two Sicilies.

The drawing has long been in the Morgan Library but the source from which it was acquired is not known.

PROVENANCE: J. Pierpont Morgan; J. P. Morgan.

The Pierpont Morgan Library
Transfer No. 1962.5

Domenico Mondo
Died Naples 1806

300 *Battle at a Bridge*

Pen and brown ink, gray and brown wash, heightened with white. 8 3/16 × 12 1/16 inches (20.3 × 30.6 cm.). Small tears and losses at margins; crease at lower right margin.

Domenico Mondo, as Walter Vitzthum points out, was the last and, as a draughtsman, the most brilliant of Solimena's artistic heirs. Mondo's drawing style involves a radical simplification of Solimena's elegant contour line and dramatic chiaroscuro. Contour is indicated by staccato dots, and wash is applied with wild abandon. A similar battle scene, in a Neapolitan tradition that goes back to Falcone and Rosa, is in the Società Napoletana di Storia Patria, Naples (*Disegni napoletani del Sei e del Settecento nel Museo di Capodimonte* [exhibition catalogue by Walter Vitzthum], Naples, Museo di Capodimonte, 1966, pl. 43). There the bridge is broken and the subject thus identifiable as Horatius Cocles.

Mr. Scholz possesses four more drawings by Mondo, and there are further characteristic examples in the Cooper-Hewitt Museum and the Metropolitan Museum.

PROVENANCE: Giovanni Piancastelli (no mark, see Lugt S. 2078a); Mr. and Mrs. Edward Brandegee (no mark, see Lugt S. 1860c).

EXHIBITIONS: Minneapolis, University of Minnesota Gallery, "The Eighteenth Century, One Hundred Drawings by One Hundred Artists," 1961, no. 59; New York, Finch College Museum of Art, "In the Shadow of Vesuvius, Neapolitan Drawings from the Collection of Janos Scholz," 1969, no. 50, repr.

Janos Scholz

Plates

1 · FRANCESCO SOLIMENA · The Arrival of Columbus in the New World

Cooper-Hewitt Museum, Smithsonian Institution

2 · FRANCESCO SOLIMENA · St. Maurus Healing an Invalid

Joseph McCrindle

3 · FRANCESCO SOLIMENA · Deborah and Barak   The Metropolitan Museum of Art

4 · FAUSTINO BOCCHI · The Mock Visit of Ceremony   The Metropolitan Museum of Art

5 (opposite) · SEBASTIANO RICCI · Figure Studies   The Metropolitan Museum of Art

6 · SEBASTIANO RICCI · Allegory with Figures of Hope, Time, and Death
The Metropolitan Museum of Art

7 · SEBASTIANO RICCI · Venus and Cupid with Other Figures before an Altar
The Pierpont Morgan Library

8 · SEBASTIANO RICCI · The Education of the Virgin   The Metropolitan Museum of Art

9 · PAOLO PAGANI · Antiochus and Stratonice

Robert and Bertina Suida Manning

10 · PAOLO DE MATTEIS · Galatea Triumphant   The Metropolitan Museum of Art

11 · GIUSEPPE MARIA CRESPI · Marcolfa Persuades Cacasenno to Mount a Horse
The Metropolitan Museum of Art

12 · BENEDETTO LUTI · Pius V and the Ambassador of the King of Poland

14 · ALESSANDRO MAGNASCO · The Peep Show

B. Augustinus nouellus Panormitanus

15 · ALESSANDRO MAGNASCO · Seated Monk in a Landscape

Janos Scholz

16 · ALESSANDRO MAGNASCO
Reclining Man in Meditation Visited by an Angel
The Metropolitan Museum of Art

17 · DONATO CRETI · Holy Family with St. John   The Pierpont Morgan Library

18 · DONATO CRETI · Satyr

Janos Scholz

M. L'abbé

19 · PIER LEONE GHEZZI · An Ecclesiastic Playing the Cello   Janos Scholz

Favinello Napolitano
famoso cantove d'Soprano de
canto nel Teavo di Eliseov nell Anno 1724.
facto da me Cav.r P.M. à L 2 Marzo 1724

20 · PIER LEONE GHEZZI · The Famous Castrato Il Farinelli   Janos Scholz

21 · AURELIANO MILANI · Christ Healing a Possessed Man

22 · AURELIANO MILANI · Hilly Landscape with Three Figures

23 · GIOVANNI ANTONIO PELLEGRINI · Head of Pompey Presented to Caesar

The Metropolitan Museum of Art

The Metropolitan Museum of Art

25 · MARCO RICCI · Brigands Attacking Two Travelers

Janos Scholz

27 · MARCO RICCI · Shepherds with their Flock and Cattle at a Stream

28 · MARCO RICCI · Pastoral Landscape

Harry G. Sperling

30 · MARCO RICCI · Figures in Roman Ruins

31 · MARCO RICCI · Figures under Ruined Arches

James Parker

Diana

IX

33 · ANTON MARIA ZANETTI THE ELDER and ANTON MARIA ZANETTI THE YOUNGER
Diana
The Pierpont Morgan Library

34 · SEBASTIANO CONCA
St. Elizabeth of
Portugal Kneeling
before the Crucified
Christ
Cooper-Hewitt Museum,
Smithsonian Institution

abᵉ Lorenzo Defferari

35 · LORENZO DE' FERRARI · The Triumph of Justice   The Metropolitan Museum of Art

36 · LORENZO DE' FERRARI · Hercules Triumphant

Robert and Bertina Suida Manning

37 · GIOVANNI BATTISTA PIAZZETTA · Study of an Executioner
The Metropolitan Museum of Art

38 · GIOVANNI BATTISTA PIAZZETTA · Young Man Embracing a Girl Dr. George M. Baer

39 · GIOVANNI BATTISTA PIAZZETTA · Head of a Levantine   Janos Scholz

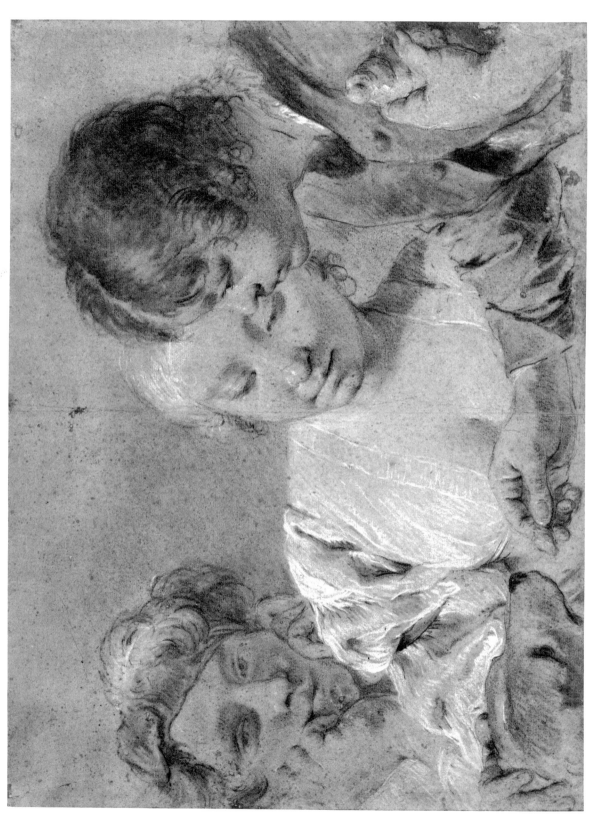

Walter C. Baker

41 · GIOVANNI BATTISTA PIAZZETTA · Young Girl Selling a Fowl

42 · GIOVANNI BATTISTA PIAZZETTA · Young Woman Holding a Pear   The Pierpont Morgan Library

43 · GIOVANNI BATTISTA PIAZZETTA · Young Woman Holding a Jingle Ring
The Pierpont Morgan Library

44 · GIOVANNI BATTISTA PIAZZETTA · Minerva's Homage to Venice
The Pierpont Morgan Library

45 · GIOVANNI BATTISTA PIAZZETTA · Apollo and the Muses   The Pierpont Morgan Library

46 · GIOVANNI BATTISTA PIAZZETTA · Surgeon and His Patient, Attended by Her Maid
The Pierpont Morgan Library

47 · GIOVANNI BATTISTA PIAZZETTA · Male Nude Lying on a Standard

Cooper-Hewitt Museum, Smithsonian Institution

49 · BALDASSARE DE CARO · Design for a Monument
Cooper-Hewitt Museum, Smithsonian Institution

50 · GASPARE DIZIANI · Hercules and Omphale   The Metropolitan Museum of Art

51 · GASPARE DIZIANI · The Virgin of Sorrows   The Pierpont Morgan Library

52 · GASPARE DIZIANI · Apollo and Daphne   Janos Scholz

53 · GASPARE DIZIANI · Adam and Eve Driven from Paradise   Janos Scholz

Gasparo Diziani Bellunese.

54 · GASPARE DIZIANI · Venice Receiving Homage   The Metropolitan Museum of Art

55 · GIOVANNI PAOLO PANNINI · Drawing of the Lottery in Piazza di Montecitorio

56
GIOVANNI PAOLO PANNINI
Young Gentleman Holding
His Hat
Harry G. Sperling

57 · GIUSEPPE GALLI BIBIENA, attributed to · Design for a Stage Set: The Temple of Jupiter

58 · FRANCESCO DE MURA · Design for the Frame of a Portrait
Cooper-Hewitt Museum, Smithsonian Institution

59 · G. B. TIEPOLO · Figures around a Pyramid   Robert Lehman Collection

60 · G. B. TIEPOLO · Group of Fighting Figures

61 · G. B. TIEPOLO · Beheading of St. Nazarius and St. Celsus in Milan
The Metropolitan Museum of Art

62 · G. B. TIEPOLO · Beheading of a Male and a Female Saint
The Metropolitan Museum of Art

63 · G. B. TIEPOLO · Enthroned Madonna Attended by St. Sebastian, St. Francis, and Angels
The Metropolitan Museum of Art

64 · G. B. TIEPOLO · Design for a Ceiling:
Truth Appearing before a Group of Elders

The Pierpont Morgan Library

65 · G. B. TIEPOLO · St. Dominic Borne Upward by Three Angels   The Pierpont Morgan Library

66 · G. B. TIEPOLO
St. Dominic with Arms Outstretched
The Pierpont Morgan Library

67 · G. B. TIEPOLO · St. Dominic, His Hands in Prayer, Borne Upward   The Pierpont Morgan Library

68 · G. B. TIEPOLO · The Adoration of the Magi   The Metropolitan Museum of Art

69 · G. B. TIEPOLO · Design for a Ceiling: The Triumph of Hercules

70 · G. B. TIEPOLO · Virgin and Child Attended by St. Sebastian and Two Monastic Saints
Robert Lehman Collection

71 · G. B. TIEPOLO · Virgin and Child Attended by Three Ecclesiastics   Janos Scholz

72 · G. B. TIEPOLO · Virgin and Child Appearing to a Group of Worshipers
Robert Lehman Collection

73 · G. B. TIEPOLO · Virgin and Child Appearing to Two Monks   Private Collection

74 · G. B. TIEPOLO · Apollo Supported by a Genius with Butterfly Wings
The Metropolitan Museum of Art

75 · G. B. TIEPOLO
Apollo, with Lyre and Quiver, His Arm Upraised
The Pierpont Morgan Library

76 · G. B. TIEPOLO · Apollo Seated on Clouds, Two Figures at Left   The Metropolitan Museum of Art

77 · G. B. TIEPOLO · Apollo Standing in His Chariot   The Metropolitan Museum of Art

79 · G. B. TIEPOLO · Two Zephyrs with a Horse of Apollo

81 · G. B. TIEPOLO · Hercules with an Attendant Male and a Female Figure

82 · G. B. TIEPOLO · Truth with Two River Gods and Putti

83 · G. B. TIEPOLO · Apollo Flanked by Two Figures and a Putto Holding a Quiver

84 · G. B. TIEPOLO
Standing Figure of Prudence and a Seated River God
The Metropolitan Museum of Art

85 · G. B. TIEPOLO
Seated Woman with Mirror and Vase, Putto with Serpent, and a River God
The Metropolitan Museum of Art

86 · G. B. TIEPOLO
Two Seated Women
and a Boy
The Metropolitan
Museum of Art

91 · G. B. TIEPOLO · Time and Cupid

The Metropolitan Museum of Art

94 · G. B. TIEPOLO · Three Zephyrs The Pierpont Morgan Library

95 · G. B. TIEPOLO · Bacchant and Bacchante   The Pierpont Morgan Library

96 · G. B. TIEPOLO · Scherzo di Fantasia: Standing Warrior and King Attended by Five Figures
The Metropolitan Museum of Art

97 · G. B. TIEPOLO · Scherzo di Fantasia: Two Standing Orientals and a Standing Youth
The Metropolitan Museum of Art

98 · G. B. TIEPOLO · Scherzo di Fantasia: Seated Warrior and Standing Youth
The Metropolitan Museum of Art

99 · G. B. TIEPOLO · Three Standing Men and an Angel   Private Collection

100 · G. B. TIEPOLO · Psyche Transported to Olympus   Dr. and Mrs. Rudolf Heinemann

101 · G. B. TIEPOLO · Psyche Transported to Olympus   The Metropolitan Museum of Art

102 · G. B. TIEPOLO · Virgin and Child Seated on a Globe   Dr. and Mrs. Rudolf Heinemann

104 · G. B. TIEPOLO · Virtue and Nobility

105 · G. B. TIEPOLO · Nobility and Virtue

107 · G. B. TIEPOLO · Virtue and Nobility   The Pierpont Morgan Library

110 · G. B. TIEPOLO · The Meeting of Anthony and Cleopatra   The Metropolitan Museum of Art

III · G. B. TIEPOLO · Bacchus and Ariadne   The Metropolitan Museum of Art

113 · G. B. TIEPOLO · Three Studies of Bacchus   The Pierpont Morgan Library

114 · G. B. TIEPOLO · Harvesters with Rakes and a Sieve

115 · G. B. TIEPOLO · Zephyr and Flora

116 · G. B. TIEPOLO · Zephyr and Flora   The Pierpont Morgan Library

117 · G. B. TIEPOLO · Three Angels in Flight   The Pierpont Morgan Library

118 · G. B. TIEPOLO · Angelica and Medoro

119 · G. B. TIEPOLO · Time and Truth   The Metropolitan Museum of Art

120 · G. B. TIEPOLO · Time and Truth   The Metropolitan Museum of Art

121 · G. B. TIEPOLO · Time and Truth   The Metropolitan Museum of Art

122 · G. B. TIEPOLO · Two Old Men, a Marine Deity, and a Putto Looking over a Balustrade

Robert Lehman Collection

123 · G. B. TIEPOLO · The Flight into Egypt   Mrs. Vincent Astor

124 · G. B. TIEPOLO · Christ Healing a Paralytic Man

126 · G. B. TIEPOLO · Elderly Man Attended by Mercury and Prudence
The Metropolitan Museum of Art

127 · G. B. TIEPOLO · Magus and His Attendants   Robert Lehman Collection

129 · G. B. TIEPOLO · Young Woman Seated on a Cloud   Dr. and Mrs. Rudolf Heinemann

130 · G. B. TIEPOLO · Design for an Overmantel   Dr. and Mrs. Rudolf Heinemann

131 · G. B. TIEPOLO · Studies of Vases   Private Collection

132 · G. B. TIEPOLO · Holy Family with an Attendant Boy at Left   Robert Lehman Collection

133 · G. B. TIEPOLO · Holy Family with St. Joseph Standing   Robert Lehman Collection

134 · G. B. TIEPOLO · Holy Family under a Tree with St. Joseph Standing at a Pedestal
Dr. and Mrs. Rudolf Heinemann

Giovanni Battista Tiepolo

135 · G. B. TIEPOLO · Holy Family with St. Joseph Kneeling

Dr. and Mrs. Rudolf Heinemann

136 · G. B. TIEPOLO · Holy Family with Child Asleep   Dr. and Mrs. Rudolf Heinemann

137 · G. B. TIEPOLO · Bishop Seated   Dr. and Mrs. Rudolf Heinemann

138 · G. B. TIEPOLO · Group of Figures

Dr. and Mrs. Rudolf Heinemann

139 · G. B. TIEPOLO · Apotheosis of a Warrior

140 · G. B. TIEPOLO · Apotheosis of Merit

141 · G. B. TIEPOLO · Apotheosis of Merit

142 · G. B. TIEPOLO · Constancy and Fame

143 · G. B. TIEPOLO · Constancy and Fame

144 · G. B. TIEPOLO · Error and Falsehood

146 · G. B. OR DOMENICO TIEPOLO · Three Putti Bearing a Mirror
The Pierpont Morgan Library

147 · G. B. OR DOMENICO TIEPOLO · Bacchus and Fauns

The Pierpont Morgan Library

148 · G. B. TIEPOLO · The Angel at the Tomb

149 · G. B. TIEPOLO · Family Group

Dr. and Mrs. Rudolf Heinemann

150 · G. B. TIEPOLO · Design for a Dedication Page to Charles III
Cooper-Hewitt Museum, Smithsonian Institution

151 · G. B. TIEPOLO · Portrait of Palma Giovane   Dr. and Mrs. Rudolf Heinemann

152 · G. B. TIEPOLO · Portrait of Palma Giovane

Janos Scholz

153 · G. B. TIEPOLO · Three Studies of Dogs, after Veronese
The Metropolitan Museum of Art

154 · G. B. TIEPOLO · Study of an Eagle

155 · CANALETTO · Lagoon Capriccio

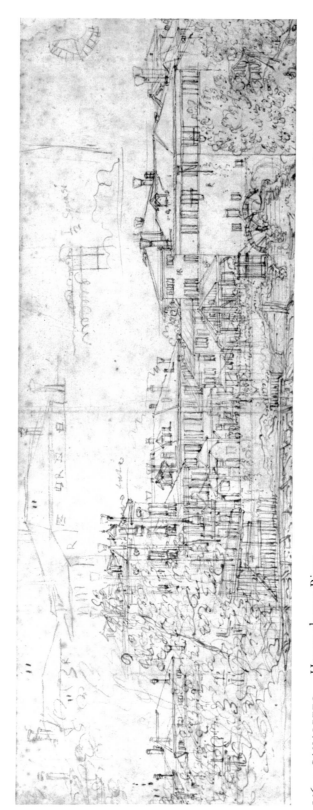

156 · CANALETTO · Houses along a River

Robert Lehman Collection

158 · CANALETTO · View of Padua from the East

159 · CANALETTO · The South Pulpit in S. Marco   Janos Scholz

161 · CANALETTO · Architectural Capriccio   Janos Scholz

162 · CANALETTO
Man Smoking a Pipe
The Metropolitan
Museum of Art

162 (verso) · CANALETTO
Standing Gentleman
and Two Studies of
His Head
The Metropolitan
Museum of Art

163 · CORRADO GIAQUINTO · St. Joseph Presented by the Virgin to the Holy Trinity

164 · CORRADO GIAQUINTO · The Relics of St. Acutius and St. Eutychetes
Transported to Naples   David Daniels

165 · G. A. GUARDI · The Good Samaritan   The Metropolitan Museum of Art

166 · G. A. GUARDI · The Taking of Padua

167 · G. A. GUARDI · The Martyrdom of St. Clement   Janos Scholz

Gianbatista Tiepolo Veneziano.

168 · G. A. GUARDI · The Education of the Virgin   Dr. Donald Tapley

169 · BARTOLOMEO NAZARI · Portrait of Giovanni Paolo Rovillio   Janos Scholz

Scala di   Palmi Sei
1   2   3   4   5   6

Petrus Bracci Rom. F.

170 · PIETRO BRACCI · Project for a Tomb   The Metropolitan Museum of Art

Scala di Palmi Otto Romani

Petrus Bracci Rom. F.

171 · PIETRO BRACCI · Project for a Tomb   The Metropolitan Museum of Art

173 · CARLO MARCHIONNI
Doorway Surmounted
by the Albani Arms
Cooper-Hewitt Museum,
Smithsonian Institution

174 · PIETRO LONGHI · Venetian Senator   The Pierpont Morgan Library

176 · FRANCESCO ZUCCARELLI · Landscape with a Lake and Horseman

Janos Scholz

The Pierpont Morgan Library

179 · POMPEO GIROLAMO BATONI · Studies for the "Fall of Simon Magus"
The Pierpont Morgan Library

Prospetto della Seconda Macchina rappresentante una Deliziosa all'uso cinese. Eretta per commando di Sua Eccellenza il Sig. DON LORENZO COLONNA Gran Contestabile del Regno di Napoli &c. come Ambasciatore straordinario di S.M. il RE delle due Sicilie &c&c. la Sera delli 29. Giugno 1760. Festa de Gloriosi Santi Apostoli PIETRO, e PAOLO in occasione d'aver presentata la Chinea alla Santità di Nostro Signore PAPA CLEMENTE XIII. Paolo Posi Architetto.

180 · PAOLO POSI · Design for the Chinea of 1760: Chinoiserie

The Pierpont Morgan Library

181 · FRANCESCO SALVATOR FONTEBASSO · Two Standing Male Figures and Seated Woman with a Child   The Metropolitan Museum of Art

182 · GIUSEPPE VALERIANI · Design for the Decoration of a Dome   The Pierpont Morgan Library

183 · GIOVANNI BATTISTA MARCOLA · The Head of Pompey Brought to Caesar

Janos Scholz

The Pierpont Morgan Library

185 · GIUSEPPE ZOCCHI · Villa Poggio Imperiale, near Florence

186 · GIUSEPPE ZOCCHI · Villa Palmieri, near Florence

187 · FRANCESCO GUARDI · Virgin and Child Seated on Clouds
The Metropolitan Museum of Art

Harry G. Sperling

190 · FRANCESCO GUARDI · The Grand Canal above the Rialto

The Metropolitan Museum of Art

The Pierpont Morgan Library

Paru Bella Piazzetta e Punta di S. Giorgio Maggiore

191 · FRANCESCO GUARDI · Ballad Singer on the Piazzetta

192 · FRANCESCO GUARDI · View of S. Marco   The Metropolitan Museum of Art

193 · FRANCESCO GUARDI · Panorama from the Bacino di S. Marco

194 · FRANCESCO GUARDI · The Stairway of the Giants   The Metropolitan Museum of Art

195 · FRANCESCO GUARDI · The Bucintoro off S. Niccolò di Lido

· FRANCESCO GUARDI · The Bucintoro on the Way to the Lido on Ascension Day

Mrs. Herbert N. Straus

The Metropolitan Museum of Art

198 · FRANCESCO GUARDI · Dice Players in a Venetian Square   The Metropolitan Museum of Art

199 · FRANCESCO GUARDI · Architectural Capriccio: Courtyard of a Palace
The Metropolitan Museum of Art

200 · FRANCESCO GUARDI · Architectural Capriccio: Courtyard of a Palace
The Metropolitan Museum of Art

201 · FRANCESCO GUARDI · Architectural Capriccio: Vaulted Colonnade of a Palace

202 · *FRANCESCO GUARDI* · Architectural Capriccio: View through an Archway
The Metropolitan Museum of Art

203 · FRANCESCO GUARDI · Capriccio with Ruins   Mr. and Mrs. Eugene Victor Thaw

204 · FRANCESCO GUARDI · Capriccio with a Tower

205 · FRANCESCO GUARDI · Capriccio with a Squall on the Lagoon

Mr. and Mrs. Eugene Victor Thaw

The Metropolitan Museum of Art

207 · FRANCESCO GUARDI · The Villa Loredan, near Treviso

208 · FRANCESCO GUARDI · View of Lévico in the Valsugana

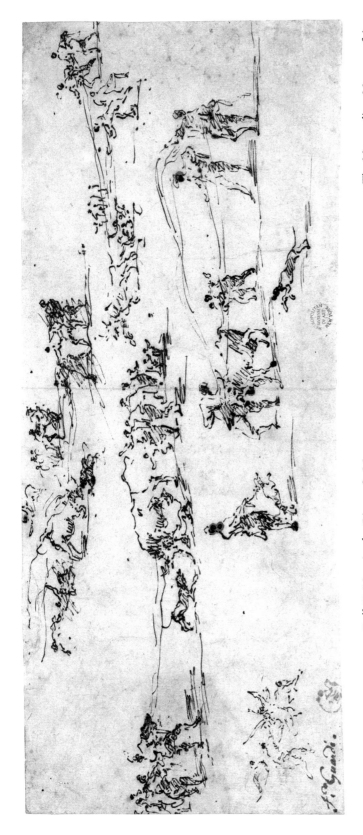

209 · FRANCESCO GUARDI · Bull Baiting in the Piazza S. Marco

211 · FRANCESCO GUARDI · The Fenice Theater in Venice

212 · FRANCESCO GUARDI · Decorative Cartouche with a Lagoon Capriccio

213 · FRANCESCO GUARDI · Design for a Framing Motif

215 · BERNARDO BELLOTTO · View of Padua from the East

Walter C. Baker

217 · GIOVANNI BATTISTA PIRANESI · Central View of a Church Interior

218 · GIOVANNI BATTISTA PIRANESI · Prison Interior

219 · GIOVANNI BATTISTA PIRANESI · Gondola

221 · GIOVANNI BATTISTA PIRANESI · Design for a Title Page

The Pierpont Morgan Library

222 · GIOVANNI BATTISTA PIRANESI · Capriccio

223 · GIOVANNI BATTISTA PIRANESI · Design for a Wall Panel   The Pierpont Morgan Library

224 · GIOVANNI BATTISTA PIRANESI · Design for a Wall Panel   The Pierpont Morgan Library

225 · GIOVANNI BATTISTA PIRANESI · Architectural Complex   The Pierpont Morgan Library

227 · GIOVANNI BATTISTA PIRANESI · S. Maria del Priorato, Rome:
Design for the Central Panel of the Vault   The Pierpont Morgan Library

228 · GIOVANNI BATTISTA PIRANESI · S. Maria del Priorato, Rome:
Sketch for the High Altar   The Pierpont Morgan Library

229 · GIOVANNI BATTISTA PIRANESI · S. Maria del Priorato, Rome: Design for the Lower Part of the High Altar   The Pierpont Morgan Library

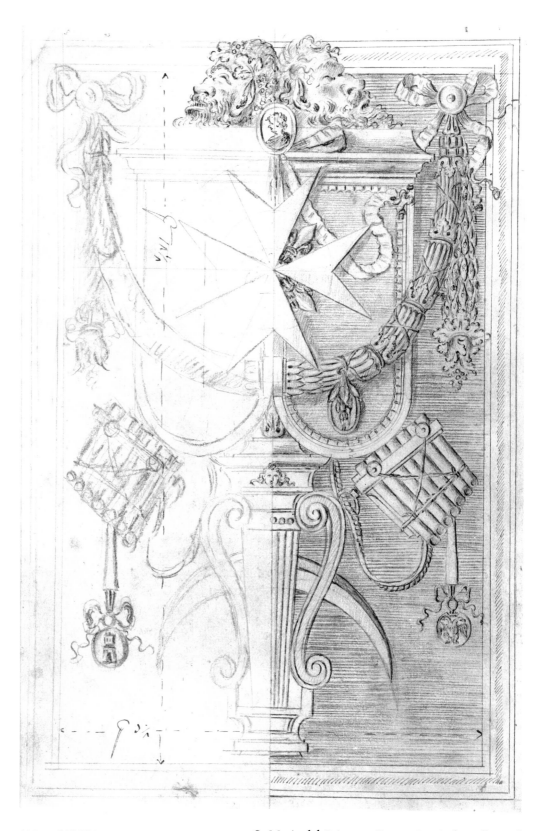

230 · GIOVANNI BATTISTA PIRANESI · S. Maria del Priorato, Rome: Vertical Wall Panel
The Pierpont Morgan Library

231 · GIOVANNI BATTISTA PIRANESI · S. Giovanni in Laterano, Rome: Longitudinal Section of Proposed Alteration of West End
The Pierpont Morgan Library

232 · GIOVANNI BATTISTA PIRANESI · S. Giovanni in Laterano, Rome: Sketch for Choir Wall; Putti
The Pierpont Morgan Library

233 · GIOVANNI BATTISTA PIRANESI · S. Giovanni in Laterano, Rome:
Design for a Papal Monument   The Pierpont Morgan Library

234 · GIOVANNI BATTISTA PIRANESI · Design for Mantelpiece with Confronted Elephant Heads

The Pierpont Morgan Library

235 · GIOVANNI BATTISTA PIRANESI · Design for Mantelpiece

The Pierpont Morgan Library

237 · GIOVANNI BATTISTA PIRANESI · Figure Studies   Janos Scholz

238 · GIOVANNI BATTISTA PIRANESI · Figure Studies

239 · DOMENICO TIEPOLO · Kneeling Woman with Two Children   Private Collection

240 · DOMENICO TIEPOLO · Two Angel Musicians on a Balustrade

241 · DOMENICO TIEPOLO · Abraham Visited by the Angels The Metropolitan Museum of Art

242 · DOMENICO TIEPOLO · The Assumption of the Virgin   The Metropolitan Museum of Art

243 · DOMENICO TIEPOLO · The Baptism of Christ   The Metropolitan Museum of Art

244 · DOMENICO TIEPOLO · Oriental Lancer Approaching a Town

The Metropolitan Museum of Art

245 · DOMENICO TIEPOLO · Two Families of Satyrs

247 · DOMENICO TIEPOLO · Caricature of a Gentleman and Other Studies
The Metropolitan Museum of Art

248 · DOMENICO TIEPOLO · Monkey Swinging on a Parapet and Two Monkey Skeletons
Dr. and Mrs. Rudolf Heinemann

249 · DOMENICO TIEPOLO · Figures around a Sacrificial Altar

250 · DOMENICO TIEPOLO · Studies of Two Orientals   Dr. and Mrs. Rudolf Heinemann

252 · DOMENICO TIEPOLO · Joachim's Offering Refused   The Pierpont Morgan Library

253 · DOMENICO TIEPOLO · The Betrothal of the Virgin   Robert Lehman Collection

254 · DOMENICO TIEPOLO · The Arrival of the Virgin in Bethlehem   Robert Lehman Collection

255 · DOMENICO TIEPOLO · The Flight into Egypt: The Holy Family Leaving Bethlehem
The Pierpont Morgan Library

256 · DOMENICO TIEPOLO · The Flight into Egypt: The Holy Family Passing a Flock of Sheep
The Pierpont Morgan Library

257 · DOMENICO TIEPOLO · The Flight into Egypt: The Rest   Robert Lehman Collection

258 · DOMENICO TIEPOLO · The Death of St. Joseph   Dr. and Mrs. Rudolf Heinemann

PORTA
SPETIOSA

259 · DOMENICO TIEPOLO · St. Peter Healing the Lame Man at the Beautiful Gate
The Pierpont Morgan Library

261 · DOMENICO TIEPOLO · Scene of Contemporary Life: A Visit to a Lawyer

The Pierpont Morgan Library

The Metropolitan Museum of Art

Dr. and Mrs. Rudolf Heinemann

Mr. and Mrs. Eugene Victor Thaw

267 · DOMENICO TIEPOLO · Scene of Contemporary Life: Bagpiper, with a Bear, Passing Peasants on a Mountain Road
Robert Lehman Collection

268 · DOMENICO TIEPOLO · Resting Traveler Watching Dogs at Play

269 · DOMENICO TIEPOLO · The Marriage Feast of Punchinello's Parents

Mr. and Mrs. Eugene Victor Thaw

270 · DOMENICO TIEPOLO · The Pregnancy of Punchinello's Mother

271 · DOMENICO TIEPOLO · Punchinello as a Baby in Bed with His Parents

272 · DOMENICO TIEPOLO · Punchinello Takes Part in a "Triumph of Flora"

Dr. and Mrs. Rudolf Heinemann

273 · DOMENICO TIEPOLO · Punchinello Riding an Ass in a Procession of His Fellows

Dr. and Mrs. Rudolf Heinemann

Robert Lehman Collection

The Pierpont Morgan Library

277 · DOMENICO TIEPOLO · Punchinello as a Tailor's Assistant

279 · DOMENICO TIEPOLO · Punchinello as a Portrait Painter

281 · DOMENICO TIEPOLO · Punchinello at a Flogging

282 · DOMENICO TIEPOLO · Punchinellos Picking Fruit and Quarreling in a Garden

Mr. and Mrs. E. Powis Jones

283 · DOMENICO TIEPOLO · Burial of Punchinello

Robert and Bertina Suida Manning

286 · UBALDO GANDOLFI · Design for a Door Knocker   Mr. and Mrs. A. Hyatt Mayor

Pierantonio Novelli Veneziano.

287 · PIER ANTONIO NOVELLI · Bacchante with Two Infant Fauns
The Pierpont Morgan Library

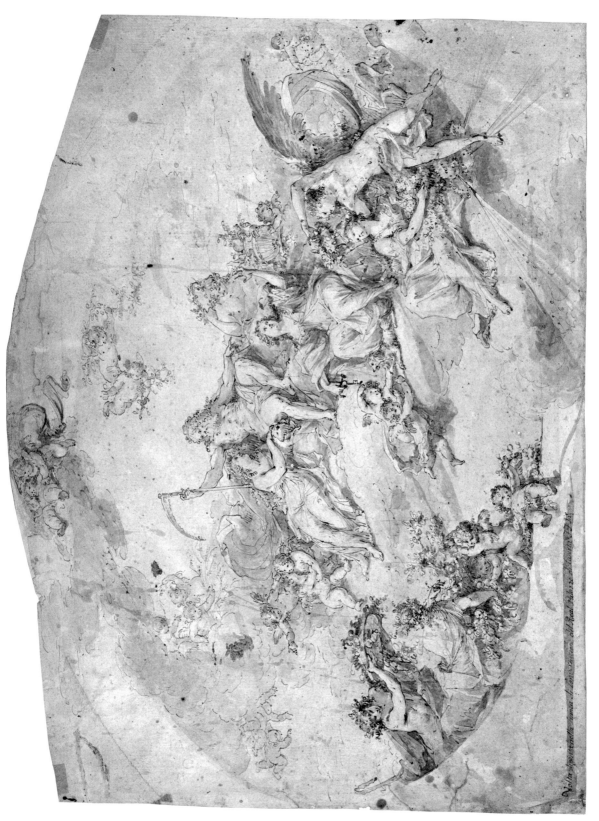

Janos Scholz

289 · GAETANO GANDOLFI · Noah

290 · GAETANO GANDOLFI · Joshua

Donald P. Gurney

292 · LORENZO BALDISSERA TIEPOLO · Head of a Bearded Man in a Turban
The Pierpont Morgan Library

The Metropolitan Museum of Art

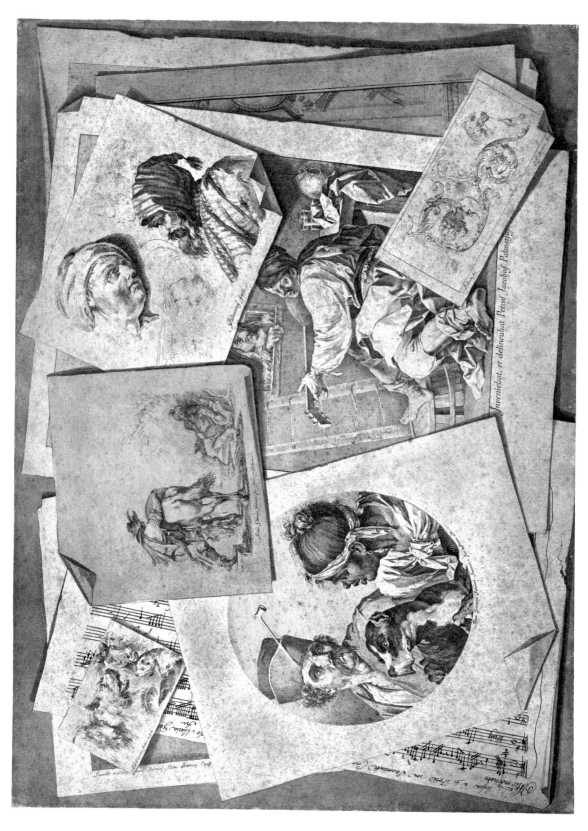

295 · GIUSEPPE CADES · The Virgin Immaculate   The Metropolitan Museum of Art

296 · GIUSEPPE CADES · Two Monks Kneeling before the Virgin   Janos Scholz

F.¹ Bison Veneziano

297 · GIUSEPPE BERNARDINO BISON · Scene of Antique Sacrifice

The Metropolitan Museum of Art

· FRANCESCO TIRONI · The Meeting of Pius VI and the Doge on the Island of S. Giorgio in Alga

The Pierpont Morgan Library

299 · ANTONIO TERRENI, attributed to · A Ball at the Pitti Palace, May 31, 1785

Janos Scholz

Watermarks

The watermarks illustrated are impressed in the paper
used by Giambattista and Domenico Tiepolo, Canaletto,
and Francesco Guardi. With the exception of no. 43,
they are reproduced actual size.

Bird–Bow (or Crossbow)

1

Opposite:
Circle–Coat of Arms

2

3

4

5

6

7

8

9

10

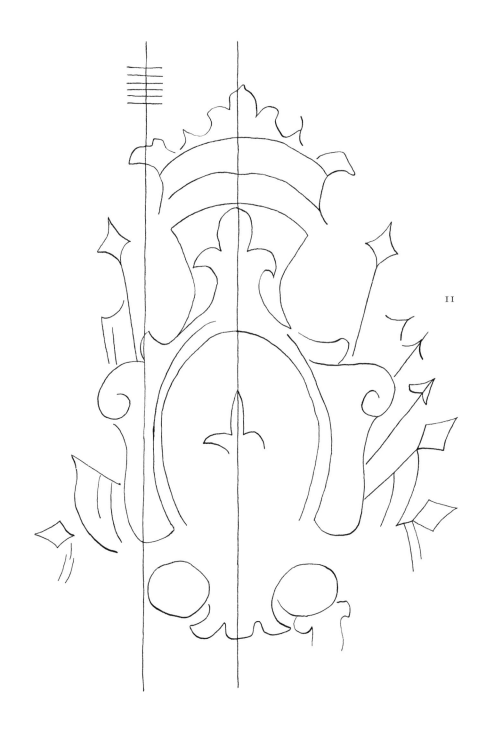

II

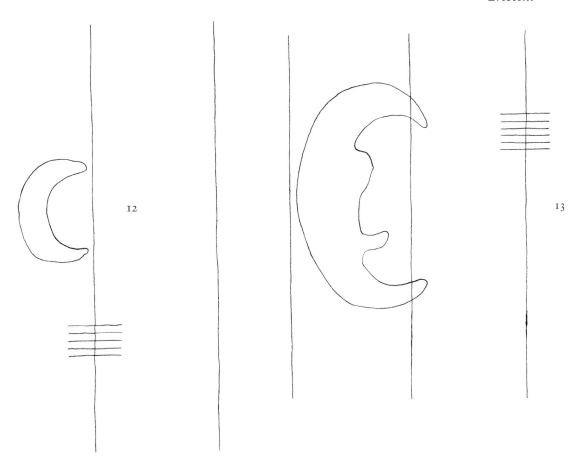

12

13

14

Crescent

15

16

17

MEZANA

Crescent

18

19

20

Crescent

21 Left side

21 Right side

Crescent

22

23

24

25

26

27

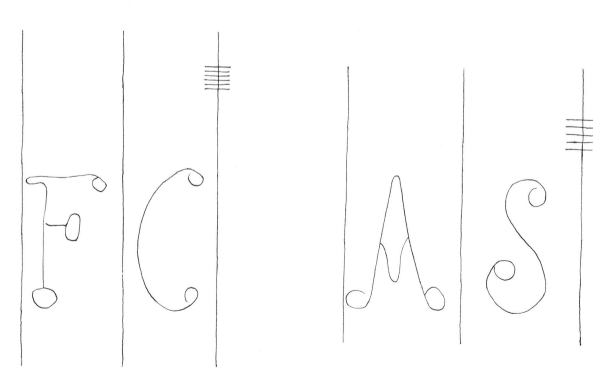

28

29

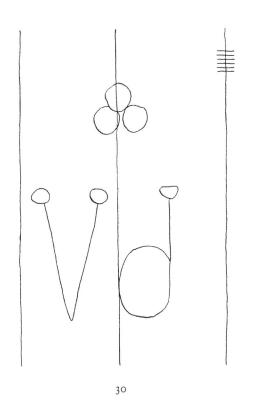

30

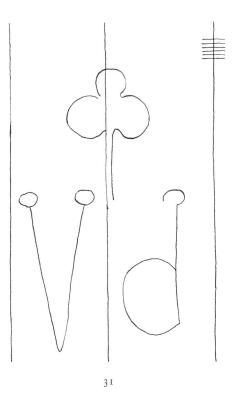

31

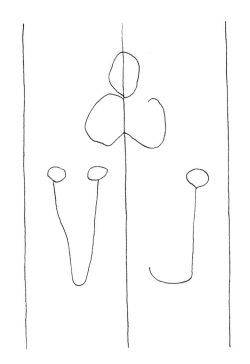

32

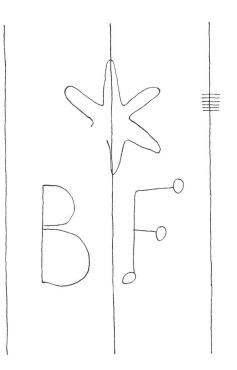

33

34

35 Left side

35 Right side

36

37 Left side

37 Right side

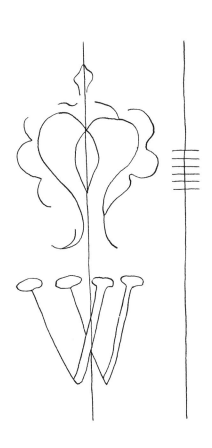

38

39

40

41

Monogram

42 Left side

42 Right side

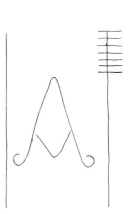

~FAVSTINO~ ~CALCIMARDI~

43 Actual size: $1\frac{3}{8} \times 26\frac{3}{8}$ inches

44 Right side

44 Left side

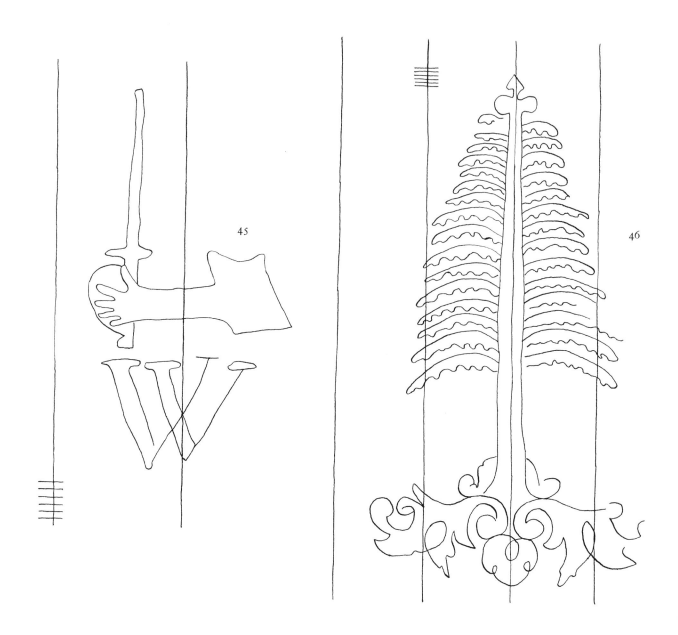

Index of Artists

Designed by Peter Oldenburg. Text composed and printed in English Monotype Bembo by The Stinehour Press, illustrations and watermarks printed by The Meriden Gravure Company, on S-N Text. Binding by Tapley-Rutter Company, Inc.
First printing, 1971, 6000 copies